Progress in Mathematics
Volume 146

J. F. Jardine

Generalized Etale Cohomology Theories

Birkhäuser Verlag
Basel · Boston · Berlin

Author:

J. F. Jardine
Mathematics Department
University of Western Ontario
London, Ontario N6A 5B7
Canada

1991 Mathematics Subject Classification 55P42, 18F25, 18F20, 19F27

A CIP catalogue record for this book is available from the Library of Congress,
Washington D.C., USA

Deutsche Bibliothek Cataloging-in-Publication Data

Jardine, John F.:
Generalized etale cohomology theories / J. F. Jardine. – Basel ;
Boston ; Berlin : Birkhäuser, 1997
  (Progress in mathematics ; Vol. 146)
    ISBN 3-7643-5494-1 (Basel ...)
    ISBN 0-8176-5494-1 (Boston)
NE: GT

© 1997 Birkhäuser Verlag, P.O. Box 133, CH-4010 Basel, Switzerland
Printed on acid-free paper produced of chlorine-free pulp. TCF ∞
Printed in Germany
ISBN 3-7643-5494-1
ISBN 0-8176-5494-1

9 8 7 6 5 4 3 2 1

PREFACE

This book is not a textbook, and does not attempt to be a definitive statement of theory. If this monograph is a compendium of anything, it is one of techniques, specifically those leading to the proof of Thomason's étale cohomological descent theorem for Bott periodic K-theory, and perhaps beyond.

The proof given here for Thomason's result exposes most of the major extant ideas of the homotopy theory of presheaves of spectra on étale sites. This theory specializes to both sheaf cohomology theories and generalized cohomology theories in the traditional topological sense: a generalized étale cohomology theory is a cohomology theory which is represented by a presheaf of spectra on an étale site, by analogy with the way an ordinary spectrum represents a cohomology theory on spaces. There are many potential examples of such, but only étale K-theory has so far been studied in depth.

The homotopy theory of presheaves of spectra is a language as well as a technical device, which the original proof of the Thomason theorem predates and partially anticipates. I have maintained for several years now that his result should be proved entirely within this language, to clarify the proof and its relation with the Lichtenbaum-Quillen conjecture. This has been done successfully here, but it's been a long time coming.

There are several reasons for this, the chief among them being the requirement for an adequate theory of smash products of presheaves of spectra. It doesn't suffice to take an arbitrary theory of smash products of spectra and try to make it functorial, because there is a constant need to manipulate the resulting objects with closed model axioms to solve homotopy coherence problems: the standard constructions of K-theory spectra are, after all, not quite functorial. A theory of smash products of spectra and smash products of diagrams of spectra is therefore required which is sensitive to closed model structures, particularly those descended from the work of Bousfield and Friedlander.

For now, Adams' theory of handicrafted smash products works best for such purposes. A handicrafted smash product, or just a smash product, is a special case of the output of a diagonal functor from bispectra, or spectrum objects in spectra, to the category of spectra. The category of bispectra carries a strict and a stable closed model structure, both of which are promoted from the corresponding Bousfield-Friedlander theories for ordinary spectra, in such a way that the diagonal functor preserves stable weak equivalences and fibrations, and also defines an equivalence of the associated stable homotopy categories. The category of bispectra is a different, but equivalent, model for the stable category. Corresponding theories exist more generally for n-fold spectra, and for presheaves of bispectra and n-fold spectra on arbitrary Grothendieck sites. The strict and stable closed model structures for presheaves of bispectra, in particular, are bootstrapped from the corresponding theories for presheaves of spectra, following the relation between bispectra and ordinary spectra. The diagonal functor from presheaves of bispectra to presheaves of spectra plays the same role as in the ordinary case, and a theory of smash products of presheaves of spectra results, which includes a sensible description of function spectrum objects.

These results about smash products are the subject of the first three chapters of this book. The first applications appear in the third chapter, and include a projection formula for the abstract transfer associated to finite Galois extensions for presheaves of spectra defined on étale sites of fields.

The applications of the theory of smash products of presheaves of spectra concern K-theory, but one has to first make sure that K-theory presheaves are acceptable input for the smash products machine. The K-theory presheaf is most generally constructed on an arbitrary diagram of schemes by feeding a pseudo-functor taking values in symmetric monoidal categories arising from vector bundles on schemes to a combination of Waldhausen's $S.$-construction and supercoherence theory. The cup product on such a diagram is induced by a pseudo-natural bilinear map given on each of the underlying schemes by tensor product. One has to make sense of this idea, and show how to use it — this is the subject of Chapter 5. Supercoherence plus $S.$ is verbose and perhaps a bit ugly, but the output in this case is worth the drudgery: in conjunction with the results from the early part of the book, the theory implies that the cup product in K-theory and étale K-theory is induced by a maps of presheaves of bispectra. Supercoherence is used to show that the K-theory transfer for a finite Galois extension is equivariant for the action of the Galois group up to canonical stable equivalence, and is natural with respect to induced field extensions; our freshly minted approach to cup products implies that the projection formula is equivariant as well. The chapter closes with a demonstration that the K-theory norm for a finite Galois extension is homotopic to an abstract norm which is defined by adding up the actions of the Galois group elements. This in itself is not new, but the homotopy preserves a rather subtle kind of equivariance which becomes crucial in the proof of Thomason's theorem.

Some attempt is made at the outset of Chapter 5 to bring the reader into the supercoherence frame of mind, but none of more technical definitions or proofs from [28] are repeated here. This is the approach taken to the literature in general: I can be mildly encouraging here and there (particularly in Chapters 2, 3 and 6) about the published theory of simplicial presheaves and presheaves of spectra ([22], [23], [24] and [27]), but I quote from it ruthlessly. Similar treatment is given to other sources that I consider to be standard, such as the book of Bousfield and Kan [9], Milne's book [42], anything written by either Serre or Quillen, and the Bousfield-Friedlander paper [8].

There are, however, no references in the text to unpublished material in the absence of specific workarounds, and any required folk theorems are actually proved. This is responsible, in particular, for the content of the Chapter 4, which either plugs little gaps in the literature, or presents certain existing results in a fashion that is more to my taste. I might have inadvertently done something new in places — the discussion of the derived category that appears in the sixth section may be an example.

The sixth chapter begins with an introduction to generalized étale cohomology theories in the large, including a formal description of the construction of the descent spectral sequence from Postnikov towers. The discussion quickly moves, in subsequent sections, to one of generalized Galois cohomology and its relationship with generalized Čech cohomology, which is the technical heart of the matter in all discussions of Galois descent for the K-theory of fields. A generalized Galois cohomology theory is generalized étale cohomology theory for a field; it is also a special case of a theory which is represented by a presheaf of spectra on the site which underlies the classifying topos of a profinite group. The latter observation is essential for the applications of the final chapter. The sixth chapter closes with a discussion of bigness of the big étale site, and its relatives. It turns out that it is often technically very convenient, and maybe even necessary, to work with sites which are bigger than the big site; the last section of Chapter 6 is supposed to alleviate any set-theoretic discomfort this may cause.

The final chapter is a bit of a giant. The first five sections are occupied with the proof of Thomason's descent theorem, and its corollaries. The key point is that Bott periodic K-theory and its associated étale (or Galois) invariants coincide for fields containing the right primitive roots of unity and having a finite Tate-Tsen filtration. This is what I call Thomason's descent theorem: everything else follows from this statement by means involving greatly reduced technical exertion. There is a parallel with the Lichtenbaum-Quillen conjecture which is drawn in the final section, in that it is explicitly shown that if you can prove Lichtenbaum-Quillen for the fields appearing in the hard case of Thomason's descent theorem, then it's all over. The slick method for going from statements about the K-theory of fields to the K-theory of more general schemes involves a separate section on the Nisnevich topology. This section contains a new and short proof of the Nisnevich descent theorem for the K-theory of regular separated Noetherian schemes. The brevity of this proof is achieved by replacing Godement resolutions with globally fibrant models.

In all, this book consists of seven chapters. Each of these has its own formal introduction.

This main part of the research and writing for the preliminary version of this monograph was conducted over a period of three years, beginning in 1991–92, while I was a visiting professor at the University of British Columbia. Work on the book continued while visiting Université Paris VII in May of 1993, and was completed while I held a Distinguished Research Professorship in the 1993–94 academic year at the University of Western Ontario. This work was supported throughout by grants from the Natural Sciences and Engineering

Research Council of Canada. I would like to take this opportunity to thank all of these institutions for their hospitality and/or support.

I would like to affectionately thank my wife Catharine and children Courtney and Bryce for their patience and emotional support during the various gestation periods of this manuscript.

This book is dedicated to the memory of

Robert W. Thomason (1952–1995).

London, Ontario, Canada

October, 1996

CONTENTS

Chapter 7. Bott periodic K-theory

Chapter 1. Smash products of spectra

I take the point of view that a spectrum X is a combinatorial object, which consists of pointed simplicial sets X^n, $n \geq 0$, and pointed simplicial set maps $S^1 \wedge X^n \to X^{n+1}$. A map of spectra has the obvious definition, and these maps organize themselves into a category that is denoted by **Spt**.

No distinction will be made between prespectra and spectra. Instead, we shall use the Bousfield-Friedlander stable closed simplicial model structure for the category of spectra. This structure involves three distinguished classes of maps in the category **Spt**, called cofibrations, stable weak equivalences and stable fibrations. A *cofibration* is a map of spectra $i : U \to V$ such that the map $i : U^0 \to V^0$ at level 0 and all of the induced maps

$$(S^1 \wedge V^n) \cup_{(S^1 \cup U^n)} U^{n+1} \to V^{n+1}$$

are inclusions of pointed simplicial sets. A *stable equivalence* is a map which induces an isomorphism in all stable homotopy groups, where the stable homotopy groups $\pi_* X$ of a spectrum X are defined to be the stable homotopy groups of the associated spectrum $|X|$ in the topological space category that is obtained by applying the realization functor to all the pointed simplicial sets involved in X. A *stable fibration* is a map which has the right lifting property with respect to all maps which are both cofibrations and stable equivalences. The basic organizing principle is that the category of spectra, together with these three classes of maps, satisfies Quillen's axioms for a closed simplicial model category. The proof of this result will not be reproduced here — the reader who is unfamiliar with it should consult [8]. I shall also assume that the reader knows the basic tricks for manipulating the closed model axioms [46]. It will be important to know in particular that X is a stably fibrant spectrum if and only if all "spaces" X^n are Kan complexes, and all induced maps $X^n \to \Omega X^{n+1}$ are weak homotopy equivalences.

This chapter contains some of the basic concepts that will be used in subsequent chapters in the study of bispectra, n-fold spectra and diagrams of such. One of the problems that is addressed here is to give a definition of the smash product $X \wedge Y$ for spectra X and Y that is manifestly functorial, so that it can be applied without change to the diagrams of spectra that are encountered in later chapters.

Everyone will probably agree that, if X and Y are spectra, then the gadget consisting of the pointed simplicial sets

$$X^n \wedge Y^n, \qquad n, m \geq 0, \tag{1.1}$$

with all the pointed maps

$$S^1 \wedge X^n \wedge Y^m \to X^{n+1} \wedge Y^m \quad \text{and} \quad S^1 \wedge X^n \wedge Y^m \to X^n \wedge Y^{m+1} \tag{1.2}$$

which are induced by the structural maps for X and Y, is a natural model for a bispectrum. A bispectrum can and will be interpreted as a spectrum object in the category of spectra. The problem of extracting a stable homotopy type from the smash product bispectrum (1.1) (which one then calls the smash product of X and Y) has been one of the great aesthetic bugbears of the foundations of stable homotopy theory.

I have found that Adams' original handicrafted smash products [2] work very well for the applications that appear in this book. The method is to construct an associated diagonal spectrum in many apparently different ways by "snaking through" the bispectrum $X^n \wedge Y^m$ with the maps (1.2) in such a way that the indices n, m both tend to infinity, and then show that all of these different constructions give the same stable homotopy type. The coincidence of these stable homotopy types is proved here as a consquence of the more general but analogous result for arbitrary bispectra (Theorem 1.27, or even for n-fold spectra: Theorem 1.32). The proof is combinatorial and functorial, and depends on a homotopy theory for "partial spectra", which is introduced in a minimalist way in Section 1.2. The key to the proof of Theorem 1.27 is that any two diagonal spectrum constructions for a bispectrum differ on a certain partial spectrum by twists of circle smash factors, which twists can be ignored up to homotopy by further refining the structure.

We shall see in Section 2.2 that any of these diagonal spectrum constructions

$$d : \mathbf{Spt}^2 \to \mathbf{Spt}$$

from the category of bispectra to the category of spectra induces an equivalence of associated stable homotopy theories.

1.1. Basic definitions

In all that follows, and as in [8], a *spectrum* X consists of pointed simplicial sets X^n and pointed maps

$$\sigma : S^1 \wedge X^n \to X^{n+1}, \qquad n \geq 0.$$

Here, S^1 is the simplicial circle $\Delta^1/\partial\Delta^1$, with the obvious choice of base point. Say that the maps σ are *bonding maps*. A *map of spectra* $f : X \to Y$ consists of pointed simplicial set maps $f^n : X^n \to Y^n$, $n \geq 0$, which preserve structure in the sense that all diagrams of the form

$$
\begin{array}{ccc}
S^1 \wedge X^n & \xrightarrow{\ \sigma\ } & X^{n+1} \\
{\scriptstyle S^1 \wedge f^n}\downarrow & & \downarrow{\scriptstyle f^{n+1}} \\
S^1 \wedge Y^n & \xrightarrow{\ \sigma\ } & Y^{n+1}
\end{array}
$$

commute.

Suppose that $m \in \mathbb{Z}$. Then a spectrum $X[m]$ is defined by $X[m]^n = X^{m+n}$ in the range of numbers n for which the definition makes sense. The spectrum $X[m]$ is a model for iterated suspensions or loops according to whether m is positive or negative.

The *fake suspension spectrum* ΣX is defined by setting

$$\Sigma X^n = S^1 \wedge X^n \qquad \text{for } n \geq 0, \text{ and}$$
$$\sigma = S^1 \wedge \sigma : S^1 \wedge S^1 \wedge X^n \to S^1 \wedge X^{n+1}.$$

Then the bonding maps $\sigma : S^1 \wedge X^n \to X^{n+1}$ for X induce a natural map of spectra

$$\sigma_* : \Sigma X \to X[1].$$

The *fake loop spectrum* ΩX is the spectrum whose space at level n is the loop space ΩX^n, and with bonding maps

$$\Omega \sigma : \Omega X^n \to \Omega X^{n+1}.$$

The space ΩX^n is the pointed function complex $\mathbf{hom}_*(S^1, X^n)$ (see below). Note also the abuse: σ is really the adjoint of the bonding map $S^1 \wedge X^n \to X^{n+1}$ — no distinction will be made between these constructions, except where it could cause confusion. There is a canonical map

$$\sigma : X \to \Omega X[1]$$

which is induced by the bonding maps

$$\sigma : X^n \to \Omega X^{n+1}.$$

The fake loop spectrum construction is natural in X. It is the basis of the construction of the associated stably fibrant spectrum QX in the case where X is strictly fibrant in the sense that each X^n is a Kan complex, for then QX may be defined to be the colimit of the diagram

$$X \xrightarrow{\sigma} \Omega X[1] \xrightarrow{\Omega \sigma} \Omega^2 X[2] \xrightarrow{\Omega^2 \sigma} \dots.$$

REMARK 1.3. As noted in the introductory paragraphs above, and according to a result of Bousfield and Friedlander [8, Lemma A.9] a *stably fibrant spectrum* X is a spectrum consisting of Kan complexes X^n, $n \geq 0$, such that each of the bonding maps $\sigma : X^n \to \Omega X^{n+1}$ is a weak equivalence. It is well known (and can be seen as a consequence of Lemma 2.3 of the next chapter) that every spectrum X has an associated natural map $\eta : X \to X_{Kan}$ such that X_{Kan} is strictly fibrant and all induced level maps $\eta : X^n \to X^n_{Kan}$ are weak equivalences of simplicial sets. One usually says that the map η is a *strictly fibrant model* for X. The object that people usually call an Ω-*spectrum* is, in this language, a spectrum whose strictly fibrant model is stably fibrant. This is the definition of Ω-spectrum that will be used here. ∎

Observe that any map of spectra $f : \Sigma X \to Y$ determines unique maps $f_*^n : X^n \to \Omega Y^n$, by adjointness. The maps f_*^n fit together to give a map of spectra $f_* : X \to \Omega Y$. Conversely, one can start with a map $g : X \to \Omega Y$ and use adjointness to produce a map of spectra $g_* : \Sigma X \to Y$. These two processes are inverse to each other, and so there is a natural bijection

$$\hom_{\mathbf{Spt}}(\Sigma X, Y) \cong \hom_{\mathbf{Spt}}(X, \Omega Y). \qquad (1.4)$$

Note that $\sigma_* : \Sigma X \to X[1]$ is the adjoint of the map $\sigma : X \to \Omega X[1]$.

The following result is well known. It is proved here mainly to establish notation.

LEMMA 1.5. *The map* $\sigma_* : \Sigma X \to X[1]$ *is a stable homotopy equivalence.*

PROOF: σ_* will be a stable homotopy equivalence if and only its realization $|\sigma_*|$ is a stable homotopy equivalence of ordinary spectra in the category of pointed topological spaces. The realization of σ is the corresponding construction for pointed topological spaces, so we shall argue completely within that category by using the topological loop space. Suppose henceforth that X is a topological spectrum.

The first step is to show that the canonical map

$$\eta : X \to \Omega \Sigma X$$

is a stable weak equivalence. But

$$X = \varinjlim X^{(i)},$$

where $X^{(i)}$ is the part of X which is generated by the first i terms, namely

$$X^0, \ldots, X^i, S^1 \wedge X^i, S^1 \wedge S^1 \wedge X^i, \ldots$$

All spaces of $X^{(i)}$ are eventually highly connected, so the Freudenthal suspension theorem implies that the map

$$\eta : X^{(i)} \to \Omega \Sigma X^{(i)}$$

is a stable weak equivalence. Pass to the filtered colimit to prove the claim.

A cofinality argument implies that the map $\sigma : X \to \Omega X[1]$ is a stable equivalence. It follows that $\sigma_* : \Sigma X \to X[1]$ is a stable equivalence if and only if the map $\Omega \sigma_* : \Omega \Sigma X \to \Omega X[1]$ is a stable equivalence. The triangle

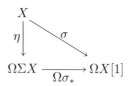

commutes, and the result is proved. ∎

Suppose that U is a pointed simplicial set and that K is arbitrary. The *half smash product* $U \ltimes K$ is the pointed simplicial set which is defined by

$$U \ltimes K = (U \times K)/(* \times K),$$

where $*$ denotes the base point of U. Equivalently, $U \ltimes K$ may be constructed by forming the smash product $U \wedge K_+$, where K_+ is the pointed simplicial set $K \sqcup \{*\}$.

If U and V are arbitrary pointed simplicial sets, then the *pointed function complex*

$$\mathbf{hom}_*(U, V)$$

is the simplicial set having for n-simplices all pointed maps of the form $U \ltimes \Delta^n \to V$. In particular, the *loop space* ΩU is defined to be the function complex $\mathbf{hom}_*(S^1, U)$. This definition is subject to the caveat that ΩU might not make any homotopical sense unless U is a Kan complex.

Suppose that Y is a spectrum and that K is a pointed simplicial set. Then there is a spectrum $\mathbf{hom}_*(K, Y)$ with space at level n given by the function complex $\mathbf{hom}_*(K, Y^n)$, and with bonding maps defined to be the composites

$$\mathbf{hom}_*(K, Y^n) \xrightarrow{\mathbf{hom}_*(K,\sigma)} \mathbf{hom}_*(K, \Omega Y^{n+1}) \cong \Omega \mathbf{hom}_*(K, Y^{n+1}).$$

The indicated isomorphism is induced by the canonical twist isomorphism

$$\tau : K \wedge S^1 \xrightarrow{\cong} S^1 \wedge K.$$

Dually, if X is a spectrum, then we may define a spectrum $X \wedge K$ by specifying the space at level n to be $X^n \wedge K$, and by defining the bonding maps to be the maps

$$\sigma \wedge K : S^1 \wedge X^n \wedge K \to X^{n+1} \wedge K.$$

Any map of spectra $f : X \to \mathbf{hom}_*(K, Y)$ consists of pointed simplicial set maps $f^n : X^n \to \mathbf{hom}_*(K, Y^n)$, each of which can be identified with a pointed map $f^n_* : X^n \wedge K \to Y^n$, by the usual exponential law. It is an elementary exercise to show that the adjoints f^n_* fit together to give a map of spectra $f_* : X \wedge K \to Y$, and conversely, implying that there is a natural isomorphism

$$\hom_{\mathbf{Spt}}(X \wedge K, Y) \cong \hom_{\mathbf{Spt}}(X, \mathbf{hom}_*(K, Y)). \tag{1.6}$$

For spectra X and Y, the *function complex*

$$\mathbf{hom}_*(X, Y)$$

is the pointed simplicial set which is defined by

$$\mathbf{hom}_*(X, Y)_n = \mathrm{hom}_{\mathbf{Spt}}(X \ltimes \Delta^n, Y).$$

The isomorphism (1.6) induces a natural isomorphism of pointed simplicial sets

$$\mathbf{hom}_*(X \wedge K, Y) \cong \mathbf{hom}_*(X, \mathbf{hom}_*(K, Y)).$$

Similarly the natural isomorphism (1.4) extends to a natural isomorphism of pointed simplicial sets

$$\mathbf{hom}_*(\Sigma X, Y) \cong \mathbf{hom}_*(X, \Omega Y). \tag{1.7}$$

We are entitled from the constructions just given to consider spectra of the form $X \wedge S^1$ and $\mathbf{hom}_*(S^1, Y)$. The spectrum $X \wedge S^1$ is the (real) *suspension spectrum* of X, and $\mathbf{hom}_*(S^1, Y)$ is the *loop spectrum* of Y. Note that $\mathbf{hom}_*(S^1, Y)$ is the loop object that arises from the various closed simplicial model structures on the category of spectra (see [8]); the adjoint construction $X \wedge S^1$ is therefore the "correct" suspension of X.

Although it might look like these spectra should be isomorphic to ΣX and ΩY respectively, they are not. Observe in particular that if we take the spaces of $X \wedge S^1$ and apply the twist isomorphism

$$X^n \wedge S^1 \xrightarrow[\cong]{\tau} S^1 \wedge X^n,$$

then $X \wedge S^1$ is isomorphic to a spectrum having spaces $S^1 \wedge X^n$, but with bonding maps $\tilde{\sigma}$ given by the composites

$$S^1 \wedge S^1 \wedge X^n \xrightarrow{S^1 \wedge \tau} S^1 \wedge X^n \wedge S^1 \xrightarrow{\sigma \wedge S^1} X^n \wedge S^1 \xrightarrow{\tau} S^1 \wedge X^n.$$

Note that there is a commutative diagram

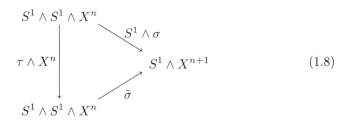

$$\tag{1.8}$$

The best that one can say about the comparison of ΣX and $X \wedge S^1$ is the following:

LEMMA 1.9. *The spectra ΣX and $X \wedge S^1$ are naturally isomorphic in the stable homotopy category.*

PROOF: The proof will follow from the commutativity of the diagram (1.8), and a technique which appears in the next section.

COROLLARY 1.10. *The spectra ΩY and $\mathbf{hom}_*(S^1, Y)$ are naturally stable homotopy equivalent, provided that Y is strictly fibrant in the sense that all of its constituent spaces are Kan complexes.*

PROOF: If X and Y are spectra such that X is cofibrant and Y is stably fibrant, then ΩY is stably fibrant and ΣX is cofibrant. Also, since $\sigma : Y \to \Omega Y[1]$ is a natural stable equivalence, if follows that the functor $Y \mapsto \Omega Y$ preserves stable equivalences. Finally, the functor $X \mapsto X \wedge S^1$ preserves stable equivalences by a cofibration sequence argument, so that $X \mapsto \Sigma X$ preserves weak equivalences as a result of Lemma 1.9.

There are natural isomorphisms

$$[X, \Omega Y] \cong \pi_0 \mathbf{hom}_*(X, \Omega Y)$$
$$\cong \pi_0 \mathbf{hom}_*(\Sigma X, Y)$$
$$\cong [\Sigma X, Y].$$

Note the use of the underlying isomorphism of pointed simplicial sets

$$\mathbf{hom}_*(\Sigma X, Y) \cong \mathbf{hom}_*(X, \Omega Y)$$

from (1.7) in the above. Similarly, $X \wedge S^1$ is cofibrant and $\mathbf{hom}_*(S^1, Y)$ is fibrant, so there is a natural isomorphism

$$[X \wedge S^1, Y] \cong [X, \mathbf{hom}_*(S^1, Y)]$$

which is induced by the appropriate isomorphisms of function complexes. But ΣX and $X \wedge S^1$ are naturally stably equivalent by Lemma 1.9, so formal nonsense implies that ΩY and $\mathbf{hom}_*(S^1, Y)$ are naturally isomorphic in the stable category. ∎

REMARK 1.11. A similar argument, based on Lemma 1.5, implies that the spectra ΩY and $Y[-1]$ are naturally isomorphic in the stable category if Y is strictly fibrant. ∎

1.2. Partial spectra
Suppose that k_i, $i \geq 0$ is an infinite list of integers, such that $k_0 = 0$, and each $k_i \geq 1$ for $i \geq 1$. Let

$$n_i = \sum_{j=0}^{i} k_j.$$

Suppose that the list $K = \{k_i\}$ is fixed in all that follows.

A *partial spectrum* (relative to the choice of list of integers K) is defined to be a collection of pointed simplicial sets X^{n_i}, $i \geq 0$, together with bonding maps

$$\sigma : X^{n_i} \to \Omega^{k_{i+1}} X^{n_{i+1}}.$$

The functor Ω^n can be interpreted in many ways. Let's assume that, if Z is a pointed simplicial set, then $\Omega^n Z$ is the pointed function complex which is obtained by applying the loop functor n times. Write S^n for the n-fold smash product $S^1 \wedge \cdots \wedge S^1$, so that there is a canonical isomorphism

$$\Omega^n Z \cong \mathbf{hom}_*(S^n, Z).$$

It is often preferable to regard a partial spectrum X as a collection of pointed simplicial sets X^{n_i}, together with pointed (bonding) maps

$$\sigma : S^{k_{i+1}} \wedge X^{n_i} \to X^{n_{i+1}}.$$

I shall not distinguish notationally between the bonding map σ and its adjoint.

A *map* $f : X \to Y$ of partial spectra consists of pointed simplicial set maps $f^{n_i} : X^{n_i} \to Y^{n_i}$, $i \geq 0$, which respect the bonding maps in the sense that the following diagrams commute

$$
\begin{array}{ccc}
X^{n_i} & \xrightarrow{\sigma} & \Omega^{k_{i+1}} X^{n_{i+1}} \\
\downarrow{\scriptstyle f^{n_i}} & & \downarrow{\scriptstyle \Omega^{k_{i+1}} f^{n_{i+1}}} \\
Y^{n_i} & \xrightarrow{\sigma} & \Omega^{k_{i+1}} X^{n_{i+1}}
\end{array}
$$

Equivalently, the adjoints of these diagrams should commute. The category of partial spectra, defined relative to the sequence K, will be denoted by $\mathbf{Spt}_K$.

Let X be a partial spectrum whose constituent spaces X^{n_i} are all fibrant, and define the simplicial set QX^{n_i} to be the filtered colimit of the sequence

$$X^{n_i} \xrightarrow{\sigma} \Omega^{k_{i+1}} X^{n_{i+1}} \xrightarrow{\Omega^{k_{i+1}}\sigma} \Omega^{k_{i+1}+k_{i+2}} X^{n_{i+2}} \xrightarrow{\Omega^{k_{i+1}+k_{i+2}}\sigma} \cdots$$

Then the diagram

$$
\begin{array}{ccccc}
X^{n_i} & \xrightarrow{\sigma} & \Omega^{k_{i+1}} X^{n_{i+1}} & \xrightarrow{\Omega^{k_{i+1}}\sigma} & \cdots \\
\downarrow{\scriptstyle \sigma} & & \downarrow{\scriptstyle \Omega^{k_{i+1}}\sigma} & & \\
\Omega^{k_{i+1}} X^{n_{i+1}} & \xrightarrow{\Omega^{k_{i+1}}\sigma} & \Omega^{k_{i+1}+k_{i+2}} X^{n_{i+2}} & \xrightarrow{\Omega^{k_{i+1}+k_{i+2}}\sigma} & \cdots
\end{array}
$$

commutes, and so there is an induced pointed simplicial set map

$$\sigma : QX^{n_i} \to \Omega^{k_{i+1}} QX^{n_{i+1}},$$

which is an isomorphism. One says that QX is the *stably fibrant* partial spectrum which is associated to X. This construction is functorial.

Suppose that Z and W are pointed simplicial sets. There is a pointed natural map

$$\chi : S|Z| \wedge S|W| \to S|Z \wedge W|$$

where $S|Z|$ denotes the effect of applying the singular functor to the realization of Z. The map χ is induced by the diagram

$$
\begin{array}{ccc}
S|X \vee Y| & \longleftarrow & S|X| \vee S|Y| \\
\downarrow & & \uparrow \\
S|X \times Y| & \xrightarrow{\cong} & S|X| \times S|Y|
\end{array}
$$

It follows that, if X is a partial spectrum, then there is a partial spectrum X_{Kan} such that

$$X^{n_i}_{Kan} = S|X^{n_i}|,$$

and with bonding maps

$$S^{k_{i+1}} \wedge S|X^{n_i}| \xrightarrow{\sigma} S|X^{n_{i+1}}|$$

induced by the transformation χ, the adjunction map $\eta : S^{k_{i+1}} \to S|S^{k_{i+1}}|$ and the original bonding maps of X. The assigment $X \mapsto X_{Kan}$ is functorial, and there is a natural (strict) weak equivalence

$$\eta : X \to X_{Kan}$$

which is defined by the adjunction maps

$$\eta : X^{n_i} \to S|X^{n_i}|.$$

X_{Kan} is called the *strictly fibrant model* for X; the point is that all of the spaces $X^{n_i}_{Kan}$ are Kan complexes. A *strictly fibrant* partial spectrum Y is a partial spectrum whose spaces Y^{n_i} are all Kan complexes. The notation $(\mathbf{Spt}_K)_{Kan}$ will be used to denote the full subcategory of strictly fibrant partial spectra, just as $\mathbf{Spt}_{Kan}$ denotes the category of strictly fibrant spectra.

A map $f : X \to Y$ of partial spectra is said to be a *stable equivalence* if the associated map $Qf : QX_{Kan} \to QY_{Kan}$ consists of space level weak equivalences $Qf^{n_i} : QX_{Kan}^{n_i} \to QY_{Kan}^{n_i}$ for all $i \geq 0$. In particular, the canonical map $\gamma : X \to QX_{Kan}$ is a stable weak equivalence.

The map f is a *strict weak equivalence* if all of the maps $f^{n_i} : X^{n_i} \to Y^{n_i}$ are weak equivalences. Thus f is a stable weak equivalence if and only if Qf is a strict weak equivalence.

Suppose that Z is a strictly fibrant spectrum. Then Z has a strictly fibrant partial spectrum LZ functorially associated to it, which is defined by

$$LZ^{n_i} = Z^{n_i},$$

and with bonding map

$$\sigma : LZ^{n_i} \to \Omega^{k_{i+1}} LZ^{n_{i+1}}$$

defined to be the composite

$$Z^{n_i} \xrightarrow{\sigma} \Omega Z^{n_i+1} \xrightarrow{\Omega\sigma} \Omega^2 Z^{n_i+2} \xrightarrow{\Omega^2\sigma} \cdots \xrightarrow{\Omega^{k_{i+1}-1}\sigma} \Omega^{k_{i+1}} Z^{n_{i+1}}.$$

For the sake of convenience, this composite will be referred to as the *canonical composite*; more generally, any composite of bonding maps of this type will be said to be canonical. The assignment $Z \mapsto LZ$ defines a functor

$$L : \mathbf{Spt}_{Kan} \to (\mathbf{Spt}_K)_{Kan}.$$

Conversely, there is a functor

$$R : (\mathbf{Spt}_K)_{Kan} \to \mathbf{Spt}_{Kan}.$$

If X is a partial spectrum, then RX is the spectrum having $RX^{n_i} = X^{n_i}$, and which is otherwise given by the sequence of spaces

$$X^0, \Omega^{k_1-1} X^{n_1}, \Omega^{k_1-2} X^{n_1}, \ldots, \Omega X^{n_1}, X^{n_1}, \Omega^{k_2-1} X^{n_2}, \ldots$$

and with bonding maps

$$X^{n_i} \xrightarrow{\sigma} \Omega^{k_{i+1}} X^{n_{i+1}} \qquad \text{for} \qquad RX^{n_i} \xrightarrow{\sigma} \Omega RX^{n_i+1},$$

and the identity everywhere else.

There is a natural map of spectra

$$\eta : Z \to RLZ.$$

η^{n_i} is defined to be the identity map

$$Z^{n_i} \to Z^{n_i} = RLZ^{n_i}$$

for all i, and, if $1 \leq j < k_{i+1}$, then η^{n_i+j} is defined to be the canonical composite

$$Z^{n_i+j} \to \Omega^{k_{i+1}-j} X^{n_{i+1}} Z^{n_i+1} = RLZ^{n_i+j}.$$

Observe also that, for any partial spectrum X, LRX is naturally isomorphic to X.

PROPOSITION 1.12. *The functors L and R preserve stable equivalences, and the natural map $\eta : Z \to RLZ$ is a stable equivalence if Z is strictly fibrant. Two spectra are stably equivalent if and only if their associated partial spectra are stably equivalent.*

PROOF: The claims in the first sentence follow from the observations that there are natural isomorphisms

$$QLZ^{n_i} \cong LQZ^{n_i} \quad \text{and} \quad QRX^{n_i} \cong RQX^{n_i}$$

for all i, and that $\eta : Z \to RLZ$ induces isomorphisms

$$Q\eta^{n_i} : QZ^{n_i} \xrightarrow{\cong} QRLZ^{n_i}$$

for all i. The claim in the second sentence is a consequence.   ∎

The functor $X \mapsto X_{Kan}$ implicitly involves partial spectrum objects in the category of pointed topological spaces. A *topological partial spectrum* Y consists of pointed topological spaces Y^{n_i} and pointed continuous maps

$$\sigma : S^{k_{i+1}} \wedge Y^{n_i} \to Y^{n_{i+1}},$$

where the notation $S^{k_{i+1}}$ means the usual thing, namely the k_{i+1}-sphere. The resulting category will be denoted by $\mathbf{Spt}_K(\mathbf{Top})$.

The strictly fibrant model functor $X \mapsto X_{Kan}$ is really a composite of two functors, namely a *realization functor*

$$|\ | : \mathbf{Spt}_K \to \mathbf{Spt}_K(\mathbf{Top}),$$

and a *singular functor*

$$S : \mathbf{Spt}_K(\mathbf{Top}) \to \mathbf{Spt}_K.$$

The reader can define these two functors. A map $f : Z \to W$ of topological partial spectra is a *stable equivalence* (respectively *strict weak equivalence*) if and only if the associated map $S(f) : S(Z) \to S(W)$ of strictly fibrant partial spectra is a stable equivalence (respectively strict weak equivalence).

Suppose the X is a partial spectrum. We shall now define the *telescope TX* of X. This definition will depend on an inductive construction of composable pairs of trivial cofibrations (and spaces) of the form

$$X^{n_i} \xrightarrow{j_i} CX^i \xrightarrow{\alpha_i} TX^{n_i}.$$

One begins in degree zero by requiring that $X^0 = CX^0 = TX^0$, and that j_0 and α_0 are identity isomorphisms.

The construction involves the mapping cylinders CX^{i+1} of the bonding maps $\sigma : S^{k_{i+1}} \wedge X^{n_i} \to X^{n_{i+1}}$, which, one recalls, are defined by the requirement that the following diagrams are pushouts:

$$
\begin{array}{ccc}
S^{k_{i+1}} \wedge X^{n_i} & \xrightarrow{\ \ \sigma\ \ } & X^{n_{i+1}} \\
\ \downarrow{\scriptstyle d^0} & & \ \downarrow{\scriptstyle j_{i+1}} \\
S^{k_{i+1}} \wedge X^{n_i} \ltimes \Delta^1 & \xrightarrow{\ \ \zeta_{i+1}\ \ } & CX^{i+1}
\end{array}
$$

Note that j_{i+1} is always a trivial cofibration. Let

$$\sigma_* : S^{k_{i+1}} \wedge X^{n_i} \to CX^{i+1}$$

denote the composite

$$S^{k_{i+1}} \wedge X^{n_i} \xrightarrow{\ d^1\ } S^{k_{i+1}} \wedge X^{n_i} \ltimes \Delta^1 \xrightarrow{\ \zeta_{i+1}\ } CX^{i+1}.$$

Suppose that $i \geq 0$, and that a trivial cofibration $\alpha_i : CX^i \to TX^{n_i}$ has been defined. Then a trivial cofibration α_{i+1} and the space $TX^{n_{i+1}}$ are defined by the requirement that the following diagram is a pushout:

$$
\begin{array}{ccc}
S^{k_{i+1}} \wedge X^{n_i} & \xrightarrow{\ \ \sigma_*\ \ } & CX^{i+1} \\
{\scriptstyle S^{k_{i+1}} \wedge j_i}\downarrow & & \\
S^{k_{i+1}} \wedge CX^i & & \downarrow{\scriptstyle \alpha_{i+1}} \\
{\scriptstyle S^{k_{i+1}} \wedge \alpha_i}\downarrow & & \\
S^{k_{i+1}} \wedge TX^{n_i} & \xrightarrow{\ \ \tilde{\sigma}\ \ } & TX^{n_{i+1}}
\end{array}
$$

Note that α_1 is forced to be an isomorphism. The spaces TX^{n_i} and the maps

$$\tilde{\sigma} : S^{k_{i+1}} \wedge TX^{n_i} \to TX^{n_{i+1}}$$

form the data for the partial spectrum TX. Observe that the mapping cylinder constructions CX^i are natural in X, so that $X \mapsto TX$ defines a functor

$$T : \mathbf{Spt}_K \to \mathbf{Spt}_K.$$

LEMMA 1.13. *Suppose that the diagrams*

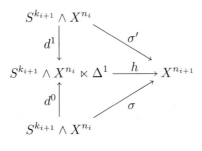

give an explicit list of homotopies from maps σ' to the bonding maps σ. Then these homotopies canonically determine a strict weak equivalence of partial spectra

$$h_* : TX \to X',$$

where X' is the partial spectrum having the same spaces X^{n_i} as X, but with bonding maps

$$\sigma' : S^{k_{i+1}} \wedge X^{n_i} \to X^{n_{i+1}}.$$

PROOF: There are unique maps $\hat{h} : CX^{i+1} \to X^{n_{i+1}}$ for $i \geq 0$ such that the following diagrams commute:

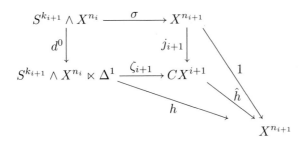

Define $\hat{h} : CX^0 \to X^0$ to be the identity on X^0.

Suppose that $h_* : TX^{n_j} \to X^{n_j}$ has been defined for $j \leq i$ such that $h_* \alpha_i = \hat{h}$, and such that the diagram

$$
\begin{array}{ccc}
S^{k_{j+1}} \wedge TX^{n_j} & \xrightarrow{\ \tilde{\sigma}\ } & TX^{n_{j+1}} \\
{\scriptstyle S^{k_{j+1}} \wedge h_*}\downarrow & & \downarrow{\scriptstyle h_*} \\
S^{k_{j+1}} \wedge X^{n_j} & \xrightarrow[\ \sigma'\ ]{} & X^{n_{j+1}}
\end{array}
$$

commutes for $j \leq i - 1$. Then there is a unique map

$$h_* : TX^{n_{i+1}} \to X^{n_{i+1}}$$

such that the following diagram commutes:

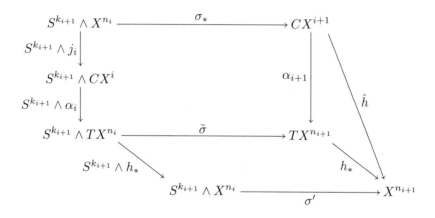

The map $h_* : TX^{n_{i+1}} \to X^{n_{i+1}}$ satisfies the conditions that were required in lower degrees, so the inductive step in the construction is complete.

Observe that j_{i+1} is a trivial cofibration, so that $\hat{h}$ is a weak equivalence in all degrees. But then α_{i+1} is also a trivial cofibration, so that h_* is a weak equivalence in all degrees. ∎

COROLLARY 1.14. *The constant homotopies*

$$S^{k_{i+1}} \wedge X^{n_i} \ltimes \Delta^1 \xrightarrow{pr} S^{k_{i+1}} \wedge X^{n_i} \xrightarrow{\sigma} X^{n_{i+1}}$$

determine a weak equivalence

$$TX \to X$$

which is natural with respect to partial spectra X.

COROLLARY 1.15. *The partial spectra X and X' of Lemma 1.13 are canonically strictly weakly equivalent.*

Since the realization functor preserves colimits, the realization $|TX|$ of the telescope TX is isomorphic to the telescope $T|X|$ (suitably defined) of the realization $|X|$. Furthermore, exactly the same method leads to a proof of the following topological analogue of Lemma 1.13

LEMMA 1.16. *Suppose that the diagrams*

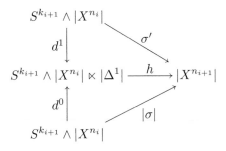

give an explicit list of homotopies from maps σ' to the bonding maps $|\sigma|$. Then these homotopies canonically determine a strict weak equivalence of partial spectra

$$h_* : T|X| \to |X|',$$

where $|X|'$ is the topological partial spectrum having the same spaces $|X^{n_i}|$ as $|X|$, but with bonding maps

$$\sigma' : S^{k_{i+1}} \wedge |X^{n_i}| \to |X^{n_{i+1}}|.$$

COROLLARY 1.17. *The topological partial spectra $|X|$ and $|X|'$ in the statement of Lemma 1.16 are canonically strictly weakly equivalent.*

REMARK 1.18. Lemma 1.9 is a consequence of Corollary 1.17. The point is that, since the diagram (1.8) commutes, there is a commutative diagram

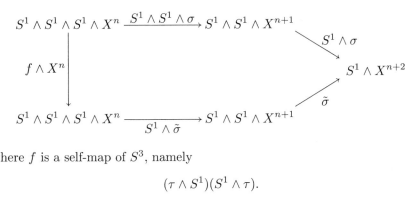

where f is a self-map of S^3, namely

$$(\tau \wedge S^1)(S^1 \wedge \tau).$$

The map f has degree 1, so that one may use Corollary 1.17 on the partial spectrum

$$\Sigma X^0, \Sigma X^2, \dots$$

to get the desired result. ∎

We have seen, in effect, that the strict homotopy type of a partial spectrum X is a homotopy invariant of its bonding maps. Our main application of this principle is the following result:

THEOREM 1.19. *Suppose that X is a partial spectrum, with bonding maps*

$$S^{k_{i+1}} \wedge X^{n_i} \xrightarrow{\sigma} X^{n_{i+1}}.$$

Choose permutations $\omega_i \in \Sigma_{k_i}$, and define

$$S^{k_{i+1}} \wedge X^{n_i} \xrightarrow{\sigma_\omega} X^{n_{i+1}}$$

to be the composites

$$S^{k_{i+1}} \wedge X^{n_i} \xrightarrow{\omega_{i+1} \wedge X^{n_i}} S^{k_{i+1}} \wedge X^{n_i} \xrightarrow{\sigma} X^{n_{i+1}},$$

where $\omega_{i+1} : S^{k_{i+1}} \to S^{k_{i+1}}$ is the map induced by the permutation ω_{i+1} which flips suspension coordinates. Let X_ω be the partial spectrum having the same spaces as X, but with bonding maps σ_ω. Then X and X_ω are naturally stably equivalent.

PROOF: We shall prove that the realizations $|X|$ and $|X_\omega|$ are naturally stably equivalent. Observe that the realization $|X_\omega|$ has bonding maps

$$S^{k_{i+1}} \wedge |X^{n_i}| \xrightarrow{\omega_{i+1} \wedge |X^{n_i}|} S^{k_{i+1}} \xrightarrow{|\sigma|} |X^{n_{i+1}}|,$$

where the induced map $\omega_{i+1} : S^{k_{i+1}} \to S^{k_{i+1}}$ of spheres is a map of degree ± 1.

If all but finitely many of the maps ω_i have degree 1, then we're done, by Lemma 1.16. Otherwise, we can find an infinite sequence of numbers i_ℓ such that each selfmap

$$\omega_{i_{\ell+1}} \wedge \omega_{i_{\ell+1}-1} \wedge \cdots \wedge \omega_{i_\ell+1}$$

of the sphere

$$S^{k_{i_{\ell+1}}} \wedge S^{k_{i_{\ell+1}-1}} \wedge \cdots \wedge S^{k_{i_\ell+1}}$$

has degree 1. Define σ_c to be the (canonical) composite

$$S^{k_{i_{\ell}+1}} \wedge \cdots \wedge S^{k_{i_{\ell}+1}} \wedge X^{n_{i_{\ell}}}$$

$$\downarrow S^{k_{i_{\ell}+1}} \wedge \cdots \wedge S^{k_{i_{\ell}+2}} \wedge \sigma$$

$$S^{k_{i_{\ell}+1}} \wedge \cdots \wedge S^{k_{i_{\ell}+2}} \wedge X^{n_{i_{\ell}}+1}$$

$$\downarrow S^{k_{i_{\ell}+1}} \wedge \cdots \wedge S^{k_{i_{\ell}+3}} \wedge \sigma$$

$$\vdots$$

$$S^{k_{i_{\ell}+1}} \wedge X^{n_{i_{\ell}+1}-1}$$

$$\downarrow \sigma$$

$$X^{n_{i_{\ell}+1}}$$

and define a corresponding map

$$(\sigma_\omega)_c : S^{k_{i_{\ell}+1}} \wedge \cdots \wedge S^{k_{i_{\ell}+1}} \wedge X^{n_{i_{\ell}}} \to X^{n_{i_{\ell}+1}}$$

using the bonding maps σ_ω. Then there is a commutative diagram

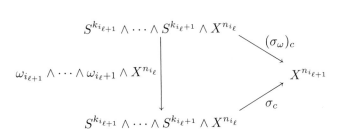

Thus, by taking a suitable partial subobject of the partial spectrum X, we reduce to the case where all of the ω_i have degree 1. ∎

1.3. Bispectra

A *bispectrum* consists of pointed simplicial sets $X^{n,m}$, $n \geq 0$, $m \geq 0$, together with pointed maps

$$\sigma_h : X^{n,m} \wedge S^1 \to X^{n+1,m}, \quad \text{and}$$
$$\sigma_v : S^1 \wedge X^{n,m} \to X^{n,m+1},$$

such that the diagram

$$
\begin{array}{ccc}
S^1 \wedge X^{n,m} \wedge S^1 & \xrightarrow{\ S^1 \wedge \sigma_h\ } & S^1 \wedge X^{n+1,m} \\
\downarrow{\scriptstyle \sigma_v \wedge S^1} & & \downarrow{\scriptstyle \sigma_v} \\
X^{n,m+1} \wedge S^1 & \xrightarrow[\ \sigma_h\ ]{} & X^{n+1,m+1}
\end{array}
\tag{1.20}
$$

commutes for all $n, m \geq 0$.

The collections of spaces $X^{n,*}$ together with the maps σ_v are spectra in the sense defined above. From this point of view, a bispectrum is a spectrum object in the category of spectra, provided that we use the functor $Z \mapsto Z \wedge S^1$ as a model for suspension.

A bispectrum may also be defined (and this is the characterization that will be used in practice) as a list of pointed simplicial sets $X^{i,j}$, $i, j \geq 0$, together with pointed simplicial set maps

$$
S^1 \wedge X^{i,j} \xrightarrow{\ \sigma_1\ } X^{i+1,j} \qquad \text{and} \qquad S^1 \wedge X^{i,j} \xrightarrow{\ \sigma_2\ } X^{i,j+1}
$$

such that the following diagram commutes for all i and j:

$$
\begin{array}{ccccc}
S^1 \wedge X^{i+1,j} & \xrightarrow{\qquad\qquad \sigma_2 \qquad\qquad} & & & X^{i+1,j+1} \\
\uparrow{\scriptstyle S^1 \wedge \sigma_1} & & & & \uparrow{\scriptstyle \sigma_1} \\
S^1 \wedge S^1 \wedge X^{i,j} & \xrightarrow[\ \tau \wedge X^{i,j}\ ]{} & S^1 \wedge S^1 \wedge X^{i,j} & \xrightarrow[\ S^1 \wedge \sigma_2\ ]{} & S^1 \wedge X^{i,j+1}
\end{array}
\tag{1.21}
$$

Here, $\tau \wedge X^{i,j}$ is the map which flips the S^1 factors and is the identity on $X^{i,j}$.

EXAMPLE 1.22. Suppose that X and Y are spectra. The *smash product* $X \wedge Y$ is the bispectrum specified by

$$
(X \wedge Y)^{n,m} = X^m \wedge Y^n,
$$

and with vertical suspension

$$
\sigma_v = \sigma \wedge Y^n : S^1 \wedge X^m \wedge Y^n \to X^{m+1} \wedge Y^n.
$$

The horizontal suspension $\sigma_h : X^m \wedge Y^n \wedge S^1 \to X^m \wedge Y^{n+1}$ is defined to be the composite

$$
X^m \wedge Y^n \wedge S^1 \xrightarrow{\ X^m \wedge \tau\ } X^m \wedge S^1 \wedge Y^n \xrightarrow{\ X^m \wedge \sigma\ } X^m \wedge Y^{n+1},
$$

where τ is the map which flips factors.   ■

Suppose that $\mathbb{N}$ denotes the set of natural numbers $\{0, 1, 2, \ldots\}$. An *admissible function* is a poset map

$$\phi : \mathbb{N} \to \mathbb{N} \times \mathbb{N}$$

such that

(1)
$$\phi(n+1) = \begin{cases} (\phi_1(n) + 1, \phi_2(n)), & \text{or} \\ (\phi_1(n), \phi_2(n) + 1), \end{cases}$$

where $\phi(n) = (\phi_1(n), \phi_2(n))$ defines the functions ϕ_1 and ϕ_2.

(2) For each $k \in \mathbb{N}$ there is a number $n \in \mathbb{N}$ such that

$$\phi_i(n) > k \qquad \text{for } i = 1, 2.$$

(3) $\phi(0) = (0, 0)$.

EXAMPLE 1.23. There is an admissible function μ which is defined by

$$\mu(2n) = (n, n), \qquad \text{and} \qquad \mu(2n+1) = (n+1, n). \qquad \blacksquare$$

Suppose that $(m_1, n_1) < (m_2, n_2)$ in the poset ordering on $\mathbb{N} \times \mathbb{N}$, and let

$$r = (n_2 - n_1) + (m_2 - m_1).$$

Then $r > 0$ by assumption.

Let $\mathbf{r}$ denote the ordinal number poset

$$0 \to 1 \to 2 \to \cdots \to r.$$

An *admissible path* from (m_1, n_1) to (m_2, n_2) is a function

$$\psi : \mathbf{r} \to \mathbb{N} \times \mathbb{N}$$

which satisfies the defining condition (1) above for an admissible function, and such that

$$\psi(0) = (m_1, n_1) \qquad \text{and} \qquad \psi(r) = (m_2, n_2).$$

The number r is called the *length* of the admissible path ψ.

An admissible function ϕ is an infinite list of admissible paths concatenated together such that condition (2) is satisfied, albeit from many points of view. In particular, any infinite list of numbers

$$0 < i_1 < i_2 < \ldots$$

determines a string of admissible paths, by defining $(m_k, n_k) = \phi(i_k)$.

EXAMPLE 1.24. Suppose that $(m_1, n_1) < (m_2, n_2)$ in $\mathbb{N} \times \mathbb{N}$, and set

$$r = (n_2 - n_1) + (m_2 - m_1)$$

as above. Somewhat arbitrarily, one defines the *canonical path* from (m_1, n_1) to (m_2, n_2) (of length r) as the path

$$\gamma : \mathbf{r} \to \mathbb{N} \times \mathbb{N}$$

which is defined by

$$\gamma(i) = \begin{cases} (m_1, n_1 + i) & \text{if } 0 \leq i \leq n_2 - n_1, \text{ and} \\ (m_1 + i - (n_2 - n_1), n_2) & \text{if } n_2 - n_1 \leq i \leq r. \end{cases}$$

The picture of the canonical path is the following:

$$(m_1, n_2) \longrightarrow (m_1 + 1, n_2) \longrightarrow \cdots \longrightarrow (m_2, n_2)$$
$$\uparrow$$
$$\vdots$$
$$\uparrow$$
$$(m_1, n_1 + 1)$$
$$\uparrow$$
$$(m_1, n_1)$$

∎

Any choice of an admissible function ϕ and a bispectrum X determines a spectrum X_ϕ such that

$$X_\phi^n = X^{\phi_1(n), \phi_2(n)},$$

and such that the bonding map, which is denoted by

$$\hat{\sigma}_n : S^1 \wedge X_\phi^n \to X_\phi^{n+1}$$

is the map

$$\sigma_2 : S^1 \wedge X^{\phi_1(n), \phi_2(n)} \to X^{\phi_1(n), \phi_2(n)+1}$$

if $\phi(n+1) = (\phi_1(n), \phi_2(n) + 1)$, or the map

$$\sigma_1 : S^1 \wedge X^{\phi_1(n), \phi_2(n)} \to X^{\phi_1(n)+1, \phi_2(n)}$$

if $\phi(n+1) = (\phi_1(n) + 1, \phi_2(n))$.

Similarly, any admissible path $\psi : \mathbf{r} \to \mathbb{N} \times \mathbb{N}$ from (m_1, n_1) to (m_2, n_2) determines a collection of bonding maps that is denoted by

$$\hat{\sigma}_i : S^1 \wedge X^{\psi(i)} \to X^{\psi(i+1)}$$

in the bispectrum X. We shall now consider strings of morphisms

$$S^r \wedge X^{\gamma(0)} \xrightarrow{S^{r-1} \wedge \hat{\sigma}_0} S^{r-1} \wedge X^{\gamma(1)} \xrightarrow{S^{r-2} \wedge \hat{\sigma}_1} \cdots \xrightarrow{\hat{\sigma}_{r-1}} X^{\gamma(r)}.$$

LEMMA 1.25. *Suppose that X is a bispectrum, and that $\gamma, \psi : \mathbf{r} \to \mathbb{N} \times \mathbb{N}$ are admissible paths from (m_1, n_1) to (m_2, n_2). Then there is an element ω of the symmetric group Σ_r such that the diagram*

commutes, where $\omega \wedge X^{m_1, n_1}$ is the map which flips suspension factors.

PROOF: By induction on r, there is a commutative diagram of the form

where $\tilde{\gamma}$ is the canonical path from (m_1, n_1) to $\psi(r-1) = \tilde{\gamma}(r-1)$. Write $\tilde{\psi}$ for the path consisting of $\tilde{\gamma}$ concatenated with the portion of ψ from $\psi(r-1)$ to $\psi(r)$.

Either $\psi(r-1) = (m_2 - 1, n_2)$ or $\psi(r-1) = (m_2, n_2 - 1)$. If $\psi(r-1) = (m_2 - 1, n_2)$ then we're done for then $\tilde{\psi}$ is canonical and the required map ω is $S^1 \wedge \omega'$.

Suppose that $\psi(r-1) = (m_2, n_2 - 1)$, and that $m_1 < m_2$ (for otherwise ψ is canonical). There are commutative diagrams

and

$$S^r \wedge X^{\psi(0)} \xrightarrow{S^{r-1} \wedge \hat\sigma_0} \cdots \xrightarrow{S^1 \wedge \hat\sigma_{r-3}} S^2 \wedge X^{\psi(r-2)}$$

with vertical map $S^{r-2} \wedge \tau \wedge X^{\psi(0)}$ on the left and $\tau \wedge X^{\psi(r-2)}$ on the right,

$$S^r \wedge X^{\psi(0)} \xrightarrow[S^{r-1} \wedge \hat\sigma_0]{} \cdots \xrightarrow[S^1 \wedge \hat\sigma_{r-3}]{} S^2 \wedge X^{\psi(r-2)}$$

where one notes that

$$\psi(r-1) = (\psi_1(r-1), \psi_2(r-1)) = (\psi_1(r-2) + 1, \psi_2(r-2)).$$

But then the portion of ψ from $\psi(r-2)$ to $\psi(r)$ may be replaced by the evident path of length 2 through

$$(\psi_1(r-2), \psi_2(r-2) + 1)$$

to obtain a path ψ'. Now use the inductive assumption to put the portion of the path ψ' from $\psi'(0)$ to $\psi'(r-1)$ into canonical form. ∎

LEMMA 1.26. *Suppose that X is a bispectrum, and that ψ and ϕ are admissible functions $\mathbb{N} \to \mathbb{N} \times \mathbb{N}$. Suppose that there is an infinite list of numbers $0 = n_0 < n_1 < n_2 < \ldots$ such that $\psi(n_i) = \phi(n_i)$ for all i. Let $(r_i, s_i) = \psi(n_i)$ and suppose further that*

$$min\{r_{i+1}, s_{i+1}\} > max\{r_i, s_i\}$$

for all i. Then the spectra X_ϕ and X_ψ are stably equivalent.

PROOF: We can suppose without loss of generality that all of the simplicial sets $X^{i,j}$ are fibrant. The lemma is proved by showing that the partial spectra LX_ϕ and LX_ψ are stably equivalent. These partial spectra are defined relative to the sequence $0 < n_1 < n_2 < \ldots$. Let

$$k_i = n_i - n_{i-1}$$

for $i \geq 1$.

The previous lemma implies that, for each i, there is a permutation $\omega_{i+1} \in \Sigma_{k_{i+1}}$ such that the following diagram commutes:

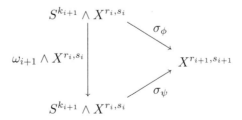

where σ_ϕ (respectively σ_ψ) refers to the bonding map of LX_ϕ (respectively LX_ψ). Now use Theorem 1.19. ∎

THEOREM 1.27. *Suppose that X is any bispectrum, and that ϕ is any admissible function. Then X_ϕ is non-canonically but naturally stably equivalent to X_μ.*

PROOF: Suppose that $\underline{n} = \{0, n_1, n_2, \dots\}$ is an infinite ascending sequence in $\mathbb{N}$, and that Z is a spectrum. Write $Z_{\underline{n}}$ for the partial spectrum

$$Z^0, Z^{n_1}, Z^{n_2}, \dots$$

which is determined by the list $\underline{n}$. We shall make repeated use of the fact that the stable homotopy type of Z is determined by $Z_{\underline{n}}$ (Proposition 1.12).

In particular, any such list $\underline{n}$ gives rise to a partial spectrum $(X_\mu)_{2\underline{n}}$

$$X^{0,0}, X^{n_1,n_1}, X^{n_2,n_2}, \dots$$

which determines the stable homotopy type of X_μ.

Similarly, since ϕ is admissible, one can inductively define an ascending list of numbers $\underline{n} = \{0, n_1, n_2, \dots\}$ in $\mathbb{N}$ by choosing n_{k+1} such that

$$\phi_j(n_{k+1}) > max\{\phi_1(n_k), \phi_2(n_k)\} \qquad \text{for } j = 1, 2.$$

Then the stable homotopy type X_ϕ is determined by the partial spectrum $(X_\phi)_{\underline{n}}$.

If the list $\underline{n}$ has a cofinal subsequence $I = \{0, i_1, i_2, \dots\}$ such that $\phi_1(i_j) = \phi_2(i_j)$ for all j, then X_ϕ is stably equivalent to X_μ, by Lemma 1.26. One may therefore assume without loss of generality that 0 is the maximal element in $\underline{n}$ at which ϕ_1 and ϕ_2 coincide.

Let B_k denote the "box" in $\mathbb{N} \times \mathbb{N}$ which is given by

$$B_k = \{(m, n) | \phi_1(n_k) \le m \le \phi_1(n_{k+1}), \phi_2(n_k) \le n \le \phi_2(n_{k+1})\}$$

Then B_k contains a point (m_k, m_k) for some number m_k — just use

$$m_k = max\{\phi_1(n_k), \phi_2(n_k)\}.$$

There is an admissible map $\gamma : \mathbb{N} \to \mathbb{N} \times \mathbb{N}$ such that

$$\gamma(n_k) = \phi(n_k)$$

for all n_k and

$$\gamma(j_k) = (m_k, m_k)$$

for some number j_k such that $n_k < j_k < n_{k+1}$. The point is that

$$n_{k+1} - n_k = (\phi_1(n_{k+1}) - \phi_1(n_k)) + (\phi_2(n_{k+1}) - \phi_2(n_k)),$$

and so any point within the box B_k appears on some admissible path joining these two points. But then the spectra X_ϕ, X_γ and X_μ have the same stable homotopy type.

The naturality assertion follows from the fact that the argument just given depends only on the admissible path ϕ. ∎

The spectrum X_μ associated to a bispectrum X is also denoted by dX, and is called the *diagonal* of X. In view of the result just proved, any of the models X_ϕ arising from an admissible function ϕ is also a candidate for such a diagonal in the stable homotopy category.

The other major elementary fact about bispectra is the following result:

LEMMA 1.28. *Suppose that $f : X \to Y$ is a map of bispectra such that each of the induced maps of spectra $f : X^{i,*} \to Y^{i,*}$ is a stable homotopy equivalence. Then the map $df : dX \to dY$ is a stable homotopy equivalence.*

PROOF: We may suppose that the bispectra X and Y consist of fibrant simplicial sets. The stable homotopy group $\pi_i^s dX$ is the colimit of the system

$$\pi_{i+2n}X^{n,n} \xrightarrow{\sigma_1} \pi_{i+1+2n}X^{n+1,n} \xrightarrow{\sigma_2} \pi_{i+2+2n}X^{n+1,n+1} \xrightarrow{\sigma_1} \cdots$$

But a cofinality argument implies that this colimit coincides with the colimit of the diagram

$$
\begin{array}{ccccccc}
\pi_{i+2n}X^{n,n} & \xrightarrow{\sigma_1} & \pi_{i+1+2n}X^{n+1,n} & \xrightarrow{\sigma_1} & \pi_{i+2+2n}X^{n+2,n} & \xrightarrow{\sigma_1} & \cdots \\
\downarrow{\scriptstyle (-1)^n\sigma_2} & & \downarrow{\scriptstyle (-1)^{n+1}\sigma_2} & & \downarrow{\scriptstyle (-1)^{n+2}\sigma_2} & & \\
\pi_{i+1+2n}X^{n,n+1} & \xrightarrow{\sigma_1} & \pi_{i+2+2n}X^{n+1,n+1} & \xrightarrow{\sigma_1} & \pi_{i+3+2n}X^{n+1,n+2} & \longrightarrow & \cdots \\
\downarrow{\scriptstyle (-1)^n\sigma_2} & & \downarrow{\scriptstyle (-1)^{n+1}\sigma_2} & & \downarrow & & \\
\pi_{i+2+2n}X^{n,n+2} & \xrightarrow{\sigma_1} & \pi_{i+3+2n}X^{n+1,n+2} & \longrightarrow & \pi_{i+4+2n}X^{n+2,n+2} & \longrightarrow & \cdots \\
\downarrow{\scriptstyle (-1)^n\sigma_2} & & \downarrow & & \downarrow & & \\
\vdots & & \vdots & & \vdots & &
\end{array}
$$

It follows that $\pi_i^s dX$ is the colimit of the string

$$\pi_{i+n}^s X^{n,*} \to \pi_{i+1+n}^s X^{n+1,*} \to \pi_{i+2+n}^s X^{n+2,*} \to \cdots \qquad \blacksquare$$

1.4. n-fold spectra

There are various ways to define the concept of n-fold spectrum. In particular, there is an "internal" description which is a generalization of the appropriate definition of bispectrum.

An *n-fold spectrum* consists of pointed simplicial sets

$$X^{i_1, i_2, \dots, i_n}, \qquad i_j \geq 0,$$

together with pointed simplicial set maps

$$\sigma_j : S^1 \wedge X^{i_1, \dots, i_j, \dots, i_n} \to X^{i_1, \dots, i_j+1, \dots, i_n},$$

$1 \leq j \leq n$ (called *bonding maps*), such that for each $1 \leq k < j \leq n$, and list of indexes i_r, $r \neq j, k$, the array of simplicial sets

$$X^{i_1, \dots, \overset{k}{*}, \dots, \overset{j}{*}, \dots, i_n},$$

together with the bonding maps σ_j and σ_k forms a bispectrum in the sense that diagrams analogous to (1.21) must commute.

The main purpose of this section is to show that one can define a realization for n-fold spectra, by analogy with the realization of bispectra. The combinatorics is a little messier, but we've already done most of the homotopical work, so some details will be left to the reader.

An *admissible function* $\phi : \mathbb{N} \to \mathbb{N}^{\times n}$ is a function such that

(1) For each $m \in \mathbb{N}$ there is a j such that

$$\phi(m+1) = (\phi_1(m), \dots, \overset{j}{\phi_j(m)} + 1, \dots, \phi_n(m)).$$

(2) For each $k \in \mathbb{N}$, there is an m such that

$$\phi_j(m) > k, \qquad \text{for all } j = 1, \dots, n$$

(3) $\phi(0) = (0, \dots, 0)$.

EXAMPLE 1.29. There is an admissible function $\mu : \mathbb{N} \to \mathbb{N}^{\times n}$ which is defined by

$$\begin{cases} \mu(nj) = (j, \dots, j) \\ \mu(nj + k) = (j+1, \dots, \overset{k}{j+1}, j, \dots, j) & \text{if } 0 < k < n. \end{cases} \qquad \blacksquare$$

Admissible paths $\mathbf{r} \to \mathbb{N}^{\times n}$ have an apparent definition, which is illustrated by the following basic example:

EXAMPLE 1.30. Suppose that

$$(m_1, \ldots, m_n) < (m'_1, \ldots, m'_n)$$

in $\mathbb{N}^{\times n}$, and set

$$r = \sum_{i=1}^{n} (m'_i - m_i).$$

Define

$$R_j = (m'_n - m_n) + \cdots + (m'_j - m_j)$$

for $j = 1, \ldots, n$, and set $R_{n+1} = 0$. Then one has relations

$$0 = R_{n+1} \leq R_n \leq \cdots \leq R_1 = r.$$

The *canonical path*

$$\gamma : \mathbf{r} \to \mathbb{N}^{\times n}$$

of length r from (m_i) to (m'_i) is the function which is defined for $R_{j+1} \leq i \leq R_j$ by

$$\gamma(i) = (m_1, \ldots, m_{j-1}, m_j + i - R_{j+1}, m'_{j+1}, \ldots, m'_n).$$ ■

Any admissible path $\psi : \mathbf{r} \to \mathbb{N}^{\times n}$ and any n-fold spectrum X together determine maps

$$\hat{\sigma}_j : S^1 \wedge X^{\psi(j)} \to X^{\psi(j+1)},$$

where $\hat{\sigma}_j$ is the map

$$S^1 \wedge X^{\psi_1(j), \ldots, \psi_k(j), \ldots, \psi_n(j)} \xrightarrow{\sigma_k} X^{\psi_1(j), \ldots, \psi_k(j)+1, \ldots, \psi_n(j)}$$

if

$$\psi(j+1) = (\psi_1(j), \ldots, \psi_k(j) + 1, \ldots, \psi_n(j)).$$

The idea is, once again, to study the associated string of pointed simplicial set maps

$$S^r \wedge X^{\psi(0)} \xrightarrow{S^{r-1} \wedge \hat{\sigma}_0} S^{r-1} \wedge X^{\psi(1)} \xrightarrow{S^{r-2} \wedge \hat{\sigma}_1} \cdots \xrightarrow{\hat{\sigma}_{r-1}} X^{\psi(r)},$$

and show that any two such composites arising from admissible paths from $\psi(0)$ to $\psi(r)$ differ by a twist of suspension factors in the source space.

LEMMA 1.31. *Suppose that X is an n-fold spectrum, and that $\psi : \mathbf{r} \to \mathbb{N}^{\times n}$ is an admissible path, and let γ be the canonical path from $\psi(0)$ to $\psi(r)$. Then there is an element ω of the symmetric group Σ_r such that the diagram*

$$
\begin{array}{c}
S^r \wedge X^{\psi(0)} \xrightarrow{\ S^{r-1} \wedge \hat{\sigma}_0\ } \cdots \xrightarrow{\ S^1 \wedge \hat{\sigma}_{r-2}\ } S^1 \wedge X^{\psi(r-1)} \\
\Big\downarrow{\omega \wedge X^{\psi(0)}} \qquad\qquad\qquad\qquad\qquad \searrow{\hat{\sigma}_{r-1}} \\
\qquad\qquad\qquad\qquad\qquad X^{m_2,n_2} \\
S^r \wedge X^{\psi(0)} \xrightarrow[\ S^{r-1} \wedge \hat{\sigma}_0\ ]{} \cdots \xrightarrow[\ S^1 \wedge \hat{\sigma}_{r-2}\ ]{} S^1 \wedge X^{\gamma(r-1)} \nearrow{\hat{\sigma}_{r-1}}
\end{array}
$$

commutes, where $\omega \wedge X^{\psi(0)}$ is the map which flips suspension factors.

PROOF: By induction on r, we may assume that there is a commutative diagram of the form

$$
\begin{array}{c}
S^{r-1} \wedge X^{\psi(0)} \xrightarrow{\ S^{r-2} \wedge \hat{\sigma}_0\ } \cdots \xrightarrow{\ S^1 \wedge \hat{\sigma}_{r-3}\ } S^1 \wedge X^{\psi(r-2)} \\
\Big\downarrow{\omega \wedge X^{\psi(0)}} \qquad\qquad\qquad\qquad\qquad \searrow{\hat{\sigma}_{r-2}} \\
\qquad\qquad\qquad\qquad\qquad X^{\psi(r-1)} \\
S^{r-1} \wedge X^{\psi(0)} \xrightarrow[\ S^{r-2} \wedge \hat{\sigma}_0\ ]{} \cdots \xrightarrow[\ S^1 \wedge \hat{\sigma}_{r-3}\ ]{} S^1 \wedge X^{\tilde{\gamma}(r-2)} \nearrow{\hat{\sigma}_{r-2}}
\end{array}
$$

where $\tilde{\gamma}$ is the canonical path from $\psi(0)$ to $\psi(r-1) = \tilde{\gamma}(r-1)$. We may therefore presume that the path ψ is canonical from $\psi(0)$ to $\psi(r-1)$.

Suppose that

$$\psi(r-1) = (\psi_1(r-2), \ldots, \psi_k(r-2) + 1, \ldots, \psi_n(r-2))$$

and that

$$\psi(r) = (\psi_1(r-1), \ldots, \psi_\ell(r-1) + 1, \ldots, \psi_n(r-1)).$$

If $\ell \le k$, then the path ψ is canonical, and we're done, so we can suppose that $\ell > k$. But then k is the minimum index that is altered by the path ψ.

We have the following commutative diagrams:

$$
\begin{array}{c}
S^2 \wedge X^{\psi(r-2)} \xrightarrow{\ \ S^1 \wedge \sigma_k\ \ } S^1 \wedge X^{\psi(r-1)} \\
\Big\downarrow{\tau \wedge X^{\psi(r-2)}} \qquad\qquad\qquad\qquad \searrow{\sigma_\ell} \\
\qquad\qquad\qquad\qquad\qquad X^{\psi(r)} \\
S^2 \wedge X^{\psi(r-2)} \xrightarrow[\ \ S^1 \wedge \sigma_\ell\ \ ]{} S^1 \wedge X^{\psi_1(r-2), \ldots, \psi_\ell(r-2)+1, \ldots, \psi_n(r-2)} \nearrow{\sigma_k}
\end{array}
$$

$$\begin{array}{ccc}
S^r \wedge X^{\psi(0)} & \xrightarrow{\ S^{r-1} \wedge \hat{\sigma}_0 \ } \cdots \xrightarrow{\ S^1 \wedge \hat{\sigma}_{r-3} \ } & S^2 \wedge X^{\psi(r-2)} \\
{\scriptstyle S^{r-2} \wedge \tau \wedge X^{\psi(0)}} \Big\downarrow & & \Big\downarrow {\scriptstyle \tau \wedge X^{\psi(r-2)}} \\
S^r \wedge X^{\psi(0)} & \xrightarrow[\ S^{r-1} \wedge \hat{\sigma}_0 \ ]{} \cdots \xrightarrow[\ S^1 \wedge \hat{\sigma}_{r-3} \ ]{} & S^2 \wedge X^{\psi(r-2)}.
\end{array}$$

Finally, assume that ψ is the concatenation of the evident admissible path of length $r-1$ from $\psi(0)$ to $(\psi_1(r-2),\dots,\psi_\ell(r-2)+1,\dots,\psi_n(r-2))$, followed by the path of length 1 from $(\psi_1(r-2),\dots,\psi_\ell(r-2)+1,\dots,\psi_n(r-2))$ to $\psi(r)$. For this path ψ if we put the path from $\psi(0)$ to $\psi(r-1)$ in canonical form, then the result is canonical, by the minimality of k. $\blacksquare$

Any admissible path $\psi : \mathbb{N} \to \mathbb{N}^{\times n}$ and any n-fold spectrum X together determine a spectrum X_ψ, just as before.

THEOREM 1.32. *Suppose that X is any n-fold spectrum, and that ψ is any admissible function. Then X_ψ is non-canonically but naturally stably equivalent to X_μ.*

SKETCH OF PROOF: One chooses an ascending sequence of numbers

$$\{0, n_1, n_2, \dots\}$$

such that

$$\psi_j(n_{i+1}) > \max_k \{\psi_k(n_i)\}.$$

The number n_i determine a sequence of boxes

$$B_i = \{(m_j)|\psi_k(n_i) < m_i < \psi_k(n_{i+1}) \text{ for all } i\}.$$

Each of these boxes B_i contains a diagonal point $(m_i,\dots,m_i)$, and so one can finish the proof by observing that there is an intermediate admissible function γ such that X_ψ and X_γ and then X_γ and X_μ give rise to stably equivalent partial spectra. $\blacksquare$

Suppose that $\psi : \mathbb{N} \to \mathbb{N}^{\times n}$ and the functions $\phi_j : \mathbb{N} \to \mathbb{N}^{\times k_j}$ are all admissible. Then the composite

$$\mathbb{N} \xrightarrow{\ \psi\ } \mathbb{N}^{\times n} \xrightarrow{\ \phi_1 \times \cdots \times \phi_n\ } \mathbb{N}^{\times k_1} \times \dots \mathbb{N}^{\times k_n}$$

is admissible. Note also that the identity map $\mathbb{N} \to \mathbb{N}$ is admissible (this is the unique admissible self-map of $\mathbb{N}$, in fact). These two observations, together with the previous theorem and Lemma 1.28, spawn an inductive machine that can be used to prove the following:

Proposition 1.33. *Suppose that $f : X \to Y$ is a map of n-fold spectra such that, for each multi-index $(i_2, \ldots, i_n)$ the induced map*

$$f : X^{*,i_2,\ldots,i_n} \to Y^{*,i_2,\ldots,i_n}$$

of spectra is a weak equivalence. Then the induced map

$$df : dX \to dY$$

of diagonal spectra is a weak equivalence.

Here, the *diagonal spectrum dX* can be defined to be X_μ, or any X_ψ arising from an admissible function ψ.

Chapter 2. Abstract homotopy theory of n-fold spectra

In this chapter, it is shown that the category $\mathbf{Spt}^n$ of n-fold spectra carries closed model structures for both the strict (ie. levelwise) and stable weak equivalences. These results appear in the first section, and are proved by analogy with the corresponding results of Bousfield and Friedlander for the category of spectra [8].

We see, in the second section, that the diagonal functors $d : \mathbf{Spt}^n \to \mathbf{Spt}$ of Section 1.3 and 1.4 induce equivalences

$$\mathrm{Ho}(\mathbf{Spt}^n) \simeq \mathrm{Ho}(\mathbf{Spt})$$

of the homotopy categories associated to the respective stable closed model structures. In other words, the category of n-fold spectra is just another model for the ordinary stable category, albeit one which is quite useful. Applications will begin to appear in Chapter 3.

A quick review of the homotopy theories for simplicial presheaves and presheaves of spectra is presented in the third section of this chapter, and then the results of the first two sections are extended to the categories of presheaves of spectra and presheaves of n-fold spectra on an arbitrary Grothendieck site in the fourth section. The stable closed model structure for the category of presheaves of n-fold spectra is established by a method which parallels the proof given in [24] for the corresponding result about presheaves of spectra.

The equivalence of homotopy categories displayed above has a trivial analogy in an equivalence of the stable homotopy categories arising from presheaves of spectra and presheaves of n-fold spectra. Keep in mind, however, that the category of presheaves of spectra on a fixed site is not necessarily a model for the ordinary stable category. The results of the third section of this chapter imply that every Grothendieck topology gives rise to its own particular stable homotopy category, and so the collection of such theories (and models for each of them) is vast. These theories are not unrelated; in a coarse sense, the interplay between them is the subject of this book.

This chapter closes with a very short final section which "shows" that the stable homotopy categories of presheaves of spectra carry a symmetric monoidal structure with multiplication given by smash product, and with the ordinary sphere spectrum as unit. The method of proof is to defer completely to Adams [2], the point being that his constructions are natural in maps of spectra, as they are defined here.

2.1. Closed model category structures for n-fold spectra

Recall, from Chapter 1, that a bispectrum may be internally defined as a list of pointed simplicial sets $X^{i,j}$, $i, j \geq 0$, together with pointed simplicial set maps

$$S^1 \wedge X^{i,j} \xrightarrow{\sigma_1} X^{i+1,j} \qquad \text{and} \qquad S^1 \wedge X^{i,j} \xrightarrow{\sigma_2} X^{i,j+1}$$

such that the following diagram commutes for all i and j:

$$
\begin{array}{ccc}
S^1 \wedge X^{i+1,j} & \xrightarrow{\quad\sigma_2\quad} & X^{i+1,j+1} \\
\Big\uparrow{\scriptstyle S^1 \wedge \sigma_1} & & \Big\uparrow{\scriptstyle \sigma_1} \\
S^1 \wedge S^1 \wedge X^{i,j} \xrightarrow{\tau \wedge X^{i,j}} S^1 \wedge S^1 \wedge X^{i,j} & \xrightarrow{S^1 \wedge \sigma_2} & S^1 \wedge X^{i,j+1}
\end{array}
\qquad (2.1)
$$

Here, $\tau \wedge X^{i,j}$ is the map which flips the S^1 factors and is the identity on $X^{i,j}$. It's not difficult to see (by drawing the appropriate large diagram) that the commutativity of diagram (2.1) is equivalent to the commutativity of

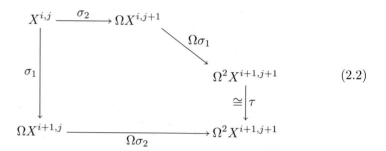

$$ (2.2) $$

The map τ is the canonical isomorphism which interchanges loop factors.

More generally, an n-fold spectrum consists of pointed simplicial sets

$$ X^{i_1,i_2,\ldots,i_n}, \qquad i_j \geq 0, $$

together with pointed simplicial set maps

$$ \sigma_j : S^1 \wedge X^{i_1,\ldots,i_j,\ldots,i_n} \longrightarrow X^{i_1,\ldots,i_j+1,\ldots,i_n}, $$

$1 \leq j \leq n$ (called *bonding maps*), such that for each $1 \leq k < j \leq n$, and list of indices i_r, $r \neq j, k$, the array of simplicial sets

$$ X^{i_1,\ldots,\overset{k}{*},\ldots,\overset{j}{*},\ldots,i_n}, $$

together with the bonding maps σ_j and σ_k forms a bispectrum in the sense that diagrams analogous to (2.1) or (2.2) must commute. Write $\mathbf{Spt}^n$ for the category of n-fold spectra.

Suppose that X is a bispectrum. Then it's elementary to check that there is a bispectrum X_{Kan} with

$$ X_{Kan}^{i,j} = S|X^{i,j}|, $$

and with bonding maps $\sigma_1 : S^1 \wedge X_{Kan}^{i,j} \to X_{Kan}^{i+1,j}$ and $\sigma_2 : S^1 \wedge X_{Kan}^{i,j} \to X_{Kan}^{i,j+1}$ defined, respectively, to be the composites

$$S^1 \wedge S|X^{i,j}| \xrightarrow{\eta \wedge X^{i,j}} S|S^1| \wedge |X^{i,j}| \xrightarrow{\text{can}} S|S^1 \wedge X^{i,j}| \xrightarrow{S|\sigma_1|} S|X^{i+1,j}|,$$

and

$$S^1 \wedge S|X^{i,j}| \xrightarrow{\eta \wedge X^{i,j}} S|S^1| \wedge |X^{i,j}| \xrightarrow{\text{can}} S|S^1 \wedge X^{i,j}| \xrightarrow{S|\sigma_2|} S|X^{i,j+1}|.$$

Furthermore, the natural maps $\eta : X^{i,j} \to S|X^{i,j}|$ define a natural map of bispectra

$$\eta : X \to X_{Kan}.$$

This construction is easily promoted to n-fold spectra for arbitrary n, giving

LEMMA 2.3. *Suppose that X is an n-fold spectrum. Then there is an n-fold spectrum X_{Kan} with*

$$X_{Kan}^{i_1,\ldots,i_n} = S|X^{i_1,\ldots,i_n}|.$$

Furthermore, the canonical weak equivalences

$$\eta : X^{i_1,\ldots,i_n} \to S|X^{i_1,\ldots,i_n}|$$

induce a natural map of n-fold spectra

$$\eta : X \to X_{Kan}.$$

Each $X_{Kan}^{i_1,\ldots,i_n}$ *is a pointed Kan complex.*

In the world of n-fold spectra, and given a pointed simplicial set K, the functors $X \mapsto X \wedge K$ and $X \mapsto \mathbf{hom}_*(K, X)$ have their obvious meanings. In other words, $X \wedge K$ is characterized by

$$(X \wedge K)^{i_1,\ldots,i_n} = X^{i_1,\ldots,i_n} \wedge K,$$

and by having bonding maps $\sigma_i \wedge K$. On the other hand,

$$\mathbf{hom}_*(K, X)^{i_1,\ldots,i_n} = \mathbf{hom}_*(K, X^{i_1,\ldots,i_n})$$

defines the spaces of $\mathbf{hom}_*(K, X)$, and this object has bonding maps

$$\mathbf{hom}_*(K, X^{i_1,\ldots,i_n}) \xrightarrow{\mathbf{hom}_*(K,\sigma_i)} \mathbf{hom}_*(K, \Omega X^{i_1,\ldots,i_n}) \xrightarrow{\tau}{\cong} \Omega\mathbf{hom}_*(K, X^{i_1,\ldots,i_n}),$$

where τ is the canonical isomorphism that switches function complex arguments.

An $(n+1)$-fold spectrum X (externally defined) consists of n-fold spectra X^i, $i \geq 0$, together with bonding maps of n-fold spectra

$$X^i \wedge S^1 \to X^{i+1}.$$

The usual adjointness relations apply, so that these bonding maps could be characterized as maps of n-fold spectra of the form

$$X^i \to \mathbf{hom}_*(S^1, X^{i+1}).$$

Say that a map $f : X \to Y$ of n-fold spectra is a *strict weak equivalence* (respectively *strict fibration*) if each of the maps

$$f : X^{i_1,\ldots,i_n} \to Y^{i_1,\ldots,i_n}$$

is a weak equivalence (respectively fibration) of simplicial sets. A *cofibration* is a map of n-fold spectra which has the left lifting property with respect to all maps which are strict fibrations and strict weak equivalences (aka. trivial strict fibrations).

PROPOSITION 2.4. *The category* $\mathbf{Spt}^n$ *of n-fold spectra, with the classes of cofibrations, strict fibrations and strict weak equivalences, satisfies the axioms for a closed model category.*

PROOF: We shall assume that $n \geq 1$, and that the category of $(n-1)$-fold spectra is a closed model category for these definitions. We shall also identify the category $\mathbf{Spt}^n$ with the category of spectrum objects in the category of $(n-1)$-fold spectra.

The category $\mathbf{Spt}^n$ is complete and cocomplete, so that the axiom **CM1** holds. The verification of the axioms **CM2** (weak equivalence) and **CM3** (retract) is clear.

The proof of the factorization axiom **CM5** is achieved by first showing that a map $i : A \to B$ of n-fold spectra has the left lifting property with respect to all (respectively trivial) strict fibrations if the following conditions are satisfied:

(1) $i^0 : A^0 \to B^0$ is a trivial cofibration (respectively cofibration) of $(n-1)$-fold spectra, and

(2) the map

$$(B^k \wedge S^1) \cup_{(A^k \wedge S^1)} A^{k+1} \to B^{k+1}$$

is a trivial cofibration (respectively cofibration) of $(n-1)$-fold spectra.

To show that any map $f : X \to Y$ has a factorization $f = qi$, where q is a trivial strict fibration and i is a cofibration, find a factorization

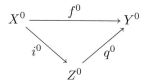

in degree 0, where i^0 is a cofibration and q^0 is a trivial strict fibration of $(n-1)$-fold spectra. Then the canonical map

$$g^1 : (Z^0 \wedge S^1) \cup_{(X^0 \wedge S^1)} X^1 \to Y^1$$

has a factorization

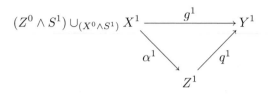

where α^1 is a cofibration and q^1 is a trivial strict fibration of $(n-1)$-fold spectra. The map q^1 is now given, and i^1 is defined to be the composite

$$X^1 \xrightarrow{(i^0 \wedge S^1)_*} (Z^0 \wedge S^1) \cup_{(X^0 \wedge S^1)} X^1 \xrightarrow{\alpha^1} Z^1.$$

This works, since cofibrations are closed under smashing with pointed simplicial sets, and closed under pushout, so that $(i^0 \wedge S^1)_*$ is a cofibration. Proceed inductively to obtain the factorization $f = qi$.

The other part of the factorization axiom is obtained by showing that f has a factorization $f = pj$, where p is a strict fibration and j is a map which is a strict weak equivalence and has the left lifting property with respect to all strict fibrations: one uses trivial cofibrations of $(n - 1)$-fold spectra in place of the cofibrations in the argument just given.

A standard argument now shows that any map j of n-fold spectra which is a cofibration and a strict weak equivalence must be a retract of a map which is a strict weak equivalence and has the left lifting property with respect to all strict fibrations. Such a map j therefore has the left lifting property with respect to all fibrations, and axiom **CM4** follows. ∎

REMARK 2.5. The proof of the factorization axioms in the previous result implies that any cofibration of n-fold spectra is a retract of a map which is composed of maps which are cofibrations of $(n - 1)$-fold spectra. It follows by induction on n that any cofibration $j : A \to B$ of n-fold spectra is a pointwise cofibration in the sense that all of the maps

$$j : A^{i_1,\dots,i_n} \to B^{i_1,\dots,i_n}$$

are cofibrations of simplicial sets. ∎

Suppose that X and Y are n-fold spectra. The *function complex*

$$\mathbf{hom}_*(X, Y)$$

is the pointed simplicial set whose m-simplices are the pointed maps of n-fold spectra of the form $X \ltimes \Delta^m \to Y$. It is a direct consequence of the corresponding result for pointed simplicial sets that there is an exponential law

$$\mathbf{hom}_*(X \wedge K, Y) \cong \mathbf{hom}_*(K, \mathbf{hom}_*(X, Y)).$$

PROPOSITION 2.6. *With the definitions of strict weak equivalence, cofibration, strict fibration and the definition of function complex given above, the category* $\mathbf{Spt}^n$ *of n-fold spectra is a proper closed simplicial model category.*

PROOF: Suppose that $p : X \to Y$ is a strict fibration of n-fold spectra, the map $i : U \to V$ is a cofibration of n-fold spectra, and that $j : K \to L$ is a trivial cofibration of pointed simplicial sets. Then the existence of the dotted arrow making the diagram commute is an equivalent condition for any of the following three (adjoint) diagrams:

$$
\begin{array}{ccc}
K & \xrightarrow{\quad \alpha \quad} & \mathbf{hom}_*(V, X) \\
{\scriptstyle j}\big\downarrow & \nearrow & \big\downarrow{\scriptstyle (i^*, p_*)} \\
L & \xrightarrow[(\beta, \gamma)]{} & \mathbf{hom}_*(U, X) \times_{\mathbf{hom}_*(U,Y)} \mathbf{hom}_*(V, Y)
\end{array}
\qquad (2.7)
$$

$$
\begin{array}{ccc}
(U \wedge L) \cup_{(U \wedge K)} (V \wedge K) & \xrightarrow{\ (\beta, \alpha)\ } & X \\
\big\downarrow & \nearrow & \big\downarrow{\scriptstyle p} \\
V \wedge L & \xrightarrow{\quad \gamma \quad} & Y
\end{array}
\qquad (2.8)
$$

$$
\begin{array}{ccc}
U & \xrightarrow{\quad \beta \quad} & \mathbf{hom}_*(L, X) \\
{\scriptstyle i}\big\downarrow & \nearrow & \big\downarrow{\scriptstyle (p_*, j^*)} \\
V & \xrightarrow[(\gamma, \alpha)]{} & \mathbf{hom}_*(L, Y) \times_{\mathbf{hom}_*(K,X)} \mathbf{hom}_*(K, Y)
\end{array}
\qquad (2.9)
$$

I have confused various maps notationwise with their adjoints in these diagrams. Note that the map

$$(p_*, j^*) : \mathbf{hom}_*(L, X) \to \mathbf{hom}_*(L, Y) \times_{\mathbf{hom}_*(K,X)} \mathbf{hom}_*(K, Y)$$

is a strict fibration, which is trivial if j or p is trivial. It follows that the map

$$(i^*, p_*) : \mathbf{hom}_*(V, X) \to \mathbf{hom}_*(U, X) \times_{\mathbf{hom}_*(U,Y)} \mathbf{hom}_*(V, Y)$$

is a fibration of pointed simplicial sets, which is trivial if i is a trivial cofibration or p is a trivial strict fibration.

Strict weak equivalences are closed under cobase change by cofibrations, by the corresponding property for simplicial sets and Remark 2.5. Similarly, strict weak equivalences are closed under base change by fibrations. ∎

Suppose that Z is an n-fold spectrum, and that $\{r_1, \ldots, r_n\}$ is a list of n integers. An n-fold spectrum $Z[r_1, \ldots, r_n]$ is defined by setting

$$Z[r_1, \ldots, r_n]^{i_1, \ldots, i_n} = Z^{i_1 + r_1, \ldots, i_n + r_n}.$$

This construction is functorial in n-fold spectra.

Suppose now that X is a strictly fibrant bispectrum. A bispectrum $\Omega_1 X$ is defined by

$$\Omega_1 X^{i,j} = \Omega X^{i,j},$$

and with bonding maps

$$\Omega \sigma_1 : \Omega X^{i,j} \to \Omega^2 X^{i+1,j},$$

for σ_1, and the composite

$$\Omega X^{i,j} \xrightarrow{\Omega \sigma_2} \Omega^2 X^{i,j+1} \xrightarrow[\cong]{\tau} \Omega^2 X^{i,j+1}$$

for σ_2. In other words,

$$\Omega_1 X^{*,j} = \Omega X^{*,j}$$

is a fake loop spectrum for each j, while

$$\Omega_1 X^{i,*} = \mathbf{hom}_*(S^1, X^{i,*})$$

is an honest loop object for each i. Similarly, there is a bispectrum $\Omega_2 X$ such that

$$\begin{cases} \Omega_2 X^{*,j} = \mathbf{hom}_*(S^1, X^{*,j}) & \text{for each } j, \text{ and} \\ \Omega_2 X^{i,*} = \Omega X^{i,*} & \text{for each } i. \end{cases}$$

Note that $\Omega_1 X$ and $\Omega_2 X$ are strictly fibrant.

The bonding maps σ_1 and σ_2 respectively determine maps of bispectra

$$\sigma_1 : X \to \Omega_1 X[1, 0] \qquad \text{and} \qquad \sigma_2 : X \to \Omega_2 X[0, 1].$$

Flipping loop factors determines a natural isomorphism of bispectra

$$\Omega_1 \Omega_2 X \xrightarrow[\cong]{\tau} \Omega_2 \Omega_1 X,$$

and there is a commutative diagram

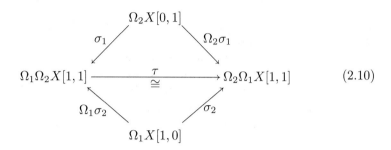

$$(2.10)$$

Similarly, if X is a strictly fibrant n-fold spectrum, where $n \geq 2$, and $1 \leq j \leq n$, there is an associated strictly fibrant n-fold spectrum $\Omega_j X$ with

$$\begin{cases} \Omega_j X^{i_1,\ldots,\overset{k}{*},\ldots,i_n} = \mathbf{hom}_*(S^1, X^{i_1,\ldots,\overset{k}{*},\ldots,i_n}) & \text{if } k \neq j, \text{ and} \\ \Omega_j X^{i_1,\ldots,\overset{k}{*},\ldots,i_n} = \Omega X^{i_1,\ldots,\overset{k}{*},\ldots,i_n} & \text{if } k = j. \end{cases}$$

Then there are natural maps

$$\sigma_j : X \to \Omega_j X[0,\ldots,\overset{j}{1},\ldots 0]$$

which are determined by the various bonding maps of X. If $i < j$, switching loop factors gives a canonical isomorphism

$$\Omega_i \Omega_j X[0,\ldots,\overset{i}{1},\ldots,\overset{j}{1},\ldots,0] \xrightarrow[\cong]{\tau} \Omega_j \Omega_i X[0,\ldots,\overset{i}{1},\ldots,\overset{j}{1},\ldots,0]$$

and a commutative diagram

$$(2.11)$$

Suppose that Z is a strictly fibrant bispectrum. One defines natural isomorphisms

$$\tau_n : \Omega_2 \Omega_1^n Z \to \Omega_1^n \Omega_2 Z$$

as follows. Let τ_1 be the isomorphism $\tau : \Omega_2 \Omega_1 Z \to \Omega_2 \Omega_1 Z$ that we constructed above. Suppose that τ_n defines an isomorphism

$$\tau_n : \Omega_2 \Omega_1^n \Omega_1 Z \to \Omega_1^n \Omega_2 \Omega_1 Z;$$

then τ_{n+1} is defined to be the composite of this map with the map

$$\Omega_1^n \tau : \Omega_1^n \Omega_2 \Omega_1 Z \to \Omega_1^n \Omega_1 \Omega_2 Z.$$

Let $Q_1 Z$ be the filtered colimit of the system

$$Z \xrightarrow{\sigma_1} \Omega_1 Z[1,0] \xrightarrow{\Omega_1 \sigma_1} \Omega_1^2 Z[2,0] \to \dots$$

and let $\mu_1 : Z \to Q_1 Z$ denote the associated canonical map. Let $Q_2 Z$ denote the filtered colimit of the system

$$Z \xrightarrow{\sigma_2} \Omega_2 Z[0,1] \xrightarrow{\Omega_2 \sigma_2} \Omega_2^2 Z[0,2] \to \dots$$

with canonical map $\mu_2 : Z \to Q_2 Z$.

The maps

$$\Omega_2 \Omega_1 Z \xrightarrow{\tau} \Omega_1 \Omega_2 Z$$

induce canonical isomorphisms

$$\Omega_2^m \Omega_1^n Z[n,m] \xrightarrow{\tau_{n,m}} \Omega_1^n \Omega_2^m Z[n,m],$$

which fit into commutative diagrams

$$
\begin{array}{ccc}
\Omega_2^m \Omega_1^{n-1} Z[n-1,m] & \xrightarrow{\tau_{n-1,m}} & \Omega_1^{n-1} \Omega_2^m Z[n-1,m] \\
{\scriptstyle \Omega_2^m \sigma_1} \downarrow & & \downarrow {\scriptstyle \sigma_1} \\
\Omega_2^m \Omega_1^n Z[n,m] & \xrightarrow{\quad \tau_{n,m} \quad} & \Omega_1^n \Omega_2^m Z[n,m] \\
{\scriptstyle \sigma_2} \uparrow & & \uparrow {\scriptstyle \Omega_1^n \sigma_2} \\
\Omega_2^{m-1} \Omega_1^n Z[n,m-1] & \xrightarrow{\quad \tau_{n,m-1} \quad} & \Omega_1^n \Omega_2^{m-1} Z[n,m-1].
\end{array}
$$

Taking filtered colimits in n and m therefore gives a commutative diagram

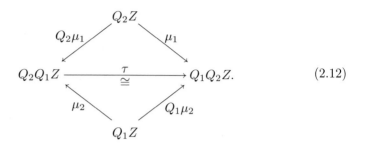

$$(2.12)$$

Analogous definitions and techniques apply to n-fold spectra for higher n. If X is a strictly fibrant n-fold spectrum and $1 \leq j \leq n$, then the n-fold spectrum $Q_j X$ is defined to be the filtered colimit of the system

$$X \xrightarrow{\sigma_j} \Omega_j X[0, \ldots, \overset{j}{1}, \ldots, 0] \xrightarrow{\Omega_j \sigma_j} \Omega_j^2 X[0, \ldots, \overset{j}{1}, \ldots, 0] \to \ldots$$

with canonical map $\mu_j : X \to Q_j X$. The same methods as were used in the bispectrum case may then be used to show:

LEMMA 2.13. *Suppose that $1 \leq i < j \leq n$. Then there is a natural isomorphism of bispectra*

$$\tau : Q_j Q_i X \xrightarrow{\cong} Q_i Q_j X,$$

and a commutative diagram

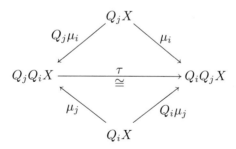

The *stabilization* QX of X is the strictly fibrant n-fold spectrum which is defined by

$$QX = Q_n Q_{n-1} \ldots Q_1 X.$$

The map $\mu : X \to QX$ is defined to be the composite

$$X \xrightarrow{\mu_1} Q_1 X \xrightarrow{\mu_2} \ldots \xrightarrow{\mu_{n-1}} Q_{n-1} \ldots Q_1 X \xrightarrow{\mu_n} Q_n \ldots Q_1 X.$$

Lemma 2.13 implies that we can permute the Q_i's in the definition of QX and get a naturally isomorphic n-fold spectrum.

The first step in the analysis of QX will be to characterize the homotopy groups of the spaces $QX^{i_1,\ldots,i_n}$.

The bonding maps

$$\sigma_r : X^{i_1,\ldots,i_n} \to \Omega X^{i_1,\ldots,i_r+1,\ldots,i_n}$$

induce maps in homotopy groups of the form

$$\sigma_r : \pi_k X^{i_1,\ldots,i_n} \to \pi_{k+1} X^{i_1,\ldots,i_r+1,\ldots,i_n}.$$

Furthermore, if $r < s$, there is a commutative diagram

$$
\begin{array}{ccc}
\pi_k X^{i_1,\ldots,i_n} & \xrightarrow{\quad \sigma_r \quad} & \pi_{k+1} X^{i_1,\ldots,i_r+1,\ldots,i_n} \\
{\scriptstyle \sigma_s} \downarrow & & \downarrow {\scriptstyle (-1)\sigma_s} \\
\pi_{k+1} X^{i_1,\ldots,i_s+1,\ldots,i_n} & \xrightarrow{\quad \sigma_r \quad} & \pi_{k+2} X^{i_1,\ldots,i_r+1,\ldots,i_s+1,\ldots i_n}
\end{array}
$$

It follows that there is an abelian group-valued functor

$$\pi_k \mathbf{X}^{i_1,\ldots,i_n} : \mathbb{N}^{\times n} \to \mathbf{Ab}$$

which is defined by associating to the n-tuple $(s_1,\ldots,s_n)$ the group

$$\pi_{k+(s_1+\cdots+s_n)} X^{i_1+s_1,i_2+s_2,\ldots,i_n+s_n}.$$

The definition of this functor is completed by the assignment of the homomorphism

$$
\begin{array}{c}
\pi_{k+(s_1+\cdots+s_n)} X^{i_1+s_1,\ldots,i_j+s_j,\ldots,i_n+s_n} \\
\\
\downarrow {\scriptstyle (-1)^{(i_1+s_1)+\cdots+(i_{j-1}+s_{j-1})}\sigma_j} \\
\\
\pi_{k+(s_1+\cdots+s_n)+1} X^{i_1+s_1,\ldots,i_j+s_j+1,\ldots,i_n+s_n}
\end{array}
$$

to the relation

$$(s_1,\ldots,s_j,\ldots,s_n) \to (s_1,\ldots,s_j+1,\ldots,s_n)$$

of $\mathbb{N}^{\times n}$.

LEMMA 2.14. *There is a natural isomorphism*

$$\pi_k Q X^{i_1,\dots,i_n} \cong \varinjlim_{\mathbb{N}^{\times n}} \pi_k \mathbf{X}^{i_1,\dots,i_n}.$$

PROOF: The colimit

$$\varinjlim_{\mathbb{N}^{\times n}} \pi_k \mathbf{X}^{i_1,\dots,i_n}$$

may be identified up to natural isomorphism with the iterated colimit

$$\varinjlim_1 \varinjlim_2 \dots \varinjlim_n \pi_k \mathbf{X}^{i_1,\dots,i_n},$$

where $\varinjlim_j$ means "take the colimit in the j direction".

The natural map $\mu_j : X \to Q_j X$ induces an isomorphism

$$\varinjlim_j \pi_k \mathbf{X}^{i_1,\dots,i_n} \xrightarrow[\cong]{\mu_j} \varinjlim_j \pi_k \mathbf{Q_j X}^{i_1,\dots,i_n},$$

by the usual cofinality argument. But then any composite $X \to Q_n \dots Q_1 X$ of instances of the μ_i maps induces an isomorphism

$$\varinjlim_n \dots \varinjlim_1 \pi_k \mathbf{X}^{i_1,\dots,i_n} \cong \varinjlim_n \dots \varinjlim_1 \pi_k \mathbf{Q_n} \dots \mathbf{Q_1 X}^{i_1,\dots,i_n}. \tag{2.15}$$

Finally, all arrows are isomorphisms in the diagram

$$\pi_k \mathbf{Q X}^{i_1,\dots,i_n}$$

of abelian groups, so that there is a canonical isomorphism

$$\varinjlim_{\mathbb{N}^{\times n}} \pi_k \mathbf{Q X}^{i_1,\dots,i_n} \cong \pi_k Q X^{i_1,\dots,i_n}. \qquad \blacksquare$$

Recall from Chapter 1 that the *diagonal spectrum* dX of an n-fold spectrum X is the spectrum having

$$dX^{nj+k} = X^{\overset{k}{j+1,\dots,j+1,j,\dots,j}},$$

and with bonding map

$$\sigma : S^1 \wedge dX^{nj+k} \to dX^{nj+k+1}$$

given by σ_{k+1} for $0 \le k \le n - 1$. This gives a diagonalization functor $d :$ $\mathbf{Spt}^n \to \mathbf{Spt}$, which will be shown in the next section to induce an equivalence of homotopy categories. We also know from the first chapter that there are many other candidates for d, but this one suffices.

Recall [8] that a map of ordinary spectra is a *stable equivalence* (or, according to the customary abuse, a *stable homotopy equivalence*) if it induces an isomorphism of all stable homotopy groups. A spectrum Z is *stably fibrant* if and only if it is strictly fibrant in the sense that that all of its constituent spaces Z^i are Kan complexes, and all of the bonding maps

$$\sigma : Z^i \to \mathbf{hom}_*(S^1, Z^{i+1})$$

are weak equivalences of simplicial sets.

COROLLARY 2.16. *Suppose that X is a strictly fibrant n-fold spectrum. Then the diagonal spectrum dQX of QX is a stably fibrant model of the diagonal spectrum dX of X in the sense that dQX is stably fibrant, and the map*

$$dX \to dQX$$

is a stable homotopy equivalence.

PROOF: The spaces $QX^{i_1,\ldots,i_n}$ are Kan complexes by construction, and each of the bonding maps '

$$\sigma_j : QX^{i_1,\ldots,i_j,\ldots,i_n} \to \Omega QX^{i_1,\ldots,i_j+1,\ldots,i_n}$$

is a weak equivalence, so dQX is stably fibrant. The stable homotopy groups of dX may be identified up to natural isomorphism (ie. by cancelling signs) with groups

$$\varinjlim_j \pi_{i+kj} \mathbf{X}^{j,\ldots,j}.$$

(see the proof of Lemma 1.28). Now use the previous result. ■

A map $f : X \to Y$ of n-fold spectra is a *pointwise cofibration* if each of the maps

$$f : X^{i_1,\ldots,i_n} \to Y^{i_1,\ldots,i_n}$$

is a cofibration of simplicial sets. To fix ideas, remember that a cofibration of n-fold spectra is a somewhat more complex object than a pointwise cofibration. Pointwise cofibrations are nevertheless "right" for the construction of long exact sequences in stable homotopy groups.

It's worth recalling that, if $i : A \to X$ is a pointwise cofibration of spectra, then there is an exact sequence in stable homotopy groups

$$\pi_n^s A \xrightarrow{i} \pi_n^s X \xrightarrow{p} \pi_n^s X/A,$$

where $p : X \to X/A$ is the cofibre. The reason is the one that is learned in school: if $\alpha : K \to X^n$ is a map of pointed topological spaces such that $p\alpha$ is pointed homotopy trivial, then the cofibration sequence can be used to show that there is a map $\beta : S^1 \wedge K \to S^1 \wedge A^n$ such that $(S^1 \wedge i)\beta = S^1 \wedge \alpha$ as maps $S^1 \wedge K \to S^1 \wedge X^n$. Note that we have not required $i : A \to X$ to be a cofibration of spectra. This, together with the definition of the diagonal functor for n-fold spectra, leads immediately to

LEMMA 2.17. *Suppose that $i : A \to X$ is a pointwise cofibration of n-fold spectra and let $p : X \to X/A$ be the cofibre. Then there is an exact sequence in stable homotopy groups of the form*

$$\pi_k^s dX \xrightarrow{p} \pi_k^s d(X/A) \to \pi_{k-1}^s dA \xrightarrow{i} \pi_{k-1}^s dX \xrightarrow{p} \pi_{k-1}^s d(X/A).$$

If $p : X \to Y$ is a strict fibration of n-fold spectra with fibre F, then the diagonal

$$p : dX \to dY$$

is a strict fibration with fibre dF. Then one has:

LEMMA 2.18. *Suppose that $p : X \to Y$ is a strict fibration of n-fold spectra with fibre F. Let $i : F \to X$ be the inclusion of the fibre. Then there is a long exact sequence in stable homotopy groups*

$$\pi_k^s dF \xrightarrow{i} \pi_k^s dX \xrightarrow{p} \pi_k^s dY \to \pi_{k-1}^s dF \xrightarrow{i} \pi_{k-1}^s dX.$$

Suppose that X is an n-fold spectrum, and let K be a pointed simplicial set. Let

$$\tau : \mathbf{hom}_*(K, \Omega X^{i_1, \dots, i_n}) \xrightarrow{\cong} \Omega \mathbf{hom}_*(K, X^{i_1, \dots, i_n})$$

denote the canonical isomorphism of function complexes, applied to the pointed simplicial sets $X^{i_1, \dots, i_n}$. Then there is a commutative diagram

$$
\begin{array}{ccc}
\mathbf{hom}_*(K, \Omega X^{i_1, \dots, i_j+1, \dots, i_n}) & \xrightarrow{\ \tau\ } & \Omega \mathbf{hom}_*(K, X^{i_1, \dots, i_j+1, \dots, i_n}) \\
{\scriptstyle (\Omega \sigma_j)_*} \downarrow & & \downarrow {\scriptstyle \Omega(\sigma_j)_*} \\
\mathbf{hom}_*(K, \Omega^2 X^{i_1, \dots, i_j+2, \dots, i_n}) & \xrightarrow{\ \tau\ } & \Omega \mathbf{hom}_*(K, \Omega X^{i_1, \dots, i_j+2, \dots, i_n}) \\
{\scriptstyle \tau} \downarrow & & \downarrow {\scriptstyle \Omega \tau} \\
\Omega \mathbf{hom}_*(K, \Omega X^{i_1, \dots, i_j+2, \dots, i_n}) & \xrightarrow{\ \Omega \tau\ } & \Omega^2 \mathbf{hom}_*(K, X^{i_1, \dots, i_j+2, \dots, i_n})
\end{array}
$$

where, for example,

$$(\sigma_j)_* : \mathbf{hom}_*(K, X^{i_1, \dots, i_j+1, \dots, i_n}) \to \mathbf{hom}_*(K, \Omega X^{i_1, \dots, i_j+2, \dots, i_n})$$

is the map induced by the bonding map σ_j. It follows that the isomorphisms τ define a natural isomorphism of n-fold spectra

$$\tau : \mathbf{hom}_*(K, \Omega_j X[0, \dots, \overset{j}{1}, \dots, 0]) \xrightarrow{\cong} \Omega_j \mathbf{hom}_*(K, X)[0, \dots, \overset{j}{1}, \dots, 0].$$

Furthermore, the natural map

$$\sigma_j : \mathbf{hom}_*(K, X) \to \Omega_j \mathbf{hom}_*(K, X)[0, \dots, \overset{j}{1}, \dots, 0]$$

and the map τ appear in a commutative diagram

$$
\begin{array}{ccc}
\mathbf{hom}_*(K, X) & \xrightarrow{(\sigma_j)_*} & \mathbf{hom}_*(K, \Omega_j X[0, \dots, \overset{j}{1}, \dots, 0]) \\
& {\scriptstyle \sigma_j} \searrow & \downarrow {\scriptstyle \cong}\ {\scriptstyle \tau} \\
& & \Omega_j \mathbf{hom}_*(K, X)[0, \dots, \overset{j}{1}, \dots, 0].
\end{array}
$$

LEMMA 2.19. *Suppose that X is an n-fold spectrum, and let K be a pointed simplicial set. Then the isomorphisms*

$$\tau : \mathbf{hom}_*(K, \Omega_j X[0, \dots, \overset{j}{1}, \dots, 0]) \to \Omega_j \mathbf{hom}_*(K, X)[0, \dots, \overset{j}{1}, \dots, 0]$$

induce a natural isomorphism

$$\tau : \mathbf{hom}_*(K, Q_j X) \overset{\cong}{\longrightarrow} Q_j \mathbf{hom}_*(K, X),$$

and there is a commutative diagram

where $\mu_j : X \to Q_j X$ is the canonical map.

PROOF: The proof is a generalization of a step in the proof of Lemma 2.13. ∎

The following result is well known. Its proof is presented here as a prototype for later results (specifically Lemma 2.46).

LEMMA 2.20. *Suppose that $f : X \to Y$ is a stable equivalence of spectra, and that K is a pointed simplicial set. Then the induced map*

$$f \wedge K : X \wedge K \to Y \wedge K$$

is a stable equivalence.

PROOF: The first step is to show that, if Z is stably fibrant, then so is the spectrum $\mathbf{hom}_*(K, Z)$. But $\mathbf{hom}_*(K, Z)$ is strictly fibrant, and the canonical map

$$\mu : Z \to QZ$$

is a strict weak equivalence. Furthermore, by Lemma 2.19, there is a commutative diagram in which the map $\mathbf{hom}_*(K, \mu)$ is a strict weak equivalence; it follows that μ is a strict weak equivalence.

The functor $X \mapsto X \wedge K$ preserves strict weak equivalences. Choose a commutative diagram

$$
\begin{array}{ccc}
X_c & \xrightarrow{\ \pi_X\ } & X \\
{\scriptstyle f_c}\downarrow & & \downarrow{\scriptstyle f} \\
Y_c & \xrightarrow[\ \pi_Y\ ]{} & Y
\end{array}
$$

in which the maps π_X and π_Y are strict fibrations and strict weak equivalences, and f_c is a cofibration which is necessarily stably trivial. Note that, since $\pi_X \wedge K$ and $\pi_Y \wedge K$ are strict weak equivalences, $f \wedge K$ is a stable equivalence if and only if $f_c \wedge K$ is a stable equivalence.

Observe that the spectra $X_c \wedge K$ and $Y_c \wedge K$ are cofibrant, and recall that Bousfield-Friedlander criterion (this is Lemma 4.5 of [8], but it is also easily proved) that a map $\theta : A \to B$ of cofibrant spectra is a stable equivalence if and only if the induced map

$$
\theta^* : \mathbf{hom}_*(B, Z) \to \mathbf{hom}_*(A, Z)
$$

of pointed simplicial sets is a weak equivalence for all stably fibrant spectra Z.

Now let Z be a stably fibrant spectrum, and form the diagram

$$
\begin{array}{ccc}
\mathbf{hom}_*(Y_c \wedge K, Z) & \xrightarrow{\ \cong\ } & \mathbf{hom}_*(Y_c, \mathbf{hom}_*(K, Z)) \\
{\scriptstyle (f_c \wedge K)^*}\downarrow & & \downarrow{\scriptstyle f_c^*} \\
\mathbf{hom}_*(X_c \wedge K, Z) & \xrightarrow[\ \cong\ ]{} & \mathbf{hom}_*(X_c, \mathbf{hom}_*(K, Z)).
\end{array}
$$

The spectrum $\mathbf{hom}_*(K, Z)$ is stably fibrant from what we have seen above, and f_c is a stable equivalence, so that f_c^* is a weak equivalence, for all Z. But then $(f_c \wedge K)^*$ is a weak equivalence for all stably fibrant Z, and so $f_c \wedge K$ is a stable equivalence. ∎

COROLLARY 2.21.

(1) *The functor $X \mapsto X \wedge K$ preserves stably trivial cofibrations of spectra.*

(2) *The functor $X \mapsto \mathbf{hom}_*(K, X)$ preserves stable fibrations of spectra.*

(3) *The functor $X \mapsto \mathbf{hom}_*(S^1, X)$ preserves stable fibrations of spectra.*

REMARK 2.22. Lemma 2.20 is the non-trivial part of the assertion that the stable structure on the category of spectra satisfies Quillen's axiom **SM7** for a closed simplicial model category. It can also be proved by using the spectral sequence techniques of Section 4.2 below. ∎

A map $f : X \to Y$ of n-fold spectra is said to be a *stable equivalence* if the associated map of diagonals

$$f : dX \to dY$$

is a stable equivalence of spectra. In view of the proof of Lemma 2.14, f is a stable equivalence of n-fold spectra if and only if

$$f : QX_{Kan} \to QY_{Kan}$$

is a strict weak equivalence of n-fold spectra. We also have the following, which is another consequence of Lemma 2.20:

COROLLARY 2.23. *The functor $X \mapsto X \wedge K$ preserves stable equivalences of n-fold spectra.*

Following [8], one says that a map $f : X \to Y$ of n-fold spectra is a *stable fibration* if it has the right lifting property with respect to all cofibrations which are stable equivalences. A cofibration which is also a stable equivalence is said to be a *stably trivial cofibration*. Similarly, *stably trivial fibrations* are maps which are both stable fibrations and stable weak equivalences.

LEMMA 2.24. *The functor $X \mapsto X \wedge K$ preserves cofibrations of n-fold spectra.*

PROOF: The proof is by induction on n, and proceeds by identifying n-fold spectra with spectrum objects in the category of $(n-1)$-fold spectra.

Recall that every cofibration $i : U \to V$ is a retract of a map $j : U \to W$ such that

(1) the map $j : U^0 \to W^0$ is a cofibration of $(n-1)$-fold spectra,

(2) each canonical map

$$(S^1 \wedge W^k) \cup_{(S^1 \wedge U^k)} U^{k+1} \to W^{k+1}$$

is a cofibration of $(n-1)$-fold spectra.

Any map j satisfying these two properties is a cofibration of n-fold spectra, and the collection of all such maps is closed under smashing with K, by the inductive assumption. But then $i \wedge K$ is a retract of $j \wedge K$, and $j \wedge K$ is a cofibration, so that $i \wedge K$ is a cofibration. ∎

COROLLARY 2.25. *The functor $X \mapsto X \wedge K$ preserves stably trivial cofibrations of n-fold spectra.*

THEOREM 2.26. *With these definitions, the category* $\mathbf{Spt}^n$ *of n-fold spectra, with the classes of cofibrations, stable equivalences and stable fibrations, satisfies the axioms for a proper closed simplicial model category.*

PROOF: One verifies the Bousfield-Friedlander axioms **A.4**, **A.5** and **A.6** (see [8] again) to get the closed model structure.

Every strict weak equivalence is a stable equivalence by Lemma 2.14, whence **A.4**. Note that $\mu_X = \mu : X \to QX$ is a strict weak equivalence for strictly fibrant n-fold spectra X if and only if each of the maps

$$\mu_j : X \to \Omega_j X[0, \ldots, \overset{j}{1}, \ldots, 0]$$

is a strict weak equivalence, and this is certainly true for QX. Thus, μ_{QX} is a strict weak equivalence. On the other hand, the fact that $Q\mu_X$ is a strict weak equivalence is a consequence of the existence of the natural isomorphism (2.15), so that **A.5** holds. Finally, **A.6** is a consequence of Lemmas 2.17 and 2.18.

Suppose that $j : K \to L$ is a cofibration of pointed simplicial sets, $i : U \to V$ is a cofibration of $\mathbf{Spt}^n$, and that $p : X \to Y$ is a stable fibration of n-fold spectra. Then p is a strict fibration, so that the map

$$(i^*, p_*) : \mathbf{hom}_*(V, X) \to \mathbf{hom}_*(U, X) \times_{\mathbf{hom}_*(U,Y)} \mathbf{hom}_*(V, Y)$$

is a fibration of simplicial sets, by Proposition 2.6. Furthermore, the canonical map

$$\theta : (U \wedge L) \cup_{(U \wedge K)} (V \wedge K) \to V \wedge L$$

is a cofibration: see the diagrams (2.7) – (2.9). It follows that (i^*, p_*) is a stably trivial fibration if p is stably trivial (diagram (2.8)). On the other hand, Corollary 2.25 implies that θ is a stably trivial cofibration if i is stably trivial. Thus, Quillen's axiom **SM7** holds.

The properness assertion is axiom **A.6**. ∎

REMARK 2.27. A result of Bousfield and Friedlander (Theorem A.7 of [8]) implies that a map $f : X \to Y$ of n-fold spectra is a stable fibration if and only if f is a strict fibration and the diagram

$$
\begin{array}{ccc}
X & \overset{\gamma}{\longrightarrow} & QX_{Kan} \\
{\scriptstyle f}\downarrow & & \downarrow{\scriptstyle Qf_{Kan}} \\
Y & \underset{\gamma}{\longrightarrow} & QY_{Kan}
\end{array}
$$

is a homotopy fibre square in the strict category, where γ denotes the composite of canonical maps

$$X \overset{\eta}{\to} X_{Kan} \overset{\mu}{\to} QX_{Kan}.$$

In particular, it's rather useful to know that an n-fold spectrum Z is stably fibrant if and only if Z is strictly fibrant, and the map $\mu : Z \to QZ$ is a strict weak equivalence.   ∎

2.2. Equivalence of homotopy categories

An n-fold spectrum X which is *truncated at level* $(m_1, \ldots, m_n)$ consists of pointed simplicial sets $X^{i_1, \ldots, i_n}$ with $0 \le i_j \le m_j$, together with bonding maps

$$\sigma_j : S^1 \wedge X^{i_1, \ldots, i_j, \ldots, i_n} \to X^{i_1, \ldots, i_j+1, \ldots, i_n}$$

for $i_j < m_j$, such that the usual defining relations for an n-fold spectrum hold, where they make sense. Write

$$\mathbf{Spt}^n(m_1, \ldots, m_n)$$

for the category of n-fold spectra truncated at level $(m_1, \ldots, m_n)$. It is convenient to let some of the m_i's be infinite, and so

$$\mathbf{Spt}^n = \mathbf{Spt}^n(\infty, \ldots, \infty).$$

If $m_j \le k_j$ for $1 \le j \le n$, there is a restriction functor

$$R : \mathbf{Spt}^n(k_1, \ldots, k_n) \to \mathbf{Spt}^n(m_1, \ldots, m_n).$$

This functor has a left adjoint

$$L : \mathbf{Spt}^n(m_1, \ldots, m_n) \to \mathbf{Spt}^n(k_1, \ldots, k_n)$$

such that the composite RL is the identity functor: one suspends in each variable inductively. Finally, each n-fold spectrum Z is naturally a colimit of n-fold spectra of the form LRZ, where the restrictions are defined with respect to some (in fact any) cofinal sequence consisting of n-tuple $(m_1, \ldots, m_n) \in \mathbb{N}^{\times n}$ — this is just a fancy way of saying that a map of an n-fold spectra is completely determined by its truncations.

LEMMA 2.28. *Suppose given an n-fold spectrum Z truncated at level*

$$(m_1, \ldots, m_n),$$

together with a map
$$f : S^1 \wedge Z^{m_1, \ldots, m_n} \to Y.$$

Then there is an n-fold spectrum $\tilde{Z}$ truncated at level $(m_1 + 1, m_2, \ldots, m_n)$ such that
$$\begin{cases} \tilde{Z}^{i_1, \ldots, i_n} = Z^{i_1, \ldots, i_n} & \text{if } i_j \le m_j \\ \tilde{Z}^{m_1+1, m_2, \ldots m_n} = Y \end{cases}$$

and such that the bonding map

$$\sigma_1 : S^1 \wedge \tilde{Z}^{m_1,\ldots,m_n} \to \tilde{Z}^{m_1+1,m_2,\ldots,m_n}$$

coincides with f. Furthermore, the maps $\tilde{Z} \to X$ of n-fold spectra truncated at level $(m_1 + 1, m_2, \ldots, m_n)$ can be identified with the set of all pairs (g, θ), where $g : Z \to RX$ is a map of n-fold spectra truncated at level $(m_1, \ldots, m_n)$ and $\theta : Y \to X^{m_1+1,\ldots,m_n}$ is a map of pointed simplicial sets, such that the following diagram commutes:

$$
\begin{array}{ccc}
S^1 \wedge Z^{m_1,\ldots,m_n} & \xrightarrow{\quad f \quad} & Y \\
{\scriptstyle S^1 \wedge g} \downarrow & & \downarrow {\scriptstyle \theta} \\
S^1 \wedge X^{m_1,\ldots,m_n} & \xrightarrow{\quad \sigma_1 \quad} & X^{m_1+1,\ldots,m_n} .
\end{array}
$$

PROOF: The proof will be by induction on n; the case $n = 1$ is a triviality.

Assume that the object $\tilde{Z}^{*,\ldots,*,m_n}$ exists for the truncated $(n-1)$-fold spectrum $Z^{*,\ldots,*,m_n}$ and the map f. The map

$$Z^{*,\ldots,*,m_n-1} \wedge S^1 \xrightarrow{\sigma_n} Z^{*,\ldots,*,m_n}$$

of $(n-1)$-fold spectra truncated at level $(m_1, \ldots, m_{n-1})$ uniquely determines a map

$$L(Z^{*,\ldots,*,m_n-1}) \wedge S^1 \cong L(Z^{*,\ldots,*,m_n-1} \wedge S^1) \xrightarrow{\sigma_n} \tilde{Z}^{*,\ldots,*,m_n}$$

of $(n-1)$-fold spectra truncated at $(m_1 + 1, m_2, \ldots, m_{n-1})$. Here, L is the left adjoint of the restriction functor

$$R : \mathbf{Spt}^{n-1}(m_1 + 1, m_2, \ldots, m_{n-1}) \to \mathbf{Spt}^{n-1}(m_1, m_2, \ldots, m_{n-1}).$$

Similarly, the maps

$$Z^{*,\ldots,*,i} \wedge S^1 \xrightarrow{\sigma_n} Z^{*,\ldots,*,i+1}$$

for $i < m_n - 1$ induce morphisms

$$L(Z^{*,\ldots,*,i}) \wedge S^1 \cong L(Z^{*,\ldots,*,i} \wedge S^1) \xrightarrow{\sigma_n} L(Z^{*,\ldots,*,i+1}).$$

Thus, the collection of objects

$$L(Z^{*,\ldots,*,0}), \ldots, L(Z^{*,\ldots,*,m_n-1}), \tilde{Z}^{*,\ldots,*,m_n}$$

externally defines an n-fold spectrum truncated at $(m_1 + 1, m_2, \ldots, m_n)$ which has the desired properties. ∎

Corollary 2.29. *The diagonal functor*

$$d : \mathbf{Spt}^n \to \mathbf{Spt}$$

has a left adjoint

$$F : \mathbf{Spt} \to \mathbf{Spt}^n.$$

Furthermore, the canonical map

$$\eta : X \to d(FX)$$

is an isomorphism for all spectra X.

Corollary 2.30. *The diagonal functor d and its left adjoint F induce an equivalence of homotopy categories*

$$\mathrm{Ho}(\mathbf{Spt}^n) \xrightleftharpoons[F]{d} \mathrm{Ho}(\mathbf{Spt}).$$

Proof: The functor F preserves stable equivalences, since the map

$$\eta : X \to d(FX)$$

is an isomorphism hence stable equivalence, by Corollary 2.29. But then the triangle identity

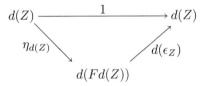

implies that the natural map of n-fold spectra

$$\epsilon_Z : Fd(Z) \to Z$$

is a stable equivalence.   ∎

2.3. Simplicial presheaves and presheaves of spectra
Suppose that $\mathcal{C}$ is an arbitrary Grothendieck site, and let

$$\mathbf{S}Pre(\mathcal{C}) \quad (\text{respectively } \mathbf{S}_*Pre(\mathcal{C}))$$

denote the category of simplicial presheaves (respectively pointed simplicial presheaves) on $\mathcal{C}$.

Recall [23] that a *cofibration* $f : X \to Y$ of (pointed) simplicial presheaves is a pointwise monomorphism in the sense that each map $f(U) : X(U) \to Y(U)$ of sections is a monomorphism of simplicial sets for all $U \in \mathcal{C}$.

A map $g : Z \to W$ in $\mathbf{S}Pre(\mathcal{C})$ is said to be a *local weak equivalence* if, for each object $U \in \mathcal{C}$ and each vertex x of $Z(U)$ the induced maps

$$\pi_n(|Z|_U|, x) \xrightarrow{f_*} \pi_n(|W|_U|, fx), \quad n \geq 0, \tag{2.31}$$

of presheaves of homotopy groups on the local site $\mathcal{C} \downarrow U$ induce isomorphisms of associated sheaves. Note that, in the presence of enough points on $\mathcal{C}$, g is a weak equivalence if and only if each induced morphism of stalks $g_x : Z_x \to W_x$ is a weak equivalence of simplicial sets; for this reason, I often refer to local weak equivalences of simplicial presheaves in the sense just defined as *stalkwise weak equivalences*. A map g is said to be a *pointwise weak equivalence*, on the other hand, if each map of sections $g(U) : Z(U) \to W(U)$ is a weak equivalence of simplicial sets. One can express the defining condition (2.31) completely in terms of simplicial homotopy groups in the case where Z and W are presheaves of Kan complexes.

A *global fibration* is a map which has the right lifting property with respect to all maps which are cofibrations and local weak equivalences.

There is a natural choice of *function complex* $\mathbf{hom}(X, Y)$ for any simplicial presheaves X and Y. Explicitly, $\mathbf{hom}(X, Y)$ is the simplicial set whose n-simplices consist of all morphisms of simplicial presheaves

$$X \times \Delta^n \to Y.$$

In the case where X and Y are globally pointed, we are entitled to construct the *pointed function complex* $\mathbf{hom}_*(X, Y)$, which is the pointed simplicial set having n-simplices

$$X \ltimes \Delta^n \to Y.$$

For our purposes, the central theorem which relates these ideas is the following (see [23], [24]):

THEOREM 2.32. *With the definitions given above, the category $\mathbf{S}Pre(\mathcal{C})$ is a proper closed simplicial model category.*

A *presheaf of spectra* X on the site $\mathcal{C}$ consists of pointed simplicial presheaves X^n, together with pointed maps $\sigma : S^1 \wedge X^n \to X^{n+1}$, $n \geq 0$. The object X can alternatively be thought of as a spectrum object in the category of pointed simplicial presheaves. The presheaves of spectra on $\mathcal{C}$ arrange themselves into a category, which I denote by $\mathbf{Spt}Pre(\mathcal{C})$.

For each presheaf of spectra X, and as in the previous section, the assignment $X(U) \mapsto X_{Kan}(U)$ determines a functor $X \mapsto X_{Kan}$ from $\mathbf{Spt}Pre(\mathcal{C})$ to itself, and there is a natural map $\eta : X \to X_{Kan}$ which is given by the natural weak equivalences $X^n(U) \to X^n_{Kan}(U)$ of simplicial sets. It's helpful to recall in particular that $X^n_{Kan}(U) = S|X^n(U)|$. Recall further that the stablization construction $X(U) \mapsto QX(U)$ is natural, and determines a natural map $\mu : X \to QX$ of presheaves of spectra.

The *sheaf of stable homotopy groups* $\tilde{\pi}^s_j X$ for a presheaf of spectra X can be constructed by taking the sheaf associated to the presheaf

$$U \mapsto \pi^s_j |X(U)|,$$

where $\pi^s_j |X(U)|$ is the jth stable homotopy group of the realized (topological) spectrum $|X(U)|$. Note also that the map $\eta : X \to X_{Kan}$ induces natural isomorphisms of presheaves

$$\pi^s_j X \cong \pi^s_j X_{Kan},$$

and the map $\mu : X_{Kan} \to QX_{Kan}$ induces isomorphisms of the form

$$\pi^s_j X_{Kan} \cong \pi^s_j QX_{Kan} \cong \pi_{j+k} QX^k_{Kan}, \tag{2.33}$$

where the last is a presheaf of ordinary simplicial homotopy groups. It follows that there are natural isomorphisms of sheaves of groups

$$\tilde{\pi}^s_j X \cong \tilde{\pi}_{j+k} QX^k_{Kan},$$

for all integers j and k that make sense. A map $f : X \to Y$ of presheaves of spectra on the site $\mathcal{C}$ is said to be a *local stable equivalence* if the induced maps

$$f_* : \tilde{\pi}^s_j X \to \tilde{\pi}^s_j Y$$

of sheaves of stable homotopy groups are isomorphisms for all integers j. This condition can be rephrased in terms of any of the invariants appearing in (2.33).

Cofibrations in the category of presheaves of spectra can be defined in two ways. Say that a map $i : A \to B$ of $\mathbf{Spt}Pre(\mathcal{C})$ is a *cofibration* if all maps in sections $i : A(U) \to B(U)$, $U \in \mathcal{C}$, are cofibrations in the ordinary spectrum category $\mathbf{Spt}$. Equivalently, i is a cofibration if and only if

(1) the map $i^0 : A^0 \to B^0$ is a cofibration of simplicial presheaves, and
(2) all induced maps

$$S^1 \wedge B^n \cup_{S^1 \wedge A_n} A^{n+1} \to B^{n+1}$$

are cofibrations of simplicial presheaves on $\mathcal{C}$.

It is important to note that the definition of cofibration of presheaves of spectra is independent of topology on the site $\mathcal{C}$, as is the definition of cofibration of simplicial presheaves.

It has become standard to say that a map $p : Z \to W$ of presheaves of spectra is a *global fibration* if it has the right lifting property with respect to all morphisms which are simultaneously cofibrations and local stable equivalences. The governing principle behind these ideas is the following result [24]:

THEOREM 2.34. *The category* $\mathbf{Spt}Pre(\mathcal{C})$ *of presheaves of spectra on a Gro-thendieck site* $\mathcal{C}$, *together with the classes of cofibrations, local stable equiva-lences and global fibrations, satisfies the axioms for a proper closed simplicial model category.*

The simplicial model structure comes from the smash products $X \wedge K$ of presheaves of spectra X with pointed simplicial sets K and the function complexes $\mathbf{hom}_*(X, Y)$, where the latter have n-simplices given by all maps of the form $X \ltimes \Delta^n \to Y$. The properness assertion follows from long exact sequence arguments, which will be repeated explicitly in a wider context below.

REMARK 2.35. The proof of Theorem 2.34, once again, follows the script of Bousfield and Friedlander [8], and in particular depends on proving a series of assertions about the composite map

$$X \xrightarrow{\eta} X_{Kan} \xrightarrow{\mu} QX_{Kan},$$

which I shall denote by $\gamma : X \to QX_{Kan}$. The argument also implies that a map $f : X \to Y$ of presheaves of spectra is a global fibration if and only if all maps $f : X^n \to Y^n$ are global fibrations of simplicial presheaves, and all diagrams

$$
\begin{array}{ccc}
X^n & \xrightarrow{\gamma} & QX^n_{Kan} \\
{\scriptstyle f}\downarrow & & \downarrow{\scriptstyle Qf_{Kan}} \\
Y^n & \xrightarrow[\gamma]{} & QY^n_{Kan}
\end{array}
$$

are homotopy fibre squares in the simplicial presheaf category. In particular, a presheaf of spectra Z is globally fibrant if and only if each simplicial presheaf Z^n is globally fibrant, and each map $\nu : Z^n \to QZ^n$ is a local weak equivalence of simplicial presheaves. Observe that I am not claiming that the stable object QZ itself is globally fibrant.   ∎

A *globally fibrant model* for a presheaf of spectra X is a local stable equiv-alence $\theta : X \to GX$, where GX is globally fibrant. Globally fibrant models always exist, by the factorization axioms, and any two globally fibrant mod-els for X are non-canonically locally stably equivalent. There is an analogous definition of globally fibrant models for simplicial presheaves. In many cases of computational interest, globally fibrant models arise from Godement resolu-tions (see [23, p.76]). It's often useful to think of a globally fibrant model as a non-abelian version of an injective resolution.

REMARK 2.36. The definitions of local weak equivalence of simplicial pre-sheaves and local stable equivalence of presheaves of spectra both depend very much on the topology on the underlying site $\mathcal{C}$. The reader has already been warned that local (stable) weak equivalences and stalkwise (stable) weak equivalences will mean the same thing in cases where the category of sheaves on the site $\mathcal{C}$ has enough points.

There is also the case where the category $\mathcal{C}$ effectively has no topology at all. The *chaotic topology* on the category $\mathcal{C}$ is the site whose covering sieves $R \subset \hom(\ ,U)$ contain the indentity 1_U, for all objects U of $\mathcal{C}$. There is no difference between sheaves and presheaves on $\mathcal{C}$ for this topology, and so in this case a map $f : X \to Y$ is a local weak equivalence of simplicial presheaves if and only if all induced maps in sections $f : X(U) \to Y(U)$, $U \in \mathcal{C}$, are weak equivalences of simplicial sets. Similarly, a map $g : Z \to W$ of presheaves of spectra on the site $\mathcal{C}$ with the chaotic topology is a local stable equivalence if and only if all maps $g : Z(U) \to W(U)$ are stable equivalences of spectra. I shall say that the local (stable) weak equivalences for the chaotic topology are *pointwise* (stable) weak equivalences. The associated closed model structures for $\mathcal{C}$-diagrams of simplicial sets and $\mathcal{C}$-diagrams of spectra are quite useful, and repeated applications will appear below.   ∎

All of the results given both here and in the following section have analogues for (small) diagrams of presheaves of spectra or n-fold spectra. This arises from the fact that the category of J-diagrams within a given Grothendieck topos has the structure of a Grothendieck topos. An explicit construction of the topos of such J-diagrams is given as follows.

Suppose that $\mathcal{C}$ is a Grothendieck site and that J is a category, and let the topology (ie. collection of covering sieves) for the site $\mathcal{C}$ be denoted by $\mathcal{T}$.

The product category $\mathcal{C} \times J$ has a Grothendieck topology, whose covering sieves are those subfunctors of the representable functors $\hom(\ ,(x,i))$ which contain a collection of morphisms $R \times \{1_i\}$, where $R \subset \hom_{\mathcal{C}}(\ ,x)$ is a member of $\mathcal{T}$.

Suppose that $in_i : \mathcal{C} \to \mathcal{C} \times J$ is the functor defined by $x \mapsto (x,i)$, and write $F(i)$ for the composite $F \circ in_J$, where F is any presheaf on $\mathcal{C} \times J$. The covering sieves $R \times \hom_J(\ ,i)$, $R \in \mathcal{T}$, are cofinal among all covering sieves for a fixed object $(x,i) \in \mathcal{C} \times J$, and it follows that F is a sheaf on $\mathcal{C} \times J$ if and only if $F(i)$ is a sheaf on $\mathcal{C}$ for each $i \in J$. Thus, if one identifies F with a contravariant functor $F : J \to PreShv(\mathcal{C})$, then F represents a sheaf on $\mathcal{C} \times J$ if and only if each $F(i)$ is a sheaf on $\mathcal{C}$, so that the sheaf category $Shv(\mathcal{C} \times J)$ can be identified up to isomorphism with the category $Shv(\mathcal{C})^{J^{op}}$ of contravariant functors on J which take values in $Shv(\mathcal{C})$. In particular, the associated sheaf for a functor $F : J \to PreShv(\mathcal{C})$ can be constructed by applying the associated sheaf functor for presheaves on $\mathcal{C}$ to get a natural transformation $\eta : F \to \tilde{F}$ for contravariant functors on J, as can be seen directly from the universal property.

Recall that a map $f : X \to Y$ of simplicial presheaves on a site $\mathcal{C}$ is a (local) weak equivalence if and only if

(1) the presheaf map $f_* : \pi_0 X \to \pi_0 Y$ induces an isomorphism of associated sheaves, and

(2) for each $U \in \mathcal{C}$ and choice of base point $x \in X_0(U)$ the presheaf map

$$f_* : \pi_i(X|_U, x) \to \pi_i(Y|_U, f(x))$$

induces an isomorphism of associated sheaves on the associated comma category site $\mathcal{C} \downarrow U$.

The topology on the comma category site

$$(\mathcal{C} \times J) \downarrow (U, i) \cong (\mathcal{C} \downarrow U) \times (J \downarrow i)$$

is induced from the topology on $\mathcal{C} \downarrow U$ in the same way that the topology on $\mathcal{C} \times J$ is induced from the topology on $\mathcal{C}$. It follows that a map $f : X \to Y$ of simplicial presheaves on $\mathcal{C} \times J$ is a local weak equivalence if and only if each of the associated maps $f : X(i) \to Y(i)$ is a weak equivalence of simplicial presheaves on the site $\mathcal{C}$.

These observations, together with the closed model structure for simplicial presheaves on an arbitrary Grothendieck site [23] now imply

PROPOSITION 2.37. *Suppose that $\mathcal{C}$ is an arbitrary Grothendieck site and that J is some index category. There is a closed simplicial model structure on the category $\mathbf{S}Pre(\mathcal{C})^J$ of J-diagrams in the category of simplicial presheaves on $\mathcal{C}$, such that*

(1) *a map $f : X \to Y$ is a weak equivalence if and only if each level map $f : X(j) \to Y(j)$, $j \in J$, is a local weak equivalence of simplicial presheaves on the site $\mathcal{C}$, and*

(2) *a map $g : U \to V$ is a cofibration if and only if each level map $g : U(j) \to V(j)$, $j \in J$ is a cofibration (ie. pointwise inclusion) of simplicial presheaves on the site $\mathcal{C}$.*

The fibrations in the category of J-diagrams in $\mathbf{S}Pre(\mathcal{C})$ are defined by a right lifting property, and are called global fibrations, as usual. One of the more important features of such objects for us in what follows is

LEMMA 2.38. *Suppose that $f : X \to Y$ is a global fibration in the category of J-diagrams of simplicial presheaves on the site $\mathcal{C}$. Then each map $f : X(j) \to Y(j)$, $j \in J$, is a global fibration of simplicial presheaves on $\mathcal{C}$.*

PROOF: The functor $\mathbf{S}Pre(\mathcal{C})^J \to \mathbf{S}Pre(\mathcal{C})$ which is defined by $X \mapsto X(j)$ has a left adjoint L_j which is defined, for $Z \in \mathbf{S}Pre(\mathcal{C})$, by

$$L_j Z(i) = \bigsqcup_{j \to i} Z.$$

The functor $L_j Z$ takes trivial cofibrations to trivial cofibrations. ∎

The following Corollary is a sample application of these ideas. This result has analogues in all of the categories of presheaves considered in this section.

COROLLARY 2.39. *Suppose that Z is a J-diagram of simplicial presheaves on the site $\mathcal{C}$. Then there is a map $\phi : Z \rightarrow GZ$ of J-diagrams of simplicial presheaves on $\mathcal{C}$ such that each map $\phi : Z(j) \rightarrow GZ(j)$, $j \in J$ is a local weak equivalence and such that each simplicial presheaf $GZ(j)$ is globally fibrant.*

PROOF: Let the map $\phi : Z \rightarrow GZ$ be a globally fibrant model within the category of simplicial presheaves on the site $\mathcal{C} \times J$. The result follows from Lemma 2.38. ∎

Corollary 2.39 solves a homotopy coherence problem, in that it's not clear a priori that a collection of globally fibrant models $Z(j) \rightarrow GZ(j)$, randomly chosen for each simplicial presheaf $Z(j)$ fits together to give a J-diagram GZ, except up to homotopy.

2.4. Presheaves of n-fold spectra

A *presheaf of n-fold spectra* on the Grothendieck site $\mathcal{C}$ is a (contravariant) functor $X : \mathcal{C}^{op} \rightarrow \mathbf{Spt}^n$ which takes values in the category of n-fold spectra. In other words X consists of pointed simplicial presheaves

$$X^{i_1,\ldots,i_n}, \quad i_j \geq 0,$$

together with pointed maps

$$\sigma_j : S^1 \wedge X^{i_1,\ldots,i_j,\ldots,i_n} \rightarrow X^{i_1,\ldots,i_j+1,\ldots,i_n}$$

of simplicial presheaves, which fit into commutative diagrams

for all relevant $j < k$, where $\tau : S^1 \wedge S^1 \rightarrow S^1 \wedge S^1$ is the map which switches factors. Write $\mathbf{Spt}^n Pre(\mathcal{C})$ for the category of presheaves of n-fold spectra on the site $\mathcal{C}$. The notation is meant to suggest that we are dealing with n-fold spectrum objects in the category of simplicial presheaves on the site $\mathcal{C}$.

The axiomatic homotopy theory for presheaves of spectra was summarized in the previous section. A corresponding theory for presheaves of n-fold spectra is given here; the method is to promote the results established for n-fold spectra in the first two sections of this chapter to the presheaf level.

A map $f : X \to Y$ of presheaves of n-fold spectra is said to be a *strict weak equivalence* if each of the maps

$$f : X^{i_1,\ldots,i_n} \to Y^{i_1,\ldots,i_n} \tag{2.40}$$

is a local weak equivalence of simplicial presheaves on the site $\mathcal{C}$. The map f is said to be a *strict fibration* if each of the maps (2.40) is a global fibration of simplicial presheaves. The *cofibrations* of $\mathbf{Spt}^n Pre(\mathcal{C})$ are those maps which have the left lifting property with respect to all maps which are strict fibrations and strict weak equivalences.

Note, first of all, that Lemma 2.3 implies

LEMMA 2.41. *There is a functor $X \mapsto X_{Kan}$ from the category $\mathbf{Spt}^n Pre(\mathcal{C})$ to itself, such that each pointed simplicial set of sections*

$$X_{Kan}^{i_1,\ldots,i_n}(U)$$

is a Kan complex. The natural weak equivalences of simplicial sets

$$\eta : X^{i_1,\ldots,i_n}(U) \to X_{Kan}^{i_1,\ldots,i_n}(U)$$

induce a natural strict weak equivalence of presheaves of n-fold spectra

$$\eta : X \to X_{Kan}.$$

For each pointed simplicial set K and each presheaf of n-fold spectra X, there are presheaves of n-fold spectra $X \wedge K$ and $\mathbf{hom}_*(K, X)$, which are given, respectively, at each multi-index by

$$X^{i_1,\ldots,i_n} \wedge K \quad \text{and} \quad \mathbf{hom}_*(K, X^{i_1,\ldots,i_n}).$$

Furthermore, there is an exponential law

$$\hom(X \wedge K, Y) \cong \hom(X, \mathbf{hom}_*(K, Y))$$

for morphisms of presheaves of n-fold spectra. In particular, a presheaf of $(n + 1)$-fold spectra Z can be regarded (in $n + 1$ different ways) as a spectrum object in the category of presheaves of n-fold spectra, meaning that Z consists of presheaves of n-fold spectra Z^j, $j \geq 0$, together with bonding maps $\sigma : Z^j \wedge S^1 \to Z^{j+1}$ in $\mathbf{Spt}^n Pre(\mathcal{C})$.

Suppose that X and Y are presheaves of n-fold spectra. The *function complex* $\mathbf{hom}_*(X, Y)$ is the pointed simplicial set whose m-simplices are the maps $X \ltimes \Delta^m \to Y$ in $\mathbf{Spt}^n Pre(\mathcal{C})$, where

$$X \ltimes \Delta^n = X \wedge (\Delta^n \sqcup \{*\}).$$

There are exponential laws

$$\mathbf{hom}_*(X \wedge K, Y) \cong \mathbf{hom}_*(K, \mathbf{hom}_*(X, Y)) \cong \mathbf{hom}_*(X, \mathbf{hom}_*(K, Y)),$$

which are valid for any X and Y in $\mathbf{Spt}^n Pre(\mathcal{C})$ and any pointed simplicial set K.

PROPOSITION 2.42. *The category* $\mathbf{Spt}^n Pre(\mathcal{C})$, *together with the classes of cofibrations, strict fibrations, and strict weak equivalences, satisfies the axioms for a proper closed simplicial model category.*

PROOF: Subject to invoking Theorem 2.32 in place of the analogous result for simplicial sets, the proof of this result is the same as that for the corresponding results for n-fold spectra, namely Proposition 2.4 and Proposition 2.6.   ∎

Say that a map $g : Z \to W$ of presheaves of n-fold spectra is a *local stable equivalence* if the induced map

$$d(g) : d(Z) \to d(W)$$

is a local stable equivalence of presheaves of spectra. Lemma 2.14 may be used to formulate this condition in terms of sheaves of homotopy groups. Every strict weak equivalence is a local stable equivalence.

Note in particular that if the natural map

$$\gamma : X \to QX_{Kan}$$

is defined to be the composite

$$X \xrightarrow{\eta} X_{Kan} \xrightarrow{\mu} QX_{Kan},$$

then the proof of Theorem 2.26 implies that the maps

$$Q\gamma : QX_{Kan} \to Q(QX_{Kan})_{Kan}$$

and

$$\gamma : QX_{Kan} \to Q(QX_{Kan})_{Kan}$$

are pointwise strict weak equivalences. In summary, we have

LEMMA 2.43. *The following hold for maps of presheaves of n-fold spectra on a Grothendieck site $\mathcal{C}$:*

(1) *Every strict weak equivalence is a local stable equivalence.*
(2) *The map* $\gamma : QX_{Kan} \to Q(QX_{Kan})_{Kan}$ *is a strict weak equivalence.*
(3) *The map* $Q\gamma : QX_{Kan} \to Q(QX_{Kan})_{Kan}$ *is a strict weak equivalence.*

It follows from Corollary 2.16 that g is a local stable equivalence if and only if the induced map

$$Qg_{Kan} : QZ_{Kan} \to QW_{Kan}$$

is a strict weak equivalence.

A map $f : A \to X$ of presheaves of n-fold spectra is said to be a *pointwise cofibration* if each of the maps

$$f : A^{i_1,\dots,i_n} \to X^{i_1,\dots,i_n}$$

is a cofibration of simplicial presheaves. One can show, by induction on n, that every cofibration of presheaves of n-fold spectra is a pointwise cofibration, just as was done for n-fold spectra. Thus, Lemma 2.17 implies that any cofibration of n-fold spectra $i : A \to X$ gives rise to an exact sequence of presheaves of abelian groups

$$\pi_k^s dX \xrightarrow{p} \pi_k^s d(X/A) \to \pi_{k-1}^s d(A) \xrightarrow{i} \pi_{k-1}^s dX \xrightarrow{p} \pi_{k-1}^s d(X/A),$$

and hence to an exact sequence of sheaves of abelian groups

$$\tilde{\pi}_k^s dX \xrightarrow{p} \tilde{\pi}_k^s d(X/A) \to \tilde{\pi}_{k-1}^s d(A) \xrightarrow{i} \tilde{\pi}_{k-1}^s dX \xrightarrow{p} \tilde{\pi}_{k-1}^s d(X/A),$$

where $p : X \to X/A$ is the canonical map to the cofibre. This gives

LEMMA 2.44. *Local stable equivalences in* $\mathbf{Spt}^n Pre(\mathcal{C})$ *are closed under cobase change by cofibrations. In other words, given a pushout diagram*

$$
\begin{array}{ccc}
A & \xrightarrow{\ g\ } & Z \\
{\scriptstyle i}\downarrow & & \downarrow \\
X & \xrightarrow[\ g_*\ ]{} & X \cup_A Z,
\end{array}
$$

where i is a cofibration, if g is a local stable equivalence, then so is g_*.

Global fibrations of simplicial presheaves are also pointwise fibrations. This fact has been alluded to in print before, usually with an injunction to see the proof of Lemma 3.4 in [23]: the essential point is that, if U is an object of the site $\mathcal{C}$, then the U-sections functor $Y \mapsto Y(U)$ has a left adjoint $X \mapsto X_U$, where

$$X_U(V) = \bigsqcup_{\phi:V \to U} X$$

defines the simplicial presheaf X_U associated to the simplicial set X (see p.68 of [23]). But then $X \mapsto X_U$ takes trivial cofibrations of simplicial sets to pointwise trivial cofibrations of simplicial presheaves, so the usual lifting property argument carries the day.

It follows that every strict fibration $p : X \to Y$ of presheaves of n-fold spectra consists (in part) of maps of n-fold spectra $p(U) : X(U) \to Y(U)$

which are strict fibrations, in all sections. It follows from Lemma 2.18 that, if $i : F \to X$ is the inclusion of the fibre of p, then there is an exact sequence of presheaves of stable homotopy groups

$$\pi_k^s dF \xrightarrow{i} \pi_k^s dX \xrightarrow{p} \pi_k^s dY \to \pi_{k-1}^s dF \xrightarrow{i} \pi_{k-1}^s dX,$$

and hence an exact sequence of sheaves of abelian groups

$$\tilde{\pi}_k^s dF \xrightarrow{i} \tilde{\pi}_k^s dX \xrightarrow{p} \tilde{\pi}_k^s dY \to \tilde{\pi}_{k-1}^s dF \xrightarrow{i} \tilde{\pi}_{k-1}^s dX.$$

This implies the following result:

LEMMA 2.45. *Local stable equivalences in* $\mathbf{Spt}^n Pre(\mathcal{C})$ *are closed under base change by strict fibrations.*

There are non-abelian analogues of the standard global ext constructions in the categories of pointed simplicial presheaves and presheaves of spectra. In particular, suppose that K and V are pointed simplicial presheaves. Then there is a pointed simplicial presheaf

$$\mathbf{Hom}_*(K, V),$$

which is defined for each $U \in \mathcal{C}$ by the equation

$$\mathbf{Hom}_*(K, V)(U) = \mathbf{hom}_*(K|_U, V|_U).$$

The simplicial presheaf $K|_U$, for example, is the restriction of K to the site $\mathcal{C} \downarrow U$ along the forgetful functor $Q : \mathcal{C} \downarrow U \to \mathcal{C}$. Furthermore, it's not hard to show that there are natural isomorphisms (ie. exponential laws)

$$\mathbf{hom}_*(X, \mathbf{Hom}_*(K, V)) \cong \mathbf{hom}_*(X \wedge K, V)$$

relating morphisms of pointed simplicial presheaves, and their function space counterparts

$$\mathbf{hom}_*(X, \mathbf{Hom}_*(K, V)) \cong \mathbf{hom}_*(X \wedge K, V).$$

This construction extends to give a presheaf of spectra $\mathbf{Hom}_*(K, Z)$ for any pointed simplicial presheaf K and presheaf of spectra Z. If X happens to be a presheaf of spectra, there is a corresponding exponential law

$$\mathbf{hom}_*(X, \mathbf{Hom}_*(K, Z)) \cong \mathbf{hom}_*(X \wedge K, Z).$$

LEMMA 2.46. *Suppose that* K *is a pointed simplicial presheaf on* $\mathcal{C}$, *and that* $f : X \to Y$ *is a local stable equivalence of presheaves of spectra on* $\mathcal{C}$. *Then the induced map*

$$f \wedge K : X \wedge K \to Y \wedge K$$

is a local stable equivalence of presheaves of spectra.

PROOF: It's a little bit fussy in cases where $Shv(\mathcal{C})$ does not have enough points, but one can show that the functor $U \mapsto U \wedge K$ preserves local weak equivalences of pointed simplicial presheaves. It follows that the functor

$$Z \mapsto \mathbf{Hom}_*(K, Z)$$

preserves global fibrations of pointed simplicial presheaves, and that the functor $X \mapsto X \wedge K$ preserves strict weak equivalences of presheaves of spectra.

Now suppose that the presheaf of spectra Z is globally fibrant. Then Z is strictly fibrant, and so $\mathbf{Hom}_*(K, Z)$ is also strictly fibrant. The canonical map $\mu : Z \to QZ$ is a strict weak equivalence of strictly fibrant presheaves of spectra, so that the map

$$\mathbf{Hom}_*(K, \mu) : \mathbf{Hom}_*(K, Z) \to \mathbf{Hom}_*(K, QZ)$$

is a strict weak equivalence. In effect, since Z^n and QZ^n are both globally fibrant, the standard construction that replaces a map between fibrant objects by a fibration, carried out within the closed model structure on the category of simplicial presheaves, guarantees that each simplicial presheaf map $\mu : Z^n \to QZ^n$ has a factorization

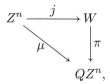

where π is a global fibration and a local weak equivalence, and j is right inverse to a map $p : W \to Z^n$ which is a global fibration and a local weak equivalence. The maps π and p induce maps $\pi_* : \mathbf{Hom}_*(K, W) \to \mathbf{Hom}_*(K, QZ^n)$ and $p_* : \mathbf{Hom}_*(K, W) \to \mathbf{Hom}_*(K, Z^n)$ which have the right lifting property with respect to all cofibrations, and are therefore local weak equivalences. There is a commutative diagram

$$
\begin{array}{ccc}
\mathbf{Hom}_*(K, Z) & \xrightarrow{\ \mathbf{Hom}_*(K, \mu)\ } & \mathbf{Hom}_*(K, QZ) \\
 & {}_{\mu}\searrow & \Big\downarrow{}^{\cong}_{\tau} \\
 & & Q\mathbf{Hom}_*(K, Z),
\end{array}
$$

so that the map

$$\mu : \mathbf{Hom}_*(K, Z) \to Q\mathbf{Hom}_*(K, Z)$$

is a strict weak equivalence. Thus, the presheaf of spectra $\mathbf{Hom}_*(K, Z)$ is globally fibrant under the assumption that Z is globally fibrant.

The rest of the argument follows the outline of proof given for Lemma 2.20. It is enough to assume that f is a cofibration and a local stable equivalence between cofibrant spectra, and show that the induced map

$$f^* : \mathbf{hom}_*(Y \wedge K, Z) \to \mathbf{hom}_*(X \wedge K, Z)$$

is a weak equivalence of simplicial sets for all globally fibrant presheaf of spectra Z. But f^* is canonically isomorphic to the map

$$\mathbf{hom}_*(Y, \mathbf{Hom}_*(K, Z)) \to \mathbf{hom}_*(X, \mathbf{Hom}_*(K, Z))$$

which is induced by f. The presheaf of spectra $\mathbf{Hom}_*(K, Z)$ is stably fibrant, so that the Bousfield-Friedlander criterion applies. ∎

Say that a map $f : X \to Y$ of presheaves of spectra which is both a local stable equivalence and a cofibration is a *locally trivial cofibration*, and that f is a *trivial global fibration* if it is both a local stable equivalence and a global fibration. Corresponding notions are defined for morphisms of presheaves of n-fold spectra. For any pointed simplicial presheaf K, the functor $X \mapsto X \wedge K$ preserves cofibrations of presheaves of spectra. This observation and Lemma 2.46 together imply

COROLLARY 2.47.

(1) *The functor* $X \mapsto X \wedge K$ *preserves locally trivial cofibrations of presheaves of spectra.*

(2) *The functor* $X \mapsto \mathbf{Hom}_*(K, X)$ *preserves global fibrations and trivial global fibrations of presheaves of spectra.*

COROLLARY 2.48. *The functor* $X \mapsto X \wedge K$ *preserves local stable equivalences of presheaves of n-fold spectra.*

LEMMA 2.49. *The functor* $X \mapsto X \wedge K$ *preserves cofibrations of n-fold spectra.*

PROOF: Use the corresponding fact for pointed simplicial presheaves (which appears in the course of proving Lemma 2.46), to give an inductive argument analogous to the proof of Lemma 2.24. ∎

COROLLARY 2.50. *The functor* $X \mapsto X \wedge K$ *preserves locally trivial cofibrations of presheaves of n-fold spectra.*

THEOREM 2.51. *The category* $\mathbf{Spt}^n Pre(\mathcal{C})$, *and the classes of cofibrations, local stable equivalences and global fibrations, together satisfy the axioms for a proper closed simplicial model category.*

PROOF: The reader would have noticed that an analogy with the proof of Theorem 2.26 has already been set up. One verifies the closed model axioms by showing that the Bousfield-Friedlander axioms are verified, as they are done in Lemmas 2.43, 2.44 and 2.45. The simplicial model structure is a consequence of Theorem 2.32 and Corollary 2.50; the proof is the same as that for the corresponding result about n-fold spectra.   ∎

The claims appearing in Remark 2.35 apply verbatim in the context of presheaves of n-fold spectra. Also, the constructions of the second section of this chapter apply without change to the presheaf case, giving:

PROPOSITION 2.52. *The diagonal functor d and its left adjoint F induce an equivalence of homotopy categories*

$$\mathrm{Ho}(\mathbf{Spt}^n Pre(\mathcal{C})) \xrightleftharpoons[F]{d} \mathrm{Ho}(\mathbf{Spt}Pre(\mathcal{C})).$$

2.5. Smash products of presheaves of spectra

It's rather interesting at this point to compare the theory that has been described here with Adams' presentation of smash products of spectra [2, pp.158-190].

We can show that all of the diagonal functors $X \mapsto X_\psi$ from n-fold spectra to spectra which are associated to admissible paths $\psi : \mathbb{N} \to \mathbb{N}^{\times n}$ are naturally stable homotopy equivalent (Theorem 1.32). We also know that there is a closed model structure on the category of n-fold spectra such that any one of these diagonal functors induces an equivalence of the ordinary stable category with the homotopy category of n-fold spectra, and this for all n (Theorem 2.26, Corollary 2.30). These results go far beyond Adams' constructions, but a way has not yet been found to use them to demonstrate that smash product of spectra and the sphere spectrum together give the stable homotopy category the structure of a symmetric monoidal category. The central problem is that the natural equivalences of Theorem 1.32 are not known to be homotopy coherent in any sense, so there is no effective way of composing them, particularly in cases where one wants to analyze symmetries.

I shall not reproduce Adams' work here. In the case of bispectra, his methods can be used to show that each bispectrum X has an associated double telescope construction, which is a spectrum that comes equipped with canonical equivalences to each of the telescopes arising from admissible paths $\psi : \mathbb{N} \to \mathbb{N}^2$. The construction of the double telescope depends, fundamentally, on first extending a particular S^2-bundle over the boundary $\partial(I \times I)$ of the box $I \times I$ to the full box (for which one uses the calculation $\pi_1 BSO(2) = 0$), and then glueing the result to a space made up of telescopes of bonding maps. The construction is therefore natural in bispectra X, and induces a natural canonical stable equivalence $X_\psi \simeq X_\gamma$ for any pair of admissible paths $\psi, \gamma : \mathbb{N} \to \mathbb{N}^{\times 2}$.

Adams uses the same general trick of glueing an extended sphere bundle to some space made up of telescopes arising from certain n-fold spectra (for low values of n) to prove all of the technical results leading to the assertion that the stable category has a symmetric monoidal category. These constructions are therefore natural in the types of n-fold spectra that arise. In particular, we can infer the following:

THEOREM 2.53. *The smash product construction* $(X, Y) \mapsto d(X \wedge Y)$ *and the (constant) sphere spectrum* S *together give the stable homotopy category* $\mathrm{Ho}(\mathbf{Spt}\,Pre(\mathcal{C}))$ *of presheaves of spectra on a Grothendieck site* $\mathcal{C}$ *the structure of a symmetric monoidal category.*

Chapter 3. First applications

One expects any theory of smash products of spectra that's worth its salt to drag a theory of function spectra into existence in an essentially formal way. The closed simplicial model structures for the various categories of n-fold spectra that were introduced in Chapter 2 have such theories associated to them, and this is the subject of the first section of this chapter.

The main idea is relatively simple (see Example 3.15): if Y is a bispectrum, and if by $Y^{*,j}$ we mean the spectrum in "vertical" degree j, and if X is a spectrum, then the pointed simplicial sets $\mathbf{hom}_*(X, Y^{*,j})$ that arise from the closed simplicial model structure for the spectrum category are part of the data for a spectrum that I denote by $\mathbf{hom}^l_*(X, Y)$. In particular, if Z is a spectrum, there is a suspension bispectrum $\Sigma^\infty Z$ which is formed in an obvious way, and a corresponding stably fibrant model $F\Sigma^\infty Z$ in the category of bispectra, and then the function spectrum of maps from X to Z is the spectrum $\mathbf{hom}^l_*(X, F\Sigma^\infty Z)$, up to stable homotopy equivalence.

This function spectrum functor is right adjoint in the stable category to smashing with X on the left. For book keeping purposes, it is also covenient to define a spectrum $\mathbf{hom}^r_*(X, Y)$ by using the pointed simplicial sets $\mathbf{hom}_*(X, Y^{i,*})$ corresponding to the spectra $Y^{i,*}$ in horizontal degrees. Then the functor $X \mapsto \mathbf{hom}^r_*(X, Y)$ is right adjoint to smashing with X on the right. Of course, the two sorts of function spectra coincide in the stable category, because smash product is commutative up to stable equivalence — this is an easy consequence of Theorem 1.27.

If Y is an m-fold spectrum and Z is a stably fibrant $(m+n)$-fold spectrum, there are analogous n-fold spectra $\mathbf{hom}^l_*(Y, Z)$ and $\mathbf{hom}^r_*(Y, Z)$, which appear as adjoints (suitably interpreted) to the respective smash product functors

$$\wedge : \mathbf{Spt}^n \times \mathbf{Spt}^m \to \mathbf{Spt}^{m+n} \quad \text{and} \quad \wedge : \mathbf{Spt}^m \times \mathbf{Spt}^n \to \mathbf{Spt}^{m+n}.$$

The adjunction formulas that we shall use are developed at this level of generality.

The second (and final) section of this chapter begins with a brief review of some explicit constructions behind addition of maps in the stable category. The most technically satisfying of the lot for our purposes makes use of the canonical stable equivalence

$$X \vee Y \xrightarrow{\simeq} X \times Y,$$

which, in effect, gives the stable category the structure of an additive category.

For example, if X is a spectrum with an action by a finite group G, then the abstract norm $N = \sum_{g \in G} g : X \to X$ is the map in the stable category which is represented by the composite

$$X \xrightarrow{\Delta_G} \prod_{g \in G} \xleftarrow{\simeq} \bigvee_{g \in G} X \xrightarrow{\nabla} X.$$

The equations $pr_g\Delta_G = g$, $g \in G$, define the map Δ_G, and ∇ is the fold map. The map $N : X \to X$ is $(G \times G)$-equivariant for the $(G \times G)$-action on the source which restricts along the projection $pr_L : G \times G \to G$ on the left hand factor, and for the $(G \times G)$-action on the target which restricts along projection on the right hand factor: such maps are called join transformations in Chapter 5. One can exploit this equivariance to show that N induces maps

$$N_* : X \to \varprojlim_{g \in G} X$$

and

$$N_h : \varinjlim_{g \in G} X \to \varprojlim_{g \in G} X.$$

The map N_h is the "hypernorm", while the map N_* is a type of abstract transfer. Both of these maps are of fundamental importance for the generalized étale (or Galois) cohomology theories that arise from presheaves of spectra on the étale site of a field k. In particular, if F is a presheaf of spectra for such a field which is globally fibrant in a suitable sense (see Example 3.20 and Chapter 6), and G is the Galois group of a finite Galois extension L/k, then G acts on the spectrum of sections $F(L)$, and the spectrum of global sections $F(k)$ is stably equivalent to $\varprojlim_{g \in G} F(L)$, so that the map N_* defines a transfer map

$$N_* : F(L) \to \varprojlim_{g \in G} F(L) \simeq F(k).$$

This chapter closes with the demonstration (Example 3.21) of a projection formula for such abstract transfer maps N_*. It is shown in Chapter 7 that the hypernorm for the G-action on $F(L)$ is a stable equivalence under a boundedness assumption on the Galois cohomological dimension of the field k — this result is called the Tate theorem there.

3.1. Function spectra

The category of spectrum objects in the category of n-fold spectra will be denoted by $\mathbf{Spt}(\mathbf{Spt}^n)$. There is a suspension object $\Sigma^\infty X$ in $\mathbf{Spt}(\mathbf{Spt}^n)$ for any n-fold spectrum X, given at level i by

$$(\Sigma^\infty X)^i = X \wedge S^i.$$

$\Sigma^\infty X$ is identified with an $(n + 1)$-fold spectrum having the same name by requiring that

$$(\Sigma^\infty X)^{i_1,\dots,i_{n+1}} = X^{i_1,\dots,i_n} \wedge S^{i_{n+1}}.$$

The bonding maps σ_j of the $(n + 1)$-fold spectrum $\Sigma^\infty X$ are defined on

$$S^1 \wedge X^{i_1,\dots,i_n} \wedge S^{i_{n+1}}$$

by
$$\sigma_j = \sigma_j \wedge S^{i_{n+1}}$$
if $j \leq n$, and σ_{n+1} is the composite
$$S^1 \wedge X^{i_1,\ldots,i_n} \wedge S^{i_{n+1}} \xrightarrow{\tau} X^{i_1,\ldots,i_n} \wedge S^{i_{n+1}} \wedge S^1 \cong X^{i_1,\ldots,i_n} \wedge S^{i_{n+1}+1},$$
where the displayed isomorphism is induced by the associativity isomorphism
$$S^{i_{n+1}} \wedge S^1 \cong S^{i_{n+1}+1}$$
(no smash factors are permuted).

There is a natural bijection
$$\hom_{\mathbf{Spt}^{n+1}}(\Sigma^\infty X, Y) \cong \hom_{\mathbf{Spt}^n}(X, Y^{*,\ldots,*,0}).$$
Recall that any $(n+1)$-fold spectrum Y can be identified with a spectrum object in $\mathbf{Spt}^n$ whose n-fold spectrum at level i is given by
$$Y^{*,\ldots,*,j}.$$

The bonding map
$$\sigma : Y^{*,\ldots,*,j} \wedge S^1 \to Y^{*,\ldots,*,j+1}$$
is a map of $(n+1)$-fold spectra which is given on the space level by the composites
$$Y^{i_1,\ldots,i_n,j} \wedge S^1 \xrightarrow{\tau} S^1 \wedge Y^{i_1,\ldots,i_n,j} \xrightarrow{\sigma_{n+1}} Y^{i_1,\ldots,i_n,j+1}.$$

Suppose that X is an n-fold spectrum and Y is an m-fold spectrum. The smash product $X \wedge Y$ is most naturally viewed as an $(n+m)$-fold spectrum with spaces
$$X^{i_1,\ldots,i_n} \wedge Y^{i_{n+1},\ldots,i_{n+m}}$$
and suitably defined bonding maps (this is discussed in more detail later in this section).

Recall that the simplicial model of the sphere spectrum S has spaces
$$S^i = S^1 \wedge \cdots \wedge S^1 \quad i \text{ factors},$$
with bonding maps
$$S^1 \wedge S^i \to S^{i+1}$$
given by associativity isomorphisms. Suppose again that X is an n-fold spectrum, and form the $(n+1)$-fold spectrum $X \wedge S$. The bonding maps σ_{n+1} of the $(n+1)$-fold spectrum $X \wedge S$ are isomorphisms, so any map
$$X \wedge S \to Y$$
of $(n+1)$-fold spectra is completely determined by the map
$$X \to Y^{*,\ldots,*,0}$$
of n-fold spectra at level 0. It follows that there is a natural isomorphism of $(n+1)$-fold spectra of the form
$$\Sigma^\infty X \cong X \wedge S.$$

LEMMA 3.1. *Suppose that X is a spectrum. Then the diagonal spectrum $d\Sigma^\infty X$ is naturally stably homotopy equivalent to X.*

Proof: Recall that the bispectrum $\Sigma^\infty X$ is specified by the spaces

$$\Sigma^\infty X^{i,j} = X^i \wedge S^j$$

and by the bonding maps

$$\sigma_1 : \ S^1 \wedge X^i \wedge S^j \xrightarrow{\ \sigma \wedge S^j\ } X^{i+1} \wedge S^j,$$

and

$$\sigma_2 : \ S^1 \wedge X^i \wedge S^j \xrightarrow{\ \tau\ } X^i \wedge S^j \wedge S^1 \cong X^i \wedge S^{j+1}.$$

Thus

$$d\Sigma^\infty X^{2n} = X^n \wedge S^n \quad \text{and} \quad d\Sigma^\infty X^{2n+1} = X^{n+1} \wedge S^n,$$

with the appropriate bonding maps (see the discussion following the proof of Theorem 1.27).

The twist maps $\tau : X^i \wedge S^j \to S^j \wedge X^i$ define a natural isomorphism of spectra

$$\tau : d\Sigma^\infty X \xrightarrow{\ \cong\ } DX,$$

where DX is the spectrum with

$$DX^{2n} = S^n \wedge X^n \quad \text{and} \quad DX^{2n+1} = S^n \wedge X^{n+1},$$

and with bonding maps given by the composites

$$\begin{cases} S^1 \wedge S^n \wedge X^n \xrightarrow{\ \tau \wedge X^n\ } S^n \wedge S^1 \wedge X^n \xrightarrow{\ S^n \wedge \sigma\ } S^n \wedge X^{n+1}, \\ S^1 \wedge S^n \wedge X^{n+1} \xrightarrow{\ \tau \wedge X^{n+1}\ } S^n \wedge S^1 \wedge X^{n+1} \cong S^{n+1} \wedge X^{n+1}. \end{cases}$$

Lemma 1.16 and the method of proof of Theorem 1.19 together imply that DX is naturally stable homotopy equivalent to a spectrum $\tilde{D}X$, with

$$\tilde{D}X^{2n} = S^n \wedge X^n \quad \text{and} \quad \tilde{D}X^{2n+1} = S^n \wedge X^{n+1},$$

and having bonding maps

$$\begin{cases} S^{n+1} \wedge X^n \xrightarrow{\ S^n \wedge \sigma\ } S^n \wedge X^{n+1}, \\ S^{n+1} \wedge X^{n+1} \xrightarrow{\ 1\ } S^{n+1} \wedge X^{n+1}. \end{cases}$$

Finally, the canonical composites

$$\sigma_* : \ S^k \wedge X^n \xrightarrow{\ S^{k-1} \wedge \sigma\ } S^{k-1} \wedge X^{n+1} \xrightarrow{\ S^{k-2} \wedge \sigma\ } \ldots \xrightarrow{\ \sigma\ } X^{n+k}$$

induce a natural map of spectra

$$\sigma_* : \tilde{D}X \to X.$$

One sees that this map is a stable homotopy equivalence by staring for a sufficient length of time at the commutative diagram

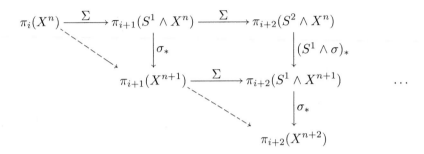

The point is that the stable homotopy groups of X and $\tilde{D}X$ can both be described as colimits of diagrams of this form.   ∎

COROLLARY 3.2. *Suppose that X in an n-fold spectrum. Then dX is naturally stable homotopy equivalent to*

$$d\Sigma^\infty X \cong d(X \wedge S).$$

PROOF: Application of the diagonalization functor d for n-fold spectra to the suspension object $\Sigma^\infty X$ gives a bispectrum (or member of **Spt(Spt)**), namely

$$d\Sigma^\infty X = \Sigma^\infty dX.$$

The diagonal spectrum $\Sigma^\infty dX$ is naturally stable homotopy equivalent to the diagonal $d\Sigma^\infty X$ of the $(n+1)$-fold spectrum $\Sigma^\infty X$, by Theorem 1.27. Now use Lemma 3.1.   ∎

LEMMA 3.3. *Suppose that X is a spectrum. Then the canonical maps*

$$(\Sigma^\infty X)^i_{Kan} \xrightarrow{\sigma_*} \mathbf{hom}_*(S^1, (\Sigma^\infty X)^{i+1}_{Kan})$$

are stable weak equivalences of spectra.

PROOF: $\Sigma^\infty X$ denotes the spectrum object in **Spt** which is given by the list of spectra

$$X, \ X \wedge S^1, \ X \wedge S^2, \ \ldots$$

and $(\Sigma^\infty X)_{Kan}$ is the associated strictly fibrant model.

Suppose that Z is a strictly fibrant spectrum, and let $|Z|^{|S^1|}$ denote the loop spectrum of the realization $|Z|$ in the category of spectrum objects in pointed topological spaces. There is a natural map of topological spectra

$$\omega : |\mathbf{hom}_*(S^1, Z)| \to |Z|^{|S^1|}$$

which is uniquely determined by the commutative diagram

$$
\begin{array}{ccc}
|\mathbf{hom}_*(S^1, Z)| \wedge |S^1| & \xrightarrow{\ \cong\ } & |\mathbf{hom}_*(S^1, Z) \wedge S^1| \\
\omega \wedge |S^1| \downarrow & & \downarrow |ev| \\
|Z|^{|S^1|} \wedge |S^1| & \xrightarrow[\ ev\ ]{} & |Z|
\end{array}
$$

This map ω is a strict weak equivalence (see [24], but mind the typos).

Note also that any map $\sigma : X \wedge S^1 \to Z$ gives rise to a commutative diagram

$$
\begin{array}{ccc}
|X| & \xrightarrow{\ |\sigma_*|\ } & |\mathbf{hom}_*(S^1, Z)| \\
 & \searrow{\scriptstyle \sigma_*} & \downarrow \omega \\
 & & |Z|^{|S^1|},
\end{array}
$$

where the diagonal map σ_* is the adjoint of the composite

$$|X| \wedge |S^1| \cong |X \wedge S^1| \xrightarrow{\ |\sigma|\ } |Z|.$$

It follows that the map

$$(\Sigma^\infty X)^i_{Kan} \xrightarrow{\ \sigma_*\ } \mathbf{hom}_*(S^1, (\Sigma^\infty X)^{i+1}_{Kan})$$

is a stable weak equivalence if and only if the map $|\sigma_*|$ of topological spectra is a stable weak equivalence, and this if and only if the induced map

$$|(\Sigma^\infty X)^i_{Kan}| \xrightarrow{\ \sigma_*\ } |(\Sigma^\infty X)^{i+1}_{Kan}|^{|S^1|}$$

is a stable weak equivalence. But there is a commutative diagram

$$
\begin{array}{ccc}
|(\Sigma^\infty X)^i_{Kan}| & \xrightarrow{\ \sigma_*\ } & |(\Sigma^\infty X)^{i+1}_{Kan}|^{|S^1|} \\
\uparrow & & \uparrow \\
|X \wedge S^i| & \xrightarrow[\ \sigma_*\ ]{} & |X \wedge S^{i+1}|^{|S^1|}
\end{array}
$$

in which the vertical maps are strict weak equivalences, and the bottom σ_* is a stable weak equivalence by standard results (see the proof of Lemma 1.1). ∎

COROLLARY 3.4. *Suppose that Y is an n-fold spectrum. Then the bonding maps*

$$(\Sigma^\infty Y)^i_{Kan} \to \mathbf{hom}_*(S^1, (\Sigma^\infty Y)^{i+1}_{Kan})$$

are stable weak equivalences of n-fold spectra.

PROOF: Use the relation

$$d(\Sigma^\infty Y)^i_{Kan} = (\Sigma^\infty dY)^i_{Kan}. \qquad \blacksquare$$

PROPOSITION 3.5. *Suppose that X is a stably fibrant bispectrum. Then the canonical map*

$$\Sigma^\infty X^{*,0} \to X$$

is a stable weak equivalence of bispectra.

PROOF: There is a commutative diagram

$$
\begin{array}{ccc}
\Sigma^\infty X^{*,0} & \xrightarrow{\;\;\lambda\;\;} & X \\
\downarrow & & \downarrow \\
(\Sigma^\infty X^{*,0})_{Kan} & \xrightarrow[\lambda_{Kan}]{} & X_{Kan}
\end{array}
$$

in which both vertical arrows are canonical strict weak equivalences. Write $\lambda = \lambda_{Kan}$; we will show that this map is a stable equivalence.

Identify the bispectrum X with a spectrum object in **Spt** by setting

$$X^i = X^{*,i}.$$

λ is a strict weak equivalence in degree 0, since it is the identity map in that degree. Since X is stably fibrant, the bonding map

$$X^i_{Kan} \xrightarrow{\;\sigma_*\;} \mathbf{hom}_*(S^1, X^{i+1}_{Kan})$$

(of spectra) is a strict weak equivalence. Consider the commutative diagram

$$
\begin{array}{ccc}
(\Sigma^\infty X^{*,0})^i_{Kan} & \xrightarrow{\;\;\lambda\;\;} & X^i_{Kan} \\
\sigma_* \downarrow & & \downarrow \sigma_* \\
\mathbf{hom}_*(S^1, (\Sigma^\infty X^{*,0})^{i+1}_{Kan}) & \xrightarrow[\lambda_*]{} & \mathbf{hom}_*(S^1, X^{i+1}_{Kan}).
\end{array}
$$

The vertical map σ_* on the right is a strict weak equivalence, and the map σ_* on the left is a stable weak equivalence by Lemma 3.3. Thus, if λ is a stable weak equivalence, then so is λ_*, and so the map

$$\lambda : (\Sigma^\infty X^{0,*})_{Kan}^{i+1} \to X_{Kan}^{i+1}$$

is a stable weak equivalence. The proof is now completed by induction on i, using Lemma 1.28.   ∎

If X is an n-fold spectrum and θ is an element of the symmetric group Σ_n, then there is an n-fold spectrum X_θ which is defined by

$$X_\theta^{i_1,\ldots,i_n} = X^{i_{\theta(1)},\ldots,i_{\theta(n)}}.$$

The bonding maps $\sigma_j^\theta : S^1 \wedge X_\theta^I \to X_\theta^{I_j}$ for X_θ are specified by $\sigma_j^\theta = \sigma_{\theta(j)}$. It is a consequence of Theorem 1.27 that dX_θ is naturally stable homotopy equivalent to dX. This is the extra ingredient that one adds to Lemma 3.1 and Proposition 3.5 to show

COROLLARY 3.6. *Suppose that X is a stably fibrant bispectrum. Then dX is naturally stable homotopy equivalent to both $X^{0,*}$ and $X^{*,0}$.*

COROLLARY 3.7. *Suppose that X is a stably fibrant n-fold spectrum. Then the spectrum dX is naturally stably equivalent to each of the spectra*

$$dX^{*,\ldots,\overset{j}{0},\ldots,*},$$

for $1 \leq j \leq n$.

PROOF: It's enough to show that dX is naturally stable homotopy equivalent to

$$dX^{*,\ldots,*,0}.$$

The other cases are obtained by permuting indices.

Identify X with the spectrum object in $\mathbf{Spt}^{n-1}$ whose $(n-1)$-fold spectrum X^j at level j is given by

$$X^j = X^{*,\ldots,*,j}.$$

Applying the $(n-1)$-fold diagonalization functor gives a stably fibrant bispectrum dX, with

$$(dX)^j = dX^{*,\ldots,*,j}.$$

The diagonal of this bispectrum is naturally stable homotopy equivalent to the diagonal of the n-fold spectrum X, by Theorem 1.32. Now apply Corollary 3.6 to the bispectrum dX.   ∎

COROLLARY 3.8. *Suppose that X is a stably fibrant n-fold spectrum. Then the diagonal spectrum dX is naturally stable homotopy equivalent to each of the spectra*

$$X^{0,\ldots,0,\overset{i}{*},0,\ldots,0}.$$

REMARK 3.9. Suppose that X is a stably fibrant spectrum, and form the suspension object $\Sigma^\infty X$ in $\mathbf{Spt(Spt)}$. Recall that this object has

$$\Sigma^\infty X^i = X \wedge S^i,$$

so that $\Sigma^\infty X^0 = X$ in particular.

Now take the associated strictly fibrant object $(\Sigma^\infty X)_{Kan}$, and form a map

$$\nu : (\Sigma^\infty X)_{Kan} \to F(\Sigma^\infty X)_{Kan}$$

in $\mathbf{Spt(Spt)}$ as follows. In degree 0, one requires that

$$(\Sigma^\infty X)^0_{Kan} \overset{\nu^0}{\longrightarrow} F(\Sigma^\infty X)^0_{Kan}$$

is a stably trivial cofibration, and that the spectrum $F(\Sigma^\infty X)^0_{Kan}$ is stably fibrant. In higher degrees, one supposes that ν^i has been constructed for $1 \leq i \leq n$ such that each ν^i is a stably trivial cofibration, and each $F(\Sigma^\infty X)^i_{Kan}$ is stably fibrant. Then ν^{i+1} is defined to be the (dotted) composite

$$
\begin{array}{c}
(\Sigma^\infty X)^i_{Kan} \wedge S^1 \\
(\nu^i \wedge S^1)_* \downarrow \qquad\qquad\qquad\qquad\qquad \\
F(\Sigma^\infty X)^i_{Kan} \wedge S^1 \cup_{(\Sigma^\infty X)^i_{Kan} \wedge S^1} (\Sigma^\infty)^{i+1}_{Kan} \xrightarrow{\quad j \quad} F(\Sigma^\infty X)^{i+1}_{Kan},
\end{array}
$$

where j is a stably trivial cofibration and $F(\Sigma^\infty X)^{i+1}_{Kan}$ is stably fibrant. Note that $(\nu^i \wedge S^1)_*$ is a stably trivial cofibration by Corollary 2.23 and Lemma 2.24.

The resulting bonding maps

$$F(\Sigma^\infty X)^i_{Kan} \to \mathbf{hom}_*(S^1, F(\Sigma^\infty X^{i+1}_{Kan}))$$

are stable and hence strict weak equivalences of stably fibrant spectra, by Lemma 3.3 and Corollary 2.21, and the bispectrum represented by $F(\Sigma^\infty X)_{Kan}$ is therefore stably fibrant. Observe also that the composite map

$$X \to (\Sigma^\infty X)^0_{Kan} \overset{\nu^0}{\longrightarrow} F(\Sigma^\infty X)^0_{Kan}$$

is a stable and hence strict weak equivalence of fibrant spectra. It follows that any stable equivalence

$$\Sigma^\infty X \xrightarrow{f} Y$$

in $\mathbf{Spt}(\mathbf{Spt})$ with Y stably fibrant induces a strict weak equivalence

$$X \to Y^0$$

of stably fibrant spectra.

The same construction obtains more generally: if X is a stably fibrant n-fold spectrum, then there is a stable weak equivalence of $(n+1)$-fold spectra

$$\Sigma^\infty X \to F(\Sigma^\infty X)_{Kan},$$

such that $F(\Sigma^\infty X)_{Kan}$ is stably fibrant and such that the induced degree 0 map is a stable (hence strict) weak equivalence

$$X \to F(\Sigma^\infty X)^0_{Kan}.$$

Furthermore, any *stably fibrant model*

$$\Sigma^\infty X \xrightarrow{\simeq} F\Sigma^\infty X$$

of $\Sigma^\infty X$ (ie. any stable weak equivalence with $F\Sigma^\infty X$ stably fibrant) has this property.   ∎

Suppose that K is a pointed simplicial set, and that X is an n-fold spectrum. Then recall that there is an n-fold spectrum $\mathbf{hom}_*(K, X)$ with

$$\mathbf{hom}_*(K, X)^J = \mathbf{hom}_*(K, X^J),$$

where J denotes a multi-index $(j_1, \ldots, j_n)$. Let

$$J_i = (j_1, \ldots, \overset{i}{j_i + 1}, \ldots, j_n).$$

The bonding maps in $\mathbf{hom}_*(K, X)$ have the form

$$S^1 \wedge \mathbf{hom}_*(K, X^J) \xrightarrow{\sigma_i} \mathbf{hom}_*(K, X^{J_i}),$$

and are defined by the requirement that the following diagram commutes:

$$
\begin{array}{ccc}
S^1 \wedge \mathbf{hom}_*(K, X^J) \wedge K & \xrightarrow{\sigma_i \wedge K} & \mathbf{hom}_*(K, X^{J_i}) \wedge K \\
{\scriptstyle S^1 \wedge ev_K} \downarrow & & \downarrow {\scriptstyle ev_K} \\
S^1 \wedge X^J & \xrightarrow{\sigma_i} & X^{J_i}.
\end{array}
$$

These maps are the adjoints of the bonding maps that have been used for this n-fold spectrum up to now. The commutativity of this diagram implies that there is a natural morphism of n-fold spectra

$$ev_K : \mathbf{hom}_*(K, X) \wedge K \to X$$

which is defined by evaluating levelwise.

Suppose that L is another pointed simplicial set. The exponential law for pointed simplicial sets implies the existence of natural isomorphisms of pointed simplicial sets

$$\mathbf{hom}_*(L, \mathbf{hom}_*(K, X^I)) \xrightarrow[\cong]{\theta^I} \mathbf{hom}_*(L \wedge K, X^I),$$

which are each defined by the requirement that the following diagram commutes:

$$
\begin{array}{ccc}
\mathbf{hom}_*(L, \mathbf{hom}_*(K, X^I)) \wedge L \wedge K & \xrightarrow{\theta^I \wedge L \wedge K} & \mathbf{hom}_*(L \wedge K, X^I) \wedge L \wedge K \\
{\scriptstyle ev_L \wedge K} \downarrow & & \downarrow {\scriptstyle ev_{L \wedge K}} \\
\mathbf{hom}_*(K, X^I) \wedge K & \xrightarrow[ev_K]{} & X^I
\end{array}
$$

These definitions are used to show that the θ^I fit together to give a natural isomorphism of n-fold spectra

$$\mathbf{hom}_*(L, \mathbf{hom}_*(K, X)) \xrightarrow[\cong]{\theta} \mathbf{hom}_*(L \wedge K, X).$$

Suppose that V is an n-fold spectrum. Then there is a natural isomorphism of pointed simplicial sets

$$\mathbf{hom}_*(V \wedge K, X) \xrightarrow[\cong]{\alpha} \mathbf{hom}_*(K, \mathbf{hom}_*(V, X)).$$

On the maps level, $\alpha(f)$ is defined for $f : V \wedge K \to X$ and an n-implex $x \in K$ by setting $\alpha(f)(x)$ equal to the composite

$$V \ltimes \Delta^n \xrightarrow{V \wedge \iota_x} V \wedge K \xrightarrow{f} X.$$

Here, $V \ltimes \Delta^n$ is the spectrum $V \wedge \Delta^n_+$, where Δ^n_+ is the simplicial set $\Delta^n_+ = \Delta^n \sqcup \{0\}$, pointed by 0. This assignment extends to the displayed isomorphism, by naturality and checking on simplices. Let

$$ev_V : V \wedge \mathbf{hom}_*(V, X) \to X$$

be the map of n-fold spectra associated to the identity map on $\mathbf{hom}_*(V, X)$ by the natural map α. Then formal nonsense implies that α is induced by composition with ev_V in the usual sense.

Let I denote the multi-index $(i_1, \ldots, i_m)$, and let

$$I_j = (i_1, \ldots, i_j \overset{j}{+} 1, \ldots, i_m).$$

Suppose that U is an m-fold spectrum and that V is an n-fold spectrum. Then there is an $(m+n)$-fold spectrum $U \wedge V$ with component spaces

$$(U \wedge V)^{i_1, \ldots, i_m, j_1, \ldots, j_n} = U^{i_1, \ldots, i_m} \wedge V^{j_1, \ldots, j_n}.$$

Write

$$(U \wedge V)^{I, J} = U^I \wedge V^J$$

to make the notation easier to deal with. The bonding maps σ_j in $U \wedge V$ have the form

$$S^1 \wedge U^I \wedge V^J \xrightarrow{\sigma_j \wedge V^J} U^{I_j} \wedge V^J$$

for $1 \le j \le m$; if $m+1 \le j \le m+n$, then σ_j is defined to be the composite

$$S^1 \wedge U^I \wedge V^J \xrightarrow{\tau \wedge V^J} U^I \wedge S^1 \wedge V^J \xrightarrow{U^I \wedge \sigma_{j-m}} U^I \wedge V^{J_{j-m}}.$$

Suppose that Z is an $(m+n)$-fold spectrum. Then there is an m-fold spectrum $\mathbf{hom}^r_*(V, Z)$ and an n-fold spectrum $\mathbf{hom}^l_*(U, Z)$, which are defined, respectively, by

$$\mathbf{hom}^r_*(V, Z)^{i_1, \ldots, i_m} = \mathbf{hom}_*(V, Z^{i_1, \ldots, i_m, *, \ldots, *}),$$

and

$$\mathbf{hom}^l_*(U, Z)^{j_1, \ldots, j_n} = \mathbf{hom}_*(U, Z^{*, \ldots, *, j_1, \ldots, j_n}).$$

In other words, $\mathbf{hom}^r_*(V, Z)$ is defined in terms of the function complex for the category of n-fold spectra by the n-fold spectra $Z^{i_1, \ldots, i_n, *, \ldots, *}$, while $\mathbf{hom}^l_*(U, Z)$ uses the function complex for the category of m-fold spectra by letting the m indices on the left in $Z^{i_1, \ldots, i_{m+n}}$ vary. If we agree that $*$ will denote variable multi-indices in contexts that make sense, then we can write

$$\mathbf{hom}^l_*(U, Z)^J = \mathbf{hom}_*(U, Z^{*, J}),$$

and

$$\mathbf{hom}^r_*(V, Z)^I = \mathbf{hom}_*(V, Z^{I, *}).$$

Then each bonding map
$$\sigma_j : S^1 \wedge \mathbf{hom}_*(V, Z^{I,*}) \to \mathbf{hom}_*(V, Z^{I_j,*})$$
for $\mathbf{hom}_*^r(V, Z)$ is adjoint to the composite

$$V \wedge S^1 \wedge \mathbf{hom}_*(V, Z^{I,*}) \xrightarrow{V \wedge \tau} V \wedge \mathbf{hom}_*(V, Z^{I,*}) \wedge S^1$$

$$ev \wedge S^1 \downarrow$$

$$Z^{I,*} \wedge S^1 \xrightarrow{\tilde{\sigma}_j} Z^{I_j,*}.$$

Similarly, the bonding map
$$\sigma_i : S^1 \wedge \mathbf{hom}_*(U, Z^{*,J}) \to \mathbf{hom}_*(U, Z^{*,J_i})$$
is adjoint to the composite

$$U \wedge S^1 \wedge \mathbf{hom}_*(U, Z^{*,J}) \xrightarrow{U \wedge \tau} U \wedge \mathbf{hom}_*(U, Z^{*,J}) \wedge S^1$$

$$ev \wedge S^1 \downarrow$$

$$Z^{*,J} \wedge S^1 \xrightarrow{\tilde{\sigma}_{m+j}} Z^{*,J_j}.$$

To make sense of the above, recall the notational convention that
$$\tilde{\sigma}_i : X^I \wedge S^1 \to X^{I_i}$$

is the composite
$$X^I \wedge S^1 \xrightarrow{\tau} S^1 \wedge X^I \xrightarrow{\sigma_i} X^{I_i},$$

for any n-fold spectrum X. Recall also that $\tilde{\sigma}_i$ can be regarded as a morphism of $(n-1)$-fold spectra.

Any map $\phi : U \wedge V \to Z$ of $(n+m)$-fold spectra consists of maps
$$\phi^J : U \wedge V^J \to Z^{*,J}$$
of m-fold spectra such that all diagrams

$$\begin{array}{ccc} U \wedge V^J \wedge S^1 & \xrightarrow{\phi^J \wedge S^1} & Z^{*,J} \wedge S^1 \\ \tilde{\sigma}_{m+i} \downarrow & & \downarrow \tilde{\sigma}_{m+i} \\ U \wedge V^{J_i} & \xrightarrow{\phi^{J_i}} & Z^{*,J_i} \end{array}$$

commute in the category of m-fold spectra. We have the relation $\tilde{\sigma}_{m+i} = U \wedge \tilde{\sigma}_i$. Then it follows that the adjoint maps
$$\phi_*^J : V^J \to \mathbf{hom}_*(U, Z^{*,J})$$

define a unique map
$$\phi_* : V \to \mathbf{hom}_*^l(U, Z),$$

and conversely, proving

LEMMA 3.10. *Suppose that U is an m-fold spectrum, V is an n-fold spectrum, and that Z is an $(n+m)$-fold spectrum. Then there is a natural isomorphism*

$$\hom_{\mathbf{Spt}^{m+n}}(U \wedge V, Z) \cong \hom_{\mathbf{Spt}^n}(V, \mathbf{hom}^l_*(U, Z)).$$

A similar argument gives

LEMMA 3.11. *Suppose that U is an m-fold spectrum, V is an n-fold spectrum, and that Z is an $(n+m)$-fold spectrum. Then there is a natural isomorphism*

$$\hom_{\mathbf{Spt}^{m+n}}(U \wedge V, Z) \cong \hom_{\mathbf{Spt}^m}(U, \mathbf{hom}^r_*(V, Z)).$$

The adjoint of the identity map on $\mathbf{hom}^l_*(U, Z)$ (ie. the evaluation map) is a map of $(m+n)$-fold spectra

$$ev : U \wedge \mathbf{hom}^l_*(U, Z) \to Z.$$

Similarly, there is an evaluation map

$$ev : \mathbf{hom}^r_*(V, Z) \wedge V \to Z,$$

which is induced by the identity map on $\mathbf{hom}^r_*(V, Z)$.

Suppose that W is an $(n+m+k)$-fold spectrum, and that U and V are as above. There is a map of k-fold spectra

$$\mathbf{hom}^r_*(V, \mathbf{hom}^l_*(U, W)) \xrightarrow{f} \mathbf{hom}^l_*(U, \mathbf{hom}^r_*(V, W)),$$

which is defined to be the unique map f such that the following diagram of $(n+m+k)$-fold spectra commutes:

$$
\begin{array}{ccc}
U \wedge \mathbf{hom}^r_*(V, \mathbf{hom}^l_*(U, W)) \wedge V & \xrightarrow{U \wedge ev} & U \wedge \mathbf{hom}^l_*(U, W) \\
\Big\downarrow{\scriptstyle U \wedge f \wedge V} & & \searrow{\scriptstyle ev} \\
 & & \qquad\qquad W \\
U \wedge \mathbf{hom}^l_*(U, \mathbf{hom}^r_*(V, W)) \wedge V & \xrightarrow[ev \wedge V]{} & \mathbf{hom}^r_*(V, W) \wedge V \quad \nearrow{\scriptstyle ev}
\end{array}
$$

There is a similarly defined map

$$\mathbf{hom}^l_*(U, \mathbf{hom}^r_*(V, W)) \xrightarrow{g} \mathbf{hom}^r_*(V, \mathbf{hom}^l_*(U, W))$$

of k-fold spectra in the opposite direction. The definitions of both of these maps f and g is in terms of evaluation maps, so they are inverse to each other, and hence isomorphisms of k-fold spectra. This proves:

LEMMA 3.12. *Suppose that U is an m-fold spectrum, V is an n-fold spectrum, and W is an $(m + n + k)$-fold spectrum. Then there is a natural isomorphism of k-fold spectra*

$$\mathbf{hom}^r_*(V, \mathbf{hom}^l_*(U, W)) \xrightarrow[\cong]{f} \mathbf{hom}^l_*(U, \mathbf{hom}^r_*(V, W)).$$

It is a consequence of Lemma 3.12 that the natural isomorphism of simplicial sets

$$\mathbf{hom}_*(U \wedge V, Z) \cong \mathbf{hom}_*(V, \mathbf{hom}^l_*(U, Z)),$$

which is implicit in Lemma 3.10, induces an isomorphism

$$\mathbf{hom}_*(U \wedge V, Z) \cong \mathbf{hom}_*(U, \mathbf{hom}^r_*(V, Z)),$$

in the case where Z is an $(n + m)$-fold spectrum and U and V are as above.

EXAMPLE 3.13. Suppose that Z is a spectrum and that W is a bispectrum The function spectra

$$\mathbf{hom}^l_*(Z, W)^j = \mathbf{hom}_*(Z, W^{*,j})$$

and

$$\mathbf{hom}^r_*(Z, W)^i = \mathbf{hom}_*(Z, W^{i,*})$$

that were introduced above enjoy a range of good properties. In particular, if W is a stably fibrant bispectrum and Z is cofibrant, then $\mathbf{hom}^l_*(Z, W)$ is stably fibrant. Furthermore, if $i : Z_1 \to Z_2$ is a weak equivalence of cofibrant spectra and W is stably fibrant, then the induced map

$$\mathbf{hom}^l_*(Z_2, W) \xrightarrow{i^*} \mathbf{hom}^l_*(Z_1, W)$$

is a strict weak equivalence of spectra. Similar statements hold for the "right hand" object $\mathbf{hom}^r_*(Z, W)$. ∎

To go further, we shall need

LEMMA 3.14. *Suppose that U is a cofibrant spectrum and that $j : V_1 \to V_2$ is a cofibration of spectra. Then $U \wedge j$ is a cofibration of bispectra.*

PROOF: Suppose that $p : X_1 \to X_2$ is a trivial strict fibration of bispectra. Then p induces a map

$$p_* : \mathbf{hom}^l_*(U, X_1) \to \mathbf{hom}^l_*(U, X_2)$$

of spectra. This map is a trivial strict fibration of spectra since each of the components $p^j : X_1^{*,j} \to X_2^{*,j}$ of p is a trivial strict fibration of spectra, and U is cofibrant.

Lemma 3.10 implies that diagrams

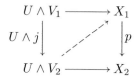

may be identified with diagrams

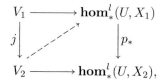

and so the required lifting exists.   ∎

EXAMPLE 3.15. Suppose that U and V are cofibrant spectra. Then Lemma 3.14 implies that $U \wedge V$ represents a cofibrant bispectrum.

Suppose that X is a stably fibrant spectrum, and identify the spectrum object $\Sigma^\infty X$ with the bispectrum specified by

$$(\Sigma^\infty X)^{i,j} = X^i \wedge S^j,$$

so that suspension degrees coincide with vertical degrees. Let $\nu : \Sigma^\infty X \to F\Sigma^\infty X$ be a stably fibrant model for the bispectrum $\Sigma^\infty X$, and recall from the construction given in Remark 3.9 that ν is a strict weak equivalence in horizontal degree 0.

The isomorphism (of Kan complexes)

$$\mathbf{hom}_*(U \wedge V, F\Sigma^\infty X) \cong \mathbf{hom}_*(V, \mathbf{hom}_*^l(U, F\Sigma^\infty X))$$

from Lemma 3.12 implies that there is a natural isomorphism

$$[U \wedge V, F\Sigma^\infty X]_{\mathbf{Spt}^2} \cong [V, \mathbf{hom}_*^l(U, F\Sigma^\infty X)]_{\mathbf{Spt}}$$

of morphisms in the respective homotopy categories. But

$$[U \wedge V, F\Sigma^\infty X]_{\mathbf{Spt}^2} \cong [d(U \wedge V), d(F\Sigma^\infty X)]_{\mathbf{Spt}}$$
$$\cong [d(U \wedge V), X]_{\mathbf{Spt}},$$

by the results of this section and Corollary 2.29. The moral is that

$$\mathbf{hom}_*^l(U, F\Sigma^\infty X)$$

is a model for the function spectrum of maps from U to X in the stable homotopy category, under the assumptions that U is cofibrant and X is stably fibrant.   ∎

3.2. The abstract norm

It is elementary and well known that one can add elements in the set $[Y, X]$ of maps from Y to X in the stable category: first observe that X is stably equivalent to some spectrum ΩZ, and then use the loop space multiplication. This addition is abelian, because Z is loops on some other spectrum. Alternatively, and perhaps more traditionally, one can play with suspensions, but that argument is the adjoint of the one just given.

The description of addition of elements in $[Y, X]$ can be made more precise by using techniques from the last section in the following way. It is, first of all, harmless to assume that Y is cofibrant and that X is stably fibrant. Form the suspension bispectrum $\Sigma^\infty X$, and take a stably fibrant model

$$j : \Sigma^\infty X \to F\Sigma^\infty X$$

for $\Sigma^\infty X$ in the category of bispectra. Then j induces a strict equivalence

$$j^0 : X \to (F\Sigma^\infty X)^0$$

at level 0 by Remark 3.9, and the bonding maps for the bispectrum $F\Sigma^\infty X$ induce a strict equivalence

$$(F\Sigma^\infty X)^0 \simeq \Omega^2 (F\Sigma^\infty X)^2.$$

This last assertion follows from Lemma 3.3.

An alternative definition of the addition operation for maps in the stable category is based on the observation that the canonical map

$$X_1 \vee \cdots \vee X_n \xrightarrow{c} X_1 \times \cdots \times X_n$$

is a weak equivalence. The map c is defined by requiring that all compositions

$$X_i \xrightarrow{in_i} X_1 \vee \cdots \vee X_n \xrightarrow{c} X_1 \times \cdots \times X_n \xrightarrow{pr_j} X_j$$

have the form

$$pr_j \cdot c \cdot in_i = \begin{cases} 1_{X_i} & \text{if } i = j, \text{ and} \\ * & \text{if } i \neq j. \end{cases}$$

Now, given two maps of spectra $f, g : Y \to X$, their sum is represented in the stable category by the composition

$$Y \xrightarrow{(f,g)} X \times X \xleftarrow[\simeq]{c} X \vee X \xrightarrow{\nabla} X,$$

where ∇ is the *fold map* which restricts to the identity on X on each wedge summand. This composition represents $[f] + [g]$ in $[Y, X]$ because the pairing

$$[Y, X] \times [Y, X] \to [Y, X]$$

which is induced by the composite

$$X \times X \xleftarrow[\simeq]{c} X \vee X \xrightarrow{\nabla} X$$

satisfies an interchange law with respect to the loop space multiplication. This follows from

Lemma 3.16. *Suppose given maps of spectra*

$$X \times X \xleftarrow{(p_1,p_2)} Z \xrightarrow{\mu} X, \tag{3.17}$$

where (p_1, p_2) is a stable equivalence. Then the pairing

$$[Y, X] \times [Y, X] \to [Y, X] \tag{3.18}$$

which is induced by the morphisms (3.17) satisfies an interchange law with respect to the standard abelian group structure on $[Y, X]$.

Proof: There is commutative diagram of the form

$$
\begin{array}{ccccc}
X \times X & \xleftarrow{(p_1,p_2)} & Z & \xrightarrow{\mu} & X \\
{\scriptstyle i \times i}\downarrow & & {\scriptstyle j}\downarrow & & \downarrow{\scriptstyle i} \\
\tilde{X} \times \tilde{X} & \xleftarrow[(\tilde{p}_1,\tilde{p}_2)]{} & \tilde{Z} & \xrightarrow[\tilde{\mu}]{} & \tilde{X}
\end{array}
$$

where $\tilde{X}$ and $\tilde{Z}$ are stably fibrant, and i and j are stably trivial cofibrations, so that $i \times i$ is a stable equivalence. We shall therefore assume that X and Z are stably fibrant spectra. We can further assume that the map $(\tilde{p}_1, \tilde{p}_2)$ is a trivial stable fibration, by a suitable factorization argument. These conditions are unchanged for the induced maps

$$\mathbf{hom}_*(S^1, X[1]) \times \mathbf{hom}_*(S^1, X[1]) \leftarrow \mathbf{hom}_*(S^1, Z[1]) \to \mathbf{hom}_*(S^1, X[1]),$$

and the pairing induced by these maps in the stable category is isomorphic to (3.18), by the Lemma 1.5. Thus, we can assume that X is loops of some stably fibrant spectrum.

We can suppose that Y is cofibrant. In this case (3.18) is induced by evaluating π_0 for the following maps of pointed simplicial sets

$$\mathbf{hom}_*(Y, X) \times \mathbf{hom}_*(Y, X) \xleftarrow{(p_1,p_2)_*} \mathbf{hom}_*(Y, Z) \xrightarrow{\mu_*} \mathbf{hom}_*(Y, X)$$

where $(p_1, p_2)_*$ is a trivial fibration. But then $(p_1, p_2)_*$ is a trivial fibration of pointed fibrant simplicial sets, so it has a pointed section. The resulting induced pairing

$$\pi_1 \mathbf{hom}_*(Y, X) \times \pi_1 \mathbf{hom}_*(Y, X) \to \pi_1 \mathbf{hom}_*(Y, X)$$

satisfies an interchange law for the group structure on $\pi_1 \mathbf{hom}_*(Y, X)$ by a standard space-level argument. ∎

Suppose that X is a spectrum, and that G is a finite group acting on X. The *abstract norm map* for the G-action on X is defined, in the stable category, to be the sum

$$N = \sum_{g \in G} g : X \to X$$

of the actions of the various elements of G on X. We shall need an explicit representative of this map, in order to keep track of various equivariance properties. In view of the results of the last section, we can take this representative to be the composite

$$X \xrightarrow{\Delta_G} \prod_{g \in G} X \xleftarrow[\simeq]{c} \bigvee_{g \in G} X \xrightarrow{\nabla} X.$$

Here, ∇ is the fold map, and Δ_G is defined by the requirement that the diagram

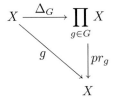

commutes for each $g \in G$, where pr_g is projection onto the factor corresponding to g.

Take $h \in G$, and define self-maps $(\cdot h)$ and $(h \cdot)$ of both $\prod_{g \in G} X$ and $\bigvee_{g \in G} X$ by the requirement that the following diagrams commute:

$$
\begin{array}{ccc}
\prod_{g \in G} X & \xrightarrow{(h\cdot)} & \prod_{g \in G} X \\
{\scriptstyle pr_{h^{-1}g}} \downarrow & & \downarrow {\scriptstyle pr_g} \\
X & \xrightarrow[1_X]{} & X
\end{array}
\qquad
\begin{array}{ccc}
\bigvee_{g \in G} X & \xrightarrow{(h\cdot)} & \bigvee_{g \in G} X \\
{\scriptstyle in_g} \uparrow & & \uparrow {\scriptstyle in_{hg}} \\
X & \xrightarrow[1_X]{} & X
\end{array}
$$

$$
\begin{array}{ccc}
\prod_{g \in G} X & \xrightarrow{(\cdot h)} & \prod_{g \in G} X \\
{\scriptstyle pr_{gh^{-1}}} \downarrow & & \downarrow {\scriptstyle pr_g} \\
X & \xrightarrow[1_X]{} & X
\end{array}
\qquad
\begin{array}{ccc}
\bigvee_{g \in G} X & \xrightarrow{(\cdot h)} & \bigvee_{g \in G} X \\
{\scriptstyle in_g} \uparrow & & \uparrow {\scriptstyle in_{gh}} \\
X & \xrightarrow[1_X]{} & X
\end{array}
$$

The assignment $h \mapsto (h\cdot)$ (respectively $h \mapsto (\cdot h)$) defines a covariant (respectively contravariant) action of G on both the product and the wedge, and the canonical map c is equivariant with respect to both actions. Note as well that there is a third action of $h \in G$ on $\bigvee_{g \in G} X$ namely the map $h : \bigvee_{g \in G} X \to \bigvee_{g \in G} X$ which restricts to $h : X \to X$ in each summand. There is a similar factorwise action $h : \prod_{g \in G} X \to \prod_{g \in G} X$, and the map $c : \bigvee_{g \in G} X \to \prod_{g \in G} X$ is equivariant for the summandwise action on the wedge and the factorwise action on the product.

These three G-actions commute with each other on both the wedge and the product. It follows that, for each pair $(g, h) \in G \times G$, the diagram

$$
\begin{array}{ccc}
\prod_{g \in G} X & \xleftarrow{\ c\ } & \bigvee_{g \in G} X \\
{\scriptstyle (h\cdot)h(\cdot g^{-1})}\Big\downarrow & & \Big\downarrow{\scriptstyle (h\cdot)h(\cdot g^{-1})} \\
\prod_{g \in G} X & \xleftarrow{\ c\ } & \bigvee_{g \in G} X
\end{array}
$$

commutes. One can also show that the diagrams

$$
\begin{array}{ccc}
X & \xrightarrow{\ \Delta_G\ } & \prod_{g \in G} X \\
{\scriptstyle g}\Big\downarrow & & \Big\downarrow{\scriptstyle (h\cdot)h(\cdot g^{-1})} \\
X & \xrightarrow{\ \Delta_G\ } & \prod_{g \in G} X
\end{array}
\qquad \text{and} \qquad
\begin{array}{ccc}
\bigvee_{g \in G} X & \xrightarrow{\ \nabla\ } & X \\
{\scriptstyle (h\cdot)h(\cdot g^{-1})}\Big\downarrow & & \Big\downarrow{\scriptstyle h} \\
\bigvee_{g \in G} X & \xrightarrow{\ \nabla\ } & X
\end{array}
$$

commute. In particular, the abstract norm map

$$ N : X \to X $$

is defined in the stable category of $(G \times G)$-spectra, where (g, h) acts via g on the copy of X in the source, and acts via h on the copy of X in the target.

Observe that any map $f : X \to Y$ of $(G \times G)$-spectra induces a map of ordinary spectra

$$ \operatorname*{holim}_{g \in G}\operatorname*{holim}_{h \in G} X \xrightarrow{\ f_*\ } \operatorname*{holim}_{g \in G}\operatorname*{holim}_{h \in G} Y, $$

where, for example, the homotopy inverse limit

$$ \operatorname*{holim}_{h \in G} X $$

is the G-spectrum obtained by taking the homotopy inverse limit for the G-action on X by restricting the $(G \times G)$-action along the group homomorphism $h \mapsto (e, h)$. If this restricted action happens to be trivial on X, then there is a map

$$\underset{g \in G}{\operatorname{holim}} X \to \underset{g \in G}{\operatorname{holim}} \underset{h \in G}{\operatorname{holim}} X$$

which is induced (in one incarnation, anyway) by the terminal map $BG \to *$. If the restricted action of G on Y which is induced by the homomorphism $g \mapsto (g, h)$ is trivial on Y, then G acts trivially on

$$\underset{h \in G}{\operatorname{holim}} Y,$$

and there's an induced map of the form

$$\underset{g \in G}{\operatorname{holim}} \underset{h \in G}{\operatorname{holim}} Y \to \underset{h \in G}{\operatorname{holim}} Y.$$

It follows that the map N in the $(G \times G)$-stable category induces a composite

$$\underset{g \in G}{\operatorname{holim}} X \to \underset{g \in G}{\operatorname{holim}} \underset{h \in G}{\operatorname{holim}} X \xrightarrow{N_*} \underset{g \in G}{\operatorname{holim}} \underset{h \in G}{\operatorname{holim}} X \to \underset{h \in G}{\operatorname{holim}} X,$$

in the ordinary stable category, which I shall denote by N_h, and call the *hypernorm*.

REMARK 3.19. Suppose that Z is a bispectrum, with an action by a finite group G. Then the maps

$$Z \xrightarrow{\Delta_G} \prod_{g \in G} Z \xleftarrow{c} \bigvee_{G \in G} Z \xrightarrow{\nabla} Z$$

make sense on the bispectrum level, and have the same $(G \times G)$-equivariance properties as their analogues in the category of spectra. The associated diagonal spectrum functor takes each of these maps to the corresponding spectrum level map. It follows that the G-bispectrum Z gives rise to a norm map $N : Z \to Z$ in the stable category of $(G \times G)$-bispectra, such that dN is the norm map for the G-spectrum dZ.

The diagonal spectrum functor also preserves homotopy limits and colimits, and all of the canonical maps associated with them, since homotopy limits and colimits are formed on the space level in the category of bispectra, just as they are in the category of spectra. The hypernorm

$$N_h : \underset{g \in G}{\operatorname{holim}} Z \to \underset{g \in G}{\operatorname{holim}} Z$$

is therefore defined in the stable category of bispectra, and it is preserved by the diagonal functor.   ∎

EXAMPLE 3.20. The fundamental application of these ideas will be to presheaves of spectra on étale sites (see Chapter 6). In particular, let $et|_k$ denote the étale site of a field k, and let L/k be a finite Galois extension of k with Galois group G. Let i denote the inclusion $k \subset L$.

If F is a presheaf of spectra on $et|_k$, then the spectrum $F(L)$ of L-sections carries a canonical G-action, so a hypernorm map

$$\varinjlim_{g \in G} F(L) \xrightarrow{N_h} \varprojlim_{g \in G} F(L)$$

is defined. If F happens to be globally fibrant, then the canonical map

$$F(k) \xrightarrow{i^*} \varprojlim_{g \in G} F(L)$$

is a stable equivalence, because it is induced on the function space level by the hypercover $EG^{op} \times_{G^{op}} Sp(L) \to *$ of the terminal simplicial presheaf [23], [24]. The induced composite

$$F(L) \to \varinjlim_{g \in G} F(L) \xrightarrow{N_*} \varprojlim_{g \in G} F(L) \xleftarrow{i^*} F(k)$$

in the stable category is the *abstract transfer* for the generalized étale cohomology theory associated to the globally fibrant presheaf of spectra F, and will, as well, be denoted by N_*. This construction specializes in particular to an abstract transfer map for étale K-theory that will be discussed in Chapters 5 and 6. ∎

EXAMPLE 3.21. Let X and Y be presheaves of spectra on the étale $et|_k$ site for the field k. Suppose as well that

$$\cup : X \wedge Y \to Z$$

is a map of presheaves of bispectra on $et|_k$. The composite

$$X(k) \wedge Y(L) \xrightarrow{i^* \wedge 1} X(L) \wedge Y(L) \xrightarrow{\cup} Z(L)$$

is G-equivariant, and it's not hard to see directly from the definitions that this composite induces a commutative diagram in the stable category of $(G \times G)$-bispectra

$$\begin{array}{ccc}
X(k) \wedge Y(L) & \xrightarrow{\cup(i^* \wedge 1)} & Z(L) \\
{\scriptstyle 1 \wedge N} \downarrow & & \downarrow {\scriptstyle N} \\
X(k) \wedge Y(L) & \xrightarrow[\cup(i^* \wedge 1)]{} & Z(L).
\end{array}$$

By playing with the adjoint map of spectra

$$Y(L) \xrightarrow{(\cup(i^* \wedge 1))_*} \mathbf{hom}_*^l(X(k), Z(L))$$

and the canonical isomorphism

$$\varprojlim_{h \in G} \mathbf{hom}_*^l(X(k), Z(L)) \cong \mathbf{hom}_*^l(X(k), \varprojlim_{h \in G} Z(L)),$$

one finds an induced map of bispectra

$$X(k) \wedge \varprojlim_{h \in G} Y(L) \xrightarrow{(\cup(i^* \times 1))_*} \varprojlim_{h \in G} Z(L)$$

which fits into a commutative diagram in the stable category of G-bispectra

$$\begin{array}{c}(3.22)\end{array}$$

The vertical maps i^* are stable equivalences if Y and Z are globally fibrant. The diagram (3.22) is the *projection formula* for the abstract transfer. ∎

Chapter 4. Auxilliary results

This is a chapter of folk theorems and slogans. The topics covered include

(1) the assertion that fibre sequences and cofibre sequences coincide in the category of spectra (Section 1),

(2) the Atiyah-Hirzebruch-Whitehead spectral sequence for the X-homology $\pi_*(X \wedge K)$ of a pointed simplicial set K (Section 2),

(3) simplicial spectra and the spectral sequence for the stable homotopy groups of their associated diagonals (Section 3),

(4) Kan spectra and the equivalence of associated strict homotopy categories with the ordinary category of spectra (Section 4),

(5) spectrum and Kan spectrum objects in the category of simplicial abelian groups and the relationship with the derived category for chain complexes of abelian groups (Sections 5 and 6), and

(6) Postnikov towers for spectra (Section 7).

I interpret the results of the first section to mean that fibre sequences and cofibre sequences are two aspects of the closed model structure for spectra that describe the same phenomenon in the stable category, and that this is somehow a defining aspect of stable homotopy theory. The proofs follows the "closed model style", proceeding axiomatically (and gently) from the existence of the long exact sequences in stable homotopy groups for fibre sequences and cofibre sequences, as one would expect.

A simplicial sets-based model for the category of spectra is manifestly the right context for any discussion of simplicial spectra (aka. spectrum objects in the category of pointed bisimplicial sets, for example). The main result of the second section identifies the differential in the E_1-term of the spectral sequence for the stable homotopy groups $\pi_*(X \wedge K)$ which arise from a spectrum X and the skeletal filtration for for a pointed simplicial set K. This identification leads immediately the the identification of the E_2-term of the Atiyah-Hirzebruch-Whitehead spectra sequence, and it is also the basis for the construction of the more general spectral sequence for the diagonal of a simplicial spectrum in Section 3. The proofs given are elementary in that they consist of manipulation of cofibre sequences only, and are obviously functorial.

The discussion of Kan spectra in the fourth section is based on the observation that there are at least two distinct suspension functors defined on the category of pointed simplicial sets. One could take a pointed simplicial set K and form the smash product $S^1 \wedge K$ as we've been doing up to now. Alternatively, one could form a cone C_*K on K by gluing together data consisting of an $(n+1)$-simplex for each n-simplex of K along the incidence relations for the simplices in a geometrically obvious way, and then collapse the image of K in C_*K to form the *Kan suspension* $\Sigma K = C_*K/K$. The smash product $S^1 \wedge K$ and the Kan suspension ΣK have naturally homeomorphic realizations, but they are distinct as simplicial sets — they really correspond to the two standard subdivisions of their common realization. A second suspension functor naturally leads to a second notion of spectrum: a *Kan spectrum* Y consists of pointed spaces Y^i and pointed simplicial maps $\Sigma Y^i \to Y^{i+1}$. Furthermore, the fact that $S^1 \wedge K$ and ΣK become naturally isomorphic after realization leads pretty quickly to the assertion that spectra and Kan spectra have the same associated strict homotopy categories.

One has to care about Kan spectra for several reasons. The category is the basis for the discussion of Postnikov towers that appears in the last section of this chapter. The reason for this is that Moore's Postnikov tower $P_n K$, $n \geq 0$ for a pointed simplicial set K is compatible with the Kan suspension, in that there is a natural map $\Sigma P_n K \to P_{n+1}\Sigma K$ that one just can't see by using the smash product suspension.

The Kan suspension is also the most technically effective basis for the discussion of spectrum objects in the category of simplicial abelian groups, since the Kan suspension *in that category* coincides up to natural isomorphism with the Eilenberg-Mac Lane $\overline{W}$-construction. A Kan spectrum object A in the category of simplicial abelian groups therefore naturally consists of simplicial abelian A^i and simplicial abelian group homomorphisms $\overline{W}A^i \to A^{i+1}$. It is well known and obvious that the normalized chains functor respects suspension in the sense that there is a natural isomorphism $N\overline{W}A \cong NA[-1]$, where $NA[-1]$ is the shifted normalized chain complex defined by $NA[-1]_i = NA_{i-1}$. It follows that the Dold-Kan equivalence of simplicial abelian groups and chain complexes can be extended, first to an equivalence of Kan spectrum objects in simplicial abelian groups with a category of spectrum objects in chain complexes, and then to an equivalence of the stable category of Kan spectrum objects in simplicial abelian groups with the derived category of chain complexes of abelian groups. These results appear in Sections 5 and 6, along with a result which asserts an equivalence of the strict homotopy categories associated to, on the one hand, Kan spectrum objects in simplicial abelian groups, and the other sort of spectrum objects which arise from the suspension functor $B \mapsto S^1 \otimes B$. These results and their proofs are completely functorial, and are therefore the basis for the assertion that any derived category is a stable homotopy category for simplicial objects in an appropriate context.

4.1. Fibres and cofibres

Let's begin by recalling something quite elementary. Consider a commutative diagram of maps of spectra

$$
\begin{array}{ccccc}
U & \xrightarrow{i} & X & \xrightarrow{p_X} & C \\
{\scriptstyle g}\downarrow & & {\scriptstyle f}\downarrow & & \| \\
A & \xrightarrow{j} & Y & \xrightarrow{p_Y} & C
\end{array}
$$

where the left hand square is a pushout, i is a stable cofibration and C is the common cofibre. Then the discussion preceding Lemma 2.17 implies that there is a long exact (Mayer-Vietoris) sequence in stable homotopy groups

$$\cdots \to \pi_j(U) \xrightarrow{(g_*,i_*)} \pi_j(A) \oplus \pi_j(X) \xrightarrow{f_*-g_*} \pi_j(Y) \xrightarrow{\Delta} \pi_{j-1}(U) \to \cdots,$$

where Δ is the composite

$$\pi_j(Y) \xrightarrow{(p_Y)_*} \pi_j(C) \xrightarrow{\delta_X} \pi_{j-1}(U),$$

and δ_X is the boundary map in the long exact sequence which is associated to the top cofibre sequence.

Consider now the cofibre sequence

$$U \xrightarrow{i} X \xrightarrow{p_X} C$$

and choose a factorization of the canonical map $* \to C$ of the form

$$* \xrightarrow{\alpha} \tilde{C} \xrightarrow{q_C} C,$$

where α is a trivial stable cofibration and q_C is a stable fibration. Form the pullback

$$
\begin{array}{ccc}
\tilde{X} & \xrightarrow{q_X} & X \\
\downarrow & & \downarrow{\scriptstyle p_X} \\
\tilde{C} & \xrightarrow{q_C} & C.
\end{array}
$$

Then $\tilde{X}$ is stably equivalent to the homotopy fibre of p_X, by a standard argument involving the closed proper simplicial model structure.

Observe that the map α induces a map $j : U \to \tilde{X}$.

LEMMA 4.1. *The map j is a stable equivalence.*

PROOF: Pulling back the pushout square

$$
\begin{array}{ccc}
U & \xrightarrow{i} & X \\
\downarrow & & \downarrow{\scriptstyle p_X} \\
* & \xrightarrow{} & C
\end{array}
$$

along the map q_C gives a pushout square

$$
\begin{array}{ccc}
\tilde{U} & \xrightarrow{\ \tilde{i}\ } & \tilde{X} \\
\tilde{p} \downarrow & & \downarrow \tilde{p}_X \\
F & \xrightarrow{\ \beta\ } & \tilde{C}.
\end{array}
\tag{4.2}
$$

in which the map $\tilde{i}$ is a pointwise cofibration.

The spectrum $\tilde{C}$ is stably contractible, so that the Mayer-Vietoris sequence for the pushout square (4.2) implies that there is an isomorphism

$$
\pi_n(\tilde{U}) \xrightarrow[\cong]{(\tilde{p}_*,\tilde{i}_*)} \pi_n(F) \oplus \pi_n(\tilde{X}),
$$

for all $n \in \mathbb{Z}$. In particular, the map

$$
\tilde{U} \xrightarrow{(\tilde{p},\tilde{i})} F \times \tilde{X}
$$

is a stable weak equivalence, and so (4.2) is a stable fibre homotopy square.

On the other hand, there is a pullback square

$$
\begin{array}{ccc}
\tilde{U} & \xrightarrow{\ \tilde{p}\ } & F \\
q_U \downarrow & & \downarrow \\
U & \xrightarrow{\qquad} & *,
\end{array}
$$

where q_U is the fibration induced by pulling q_C back along $p_X i$. It follows that the map

$$
\tilde{U} \xrightarrow{(\tilde{p},q_U)} F \times U
$$

is an isomorphism of spectra.

We therefore have a commutative diagram

$$
\begin{array}{ccccc}
F \times U & \xleftarrow[\cong]{(\tilde{p},\,q_U)} & \tilde{U} & \xrightarrow[\simeq]{(\tilde{p},\,\tilde{i})} & F \times \tilde{X} \\
& {}_{pr_L}\searrow & \downarrow \tilde{p} & \swarrow {}_{pr_L} & \\
& & F & &
\end{array}
\tag{4.3}
$$

Thus, the homotopy fibre of $\tilde{p}$ is stably equivalent to both U and $\tilde{X}$.

Note further that the map $q_U : \tilde{U} \to U$ is split by a map $\sigma : U \to \tilde{U}$ which is induced by the pointed section of $F \to *$. Then $\tilde{i}\sigma = j$, and $\tilde{p}\sigma = *$. It follows from the commutativity of (4.3) that σ induces a map from U to the homotopy fibre of $\tilde{p}$ which is a stable weak equivalence.

The square (4.2) is a stable fibre homotopy square, and so it induces a stable equivalence on the level of homotopy fibres. The inclusion of the homotopy fibre of $\tilde{p}_X$ in $\tilde{X}$ is a stable equivalence, since $\tilde{C}$ is contractible. It follows that j is a stable equivalence.   ∎

Suppose given a pullback square

$$
\begin{array}{ccc}
F & \xrightarrow{\ i\ } & E \\
\downarrow & & \downarrow{\scriptstyle p} \\
* & \longrightarrow & B
\end{array}
$$

where p is a stable fibration, and choose a factorization

$$F \xrightarrow{\ j\ } U \xrightarrow{\ \pi\ } E$$

of the map i, where j is a cofibration and π is a trivial stable fibration. Let $q : U \to C$ be the cofibre of j. Then there is a map $\nu : C \to B$ which fits into a commutative diagram

$$
\begin{array}{ccccc}
F & \xrightarrow{\ i\ } & E & \xrightarrow{\ p\ } & B \\
\| & & \uparrow{\scriptstyle \simeq}{\scriptstyle \pi} & & \uparrow{\scriptstyle \nu} \\
F & \xrightarrow{\ j\ } & U & \xrightarrow{\ q\ } & C.
\end{array}
$$

COROLLARY 4.4. *The map ν is a stable equivalence.*

PROOF: The map j induces a weak equivalence of F onto any choice of homotopy fibre for q. But then, a comparison of long exact sequences shows that ν is a weak equivalence.   ∎

More colloquially, Lemma 4.1 says that every cofibre sequence is a fibre sequence, while Corollary 4.4 says that every fibre sequence is a cofibre sequence, up to stable equivalence.

REMARK 4.5. The input for the constructions above consisted of the Mayer-Veitoris sequence, the long exact sequence for a fibration, and the closed proper simplicial model structure of the category **Spt** of spectra. These tools also exist for n-fold spectra, as well as for presheaves of spectra and n-fold spectra on any Grothendieck site, by the results of Chapter 2, so that analogues of Lemma 4.1 and Corollary 4.4 exist in all of these contexts.   ∎

4.2. Boundary maps

Suppose that X is a spectrum, and that K is a pointed simplicial set. Filter K by skeleta, and observe that each inclusion $i : sk_{p-1}K \hookrightarrow sk_pK$ determines a cofibre sequence

$$X \wedge sk_{p-1}K \xrightarrow{X \wedge i} X \wedge sk_pK \xrightarrow{X \wedge p} X \wedge (sk_pK/sk_{p-1}K),$$

where $p : sk_pK \to sk_pK/sk_{p-1}K$ is the canonical projection. Let

$$
\begin{array}{l}
\pi_{p+q}(X \wedge sk_{p-1}K) \\
\quad \downarrow{i_*} \\
\pi_{p+q}(X \wedge sk_pK) \xrightarrow{p_*} \pi_{p+q}(X \wedge (sk_pK/sk_{p-1}K)) \xrightarrow{\partial} \pi_{p+q-1}(X \wedge sk_{p-1}K) \qquad (4.6) \\
\hphantom{\pi_{p+q}(X \wedge sk_pK) \xrightarrow{p_*} \pi_{p+q}(X \wedge (sk_pK/sk_{p-1}K)) \xrightarrow{\partial}} \downarrow{i_*} \\
\hphantom{\pi_{p+q}(X \wedge sk_pK) \xrightarrow{p_*} \pi_{p+q}(X \wedge (sk_pK/sk_{p-1}K)) \xrightarrow{\partial}} \pi_{p+q-1}(X \wedge sk_pK)
\end{array}
$$

be the resulting long exact sequence.

Consider the composite

$$
\begin{array}{l}
\pi_{p+q}(X \wedge (sk_pK/sk_{p-1}K)) \xrightarrow{\quad\partial\quad} \pi_{p+q-1}(X \wedge sk_{p-1}K) \\
\hphantom{\pi_{p+q}(X \wedge (sk_pK/sk_{p-1}K)) \xrightarrow{\quad\partial\quad}} \downarrow{p_*} \qquad\qquad (4.7) \\
\hphantom{\pi_{p+q}(X \wedge (sk_pK/sk_{p-1}K)) \xrightarrow{\quad\partial}} \pi_{p+q-1}(X \wedge (sk_{p-1}K/sk_{p-2}K)).
\end{array}
$$

Let

$$NK_p = \begin{cases} \{\text{non-degenerate } p\text{-simplices of } K\} & \text{if } p > 0, \text{ and} \\ K_0 - \{*\} & \text{if } p = 0. \end{cases}$$

Then there is an isomorphism of pointed simplicial sets

$$sk_pK/sk_{p-1}K \cong \bigvee_{\sigma \in NK_p} S^p,$$

for $p \geq 0$, which induces isomorphisms

$$\pi_{p+q}(X \wedge (sk_pK/sk_{p-1}K)) \cong \bigoplus_{\sigma \in NK_p} \pi_{p+q}(X \wedge S^p) \cong \bigoplus_{\sigma \in NK_p} \pi_q X. \qquad (4.8)$$

Note that, strictly speaking, S^p is the simpicial p-sphere $\Delta^p/\partial\Delta^p$, and the isomorphisms

$$\pi_{p+q}(X \wedge S^p) \cong \pi_q(X)$$

implicit in (4.8) are induced topologically by repeated appeals to cofibre sequences

$$|S^{p-1}| \subset e^p \twoheadrightarrow |S^p|.$$

Recall that the chain complex $\tilde{\mathbb{Z}}K$ which computes the reduced homology

$$\tilde{H}_*(K, \mathbb{Z})$$

of K is defined by the (split) exact sequence

$$0 \to \tilde{\mathbb{Z}}K \to \mathbb{Z}K \to \mathbb{Z}* \to 0.$$

The skeletal filtration of K determines exact sequences

$$0 \to \tilde{\mathbb{Z}}sk_{p-1}K \to \tilde{\mathbb{Z}}sk_pK \to \tilde{\mathbb{Z}}(sk_pK/sk_{p-1}K) \to 0$$

with a corresponding filtration of the chain complex $\tilde{\mathbb{Z}}K$. There are isomorphisms

$$H_{p+q}(\tilde{\mathbb{Z}}(sk_pK/sk_{p-1}K)) \cong \begin{cases} \bigoplus_{\sigma \in NK_p} \mathbb{Z} & \text{if } q = 0, \text{ and} \\ 0 & \text{otherwise.} \end{cases}$$

Furthermore, the composite

$$H_p(\tilde{\mathbb{Z}}(sk_pK/sk_{p-1}K)) \xrightarrow{\partial} H_{p-1}(\tilde{\mathbb{Z}}sk_{p-1}K) \to H_{p-1}(\tilde{\mathbb{Z}}(sk_{p-1}K/sk_{p-2}K))$$

can be identified via this isomorphism with the map

$$\bigoplus_{\sigma \in NK_p} \mathbb{Z} \to \bigoplus_{\sigma \in NK_{p-1}} \mathbb{Z}$$

which is induced from the standard boundary $\Sigma_{i=0}^p (-1)^i d_i$ by killing degeneracies. The resulting chain complex is the *normalized chain complex* for K, and is denoted by $N\tilde{\mathbb{Z}}K$. Note that there is a natural isomorphism

$$H_*(N\tilde{\mathbb{Z}}K) \cong \tilde{H}(K, \mathbb{Z}),$$

by the spectral sequence argument that is implicit in the foregoing.

LEMMA 4.9. *The map*

$$\bigoplus_{\sigma \in NK_p} \pi_q X \to \bigoplus_{\sigma \in NK_{p-1}} \pi_q X,$$

which is induced by the composition (4.7), coincides up to isomorphism with the boundary map in the normalized chain complex $N\tilde{\mathbb{Z}}K \otimes \pi_q X$.

Proof: It is harmless to assume that X is stably fibrant, since the functor $X \mapsto X \wedge K$ preserves stable equivalences, by Lemma 2.20.

The stable homotopy groups $\pi_j(X \wedge L)$ which arise from the spectrum X and an arbitrary pointed simplicial set L are the stable homotopy groups of the realized spectrum

$$|X \wedge L| \cong |X| \wedge |L|.$$

There is a natural stable equivalence

$$\eta : X \to \Omega\Sigma X,$$

by the proof of Lemma 1.5. There are also natural stable equivalences of the form

$$\Omega\Sigma X \simeq \Sigma X[-1] \simeq (X \wedge S^1)[-1]$$

by the results of Section 1.1. But then there are natural stable equivalences

$$\begin{aligned}
|\Omega\Sigma X \wedge L| &\simeq |(X \wedge S^1)[-1] \wedge L| \\
&\cong |X \wedge S^1 \wedge L|[-1] \\
&\cong (|X| \wedge |S^1 \wedge L|)[-1] \\
&\cong (|X| \wedge |\Sigma L|)[-1],
\end{aligned}$$

where ΣL denotes the Kan suspension of the pointed simplicial set L (the definition of Kan suspension is in Section 4.4). Thus, we can replace the spaces $sk_p K$ in the composition (4.7) by their Kan suspensions [27]. This is done so that the universal case

$$K = \Delta^p_+ = \Delta^p \sqcup *$$

gives a spectrum $X \wedge \Sigma\Delta^p_+$ which can be compared to a contractible spectrum in a relatively painless way.

It suffices to prove the Lemma for the universal case. Substituting into (4.7) gives the maps

$$\pi_{p+q+1}(X \wedge \Sigma S^p) \xrightarrow{\partial} \pi_{p+q}(X \wedge \Sigma\partial\Delta^p_+) \xrightarrow{p_*} \pi_{p+q}(X \wedge \Sigma(\partial\Delta^p/sk_{p-2}\partial\Delta^p)).$$

The inclusion

$$\Sigma\partial\Delta^p_+ \hookrightarrow \Sigma\Delta^p_+$$

of Kan suspensions can be identified up to isomorphism with the map

$$i_* : \partial\Delta^{p+1}/(d^{p+1}(\Delta^p) \sqcup \{p+1\}) \to \Delta^{p+1}/(d^{p+1}(\Delta^p) \sqcup \{p+1\}),$$

which is induced by the canonical inclusion $i : \partial\Delta^{p+1} \hookrightarrow \Delta^{p+1}$. Furthermore, there is a pushout diagram

$$\begin{array}{ccc}
\partial\Delta^{p+1} & \xrightarrow{\quad i \quad} & \Delta^{p+1} \\
{\scriptstyle p}\downarrow & & \downarrow{\scriptstyle p} \\
\partial\Delta^{p+1}/(d^{p+1}(\Delta^p) \sqcup \{p+1\}) & \xrightarrow{\quad i_* \quad} & \Delta^{p+1}/(d^{p+1}(\Delta^p) \sqcup \{p+1\})
\end{array} \qquad (4.10)$$

in which the vertical maps are the projections. This is a diagram of pointed maps if one presumes that the base point for Δ^{p+1} and $\partial\Delta^{p+1}$ is the vertex $p+1$. Comparing cofibre sequences therefore gives a commutative diagram

$$
\begin{array}{ccc}
\pi_{p+q+1}(X \wedge \Sigma S^p) & \xrightarrow[\cong]{\partial} & \pi_{p+q}(X \wedge \partial\Delta^{p+1}) \\
1 \downarrow & & \downarrow p_* \\
\pi_{p+q+1}(X \wedge \Sigma S^p) & \xrightarrow{\partial} & \pi_{p+q}(X \wedge \Sigma\partial\Delta^p_+).
\end{array}
$$

The isomorphism

$$
\pi_{p+q+1}(X \wedge \Sigma S^p) \xrightarrow[\cong]{\partial} \pi_{p+q}(X \wedge \partial\Delta^{p+1})
$$

commutes with the respective identifications of both groups with $\pi_q X$. Finally, collapsing all but the summand corresponding to the ith face in

$$
\Sigma(\partial\Delta^p / sk_{p-2}\Delta^p)
$$

gives a composite map

$$
\partial\Delta^{p+1} \xrightarrow{p} \Sigma\partial\Delta^p_+ \to \Sigma(\partial\Delta^p / sk_{p-2}\Delta^p) \xrightarrow{p_i} S^p.
$$

The induced map

$$
\pi_{p+q}(X \wedge \partial\Delta^{p+1}) \to \pi_{p+q}(X \wedge S^p)
$$

is multiplication by the degree of the corresponding map of spheres. This degree can be computed homologically, and one shows that it is $(-1)^i$ by chasing the generator

$$
[\sum_{i=0}^{p+1}(-1)^i d_i \iota_{p+1}] \in H_p(\partial\Delta^{p+1}, \mathbb{Z}). \qquad \blacksquare
$$

PROPOSITION 4.11. *There is a spectral sequence with*

$$
E_2^{p,q} = \tilde{H}_p(K, \pi_q X) \Rightarrow \pi_{p+q}(X \wedge K).
$$

The differentials of this spectral sequence have the form

$$
d_r : E_r^{p,q} \to E_r^{p-r, q+r-1}.
$$

PROOF: Use the exact sequences (4.6) to construct the spectral sequence. Then Lemma 4.9 calculates the E_2 term. $\qquad \blacksquare$

The spectral sequence of Proposition 4.11 is often called the *Atiyah-Hirzebruch-Whitehead spectral sequence* [54, p.341]. Its consequences include another, and perhaps more standard, proof of the fact (Lemma 2.20) that the functor $X \mapsto X \wedge K$ preserves stable equivalences in X.

4.3. Simplicial spectra

Suppose that X is a *simplicial spectrum*. One way to define such an object is to say that X consists of pointed bisimplicial sets X^n, $n \geq 0$, together with maps $\sigma : X^n \wedge S^1 \to X^{n+1}$ of pointed bisimplicial sets.

The diagonal functor d from pointed bisimplicial sets to pointed simplicial sets commutes with smashing with a fixed simplicial set, so that there is a canonical isomorphism

$$d(X^n \wedge S^1) \cong d(X^n) \wedge S^1,$$

for each n, and applying the diagonal functor levelwise gives a spectrum $d(X)$ with $d(X)^n = d(X^n)$. I shall refer to $d(X)$ as the *diagonal spectrum* associated to the simplicial spectrum X.

REMARK 4.12. A venal sin has just been committed, in that the notation dX and the term "diagonal spectrum" has been previously used to describe a construction which associates spectra to bispectra or n-fold spectra. This is *not* the same construction as the diagonal of a simplicial spectrum. There are perfectly good cultural reasons for using this notation and terminology for these two very different constructions, and so the apparent ambiguity will persist, but the intended meaning should be clear from the context.   ∎

An alternative but equivalent view is that a simplicial spectrum X consists of spectra X_n, $n \geq 0$, together with maps of spectra of the form $\theta^* : X_n \to X_m$ for each ordinal number map $\theta : \mathbf{m} \to \mathbf{n}$, satisfying the simplicial identities.

The diagonal spectrum $d(X)$ can be thought of as a type of coend, in the sense that there is a coequalizer in the category of spectra

$$\bigvee_{\theta:\mathbf{m}\to\mathbf{n}} X_n \ltimes \Delta^m \rightrightarrows \bigvee_{n\geq 0} X_n \ltimes \Delta^n \xrightarrow{\lambda} d(X),$$

where λ is the map of spectra which is defined on the space $X_n^i \ltimes \Delta^n$ at level i of the nth summand $X_n \ltimes \Delta^n$ to be the map $X_n^i \ltimes \Delta^n \to d(X)^i$ which takes a pair (x, γ) consisting of a k-simplex of X_n^i and an ordinal number map $\gamma : \mathbf{k} \to \mathbf{n}$ to the k-simplex $\gamma^*(x)$ of $d(X)^i$. The point is that the corresponding space level construction extends to spectra (see also [26]).

Write $d(X)^{(p)}$ for the image in the diagonal spectrum $d(X)$ of the union of the spectra $X_i \ltimes \Delta^i$ for $0 \leq i \leq p$ under the map λ. Then the spectra $d(X)^{(p)}$ form an ascending filtration of the spectrum $d(X)$. Furthermore, if we let $s_{[r]}X_{p-1} \subset X_p$ be the union of the images $s_i(X_{p-1})$ of the degeneracies s_i for $0 \leq i \leq r$ in X_p, we find that there are pushout diagrams

$$
\begin{array}{ccc}
s_{[r]}X_{p-1} & \xrightarrow{\ s_{r+1}\ } & s_{[r]}X_p \\
\downarrow & & \downarrow \\
X_p & \xrightarrow{\ s_{r+1}\ } & s_{[r+1]}X_p
\end{array}
\tag{4.13}
$$

and

$$(s_{[p-1]}X_{p-1} \ltimes \Delta^p) \cup (X_p \ltimes \partial\Delta^p) \longrightarrow d(X)^{(p-1)}$$

$$\begin{array}{ccc} & & \\ \downarrow & & \downarrow \\ & & \end{array}$$

(4.14)

$$X_p \ltimes \Delta^p \xrightarrow{\quad \lambda \quad} d(X)^{(p)}$$

in which the vertical maps are pointwise cofibrations in the sense of Remark 2.5.

LEMMA 4.15. *Suppose that X is a simplicial spectrum. Then there is a natural isomorphism*

$$\pi_n(s_{[r]}X_p) \cong s_{[r]}(\pi_n X_p),$$

where $s_{[r]}(\pi_n X_p)$ denotes the subgroup of $\pi_n X_{p+1}$ which is generated by the images $s_i(\pi_n X_p)$ of the degeneracies s_i, for $0 \le i \le r$.

PROOF: Suppose that A is a simplicial abelian group, and define a subgroup $s_{[r]}A_p$ of A_{p+1} by

$$s_{[r]}A_p = \sum_{0 \le i \le r} s_i(A_p).$$

Then the diagram of abelian group homomorphisms

$$\begin{array}{ccc} s_{[r]}A_{p-1} & \xrightarrow{\ s_{r+1}\ } & s_{[r]}A_p \\ \uparrow & & \uparrow \\ A_p & \xrightarrow{\ s_{r+1}\ } & s_{[r+1]}A_p \end{array}$$

is a pullback. In effect, if

$$s_{r+1}x = s_0 y_0 + s_1 y_1 + \cdots + s_r y_r$$

for some x and y_i in A_p, then

$$x = d_{r+2}s_{r+1}x = d_{r+2}s_0 y_0 + d_{r+2}s_1 y_1 + \cdots + d_{r+2}s_r y_r$$
$$= s_0 d_{r+1}y_0 + s_1 d_{r+1}y_1 + \cdots + s_r d_{r+1}y_r.$$

But then x is a member of $s_{[r]}A_{p-1}$.

Suppose inductively that the inclusion $i : s_{[r]}\pi_n X_p \hookrightarrow \pi_n X_p$ admits a factorization

$$\begin{array}{ccc} s_{[r]}\pi_n X_p & \xrightarrow{\quad i \quad} & \\ \cong \downarrow & \searrow & \\ & & \pi_n X_p \\ \pi_n(s_{[r]}X_p) & \nearrow_{i_*} & \end{array}$$

(4.16)

for all $p \geq r$. Then the long exact sequence associated to the cofibre square (4.13) breaks up into short exact sequences

$$0 \to \pi_n(s_{[r]}X_{p-1}) \to \pi_n X_p \oplus \pi_n(s_{[r]}X_p) \to \pi_n(s_{[r+1]}X_p) \to 0$$

since the map i_* in the diagram (4.16) is monic, whereas the sequence

$$0 \to s_{[r]}(\pi_n X_{p-1}) \to \pi_n X_p \oplus s_{[r]}(\pi_n X_p) \to s_{[r+1]}(\pi_n X_p) \to 0$$

is exact, by the claim above applied to the simplicial abelian group $\pi_n X_*$. The resulting comparison

$$
\begin{array}{ccccccccc}
0 & \longrightarrow & s_{[r]}\pi_n X_{p-1} & \longrightarrow & \pi_n X_p \oplus s_{[r]}(\pi_n X_p) & \longrightarrow & s_{[r+]}\pi_n X_p & \longrightarrow & 0 \\
& & \cong \downarrow & & \cong \downarrow & & & & \\
0 & \longrightarrow & \pi_n(s_{[r]}X_{p-1}) & \longrightarrow & \pi_n X_p \oplus \pi_n(s_{[r]}X_p) & \longrightarrow & \pi_n(s_{[r+1]}X_p) & \longrightarrow & 0
\end{array}
$$

therefore induces an isomorphism

$$\pi_n(s_{[r+1]}X_p) \cong s_{[r+1]}(\pi_n X_p). \qquad \blacksquare$$

Write

$$PO = (s_{[p-1]}X_{p-1} \ltimes \Delta^p) \cup (X_p \ltimes \partial\Delta^p),$$

and observe that there is a commutative diagram of maps of spectra

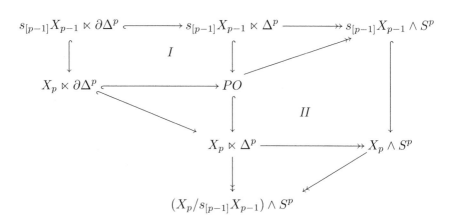

in which the indicated squares are pushouts. It follows that the cofibres of $PO \hookrightarrow X_p \ltimes \Delta^p$ and $dX^{(p-1)} \hookrightarrow dX^{(p)}$ coincide up to isomorphism with the spectrum $(X_p/s_{[p-1]}X_{p-1}) \wedge S^p$. In particular, there are induced natural isomorphisms

$$\pi_{p+q}(dX^{(p)}/dX^{(p-1)}) \cong \pi_{p+q}((X_p/s_{[p-1]}X_{p-1}) \wedge S^p)$$
$$\cong \pi_q(X_p/s_{[p-1]}X_{p-1})$$
$$\cong \pi_q(X_p)/s_{[p-1]}\pi_q(X_{p-1}),$$

by Lemma 4.15.

There is a commutative diagram

where λ is the canonical map of (4.14). We therefore have a diagram of abelian group homomorphisms

$$\pi_{p+q}(X_p \wedge S^p) \xrightarrow{\partial} \pi_{p+q-1}(X_p \ltimes \partial \Delta^p) \xrightarrow{p_*} \pi_{p+q-1}(X_p \wedge (\partial \Delta^p/sk_{p-2}\Delta^p))$$

$$\lambda_* \downarrow \qquad\qquad \lambda_* \downarrow \qquad\qquad \downarrow \lambda_* \qquad\qquad (4.17)$$

$$\pi_{p+q}(dX^{(p)}/dX^{(p-1)}) \xrightarrow{\partial} \pi_{p+q-1}(dX^{(p-1)}) \xrightarrow{p_*} \pi_{p+q-1}(dX^{(p-1)}/dX^{(p-2)})$$

Lemma 4.9 implies that there is a commutative square

$$\pi_q(X_p) \xrightarrow{((-1)^i)} \bigoplus_{0 \le i \le p} \pi_q(X_p)$$

$$\cong \downarrow \qquad\qquad \cong \downarrow \sum_{0 \le i \le p} in_i \qquad\qquad (4.18)$$

$$\pi_{p+q}(X_p \wedge S^p) \xrightarrow{p_*\partial} \pi_{p+q-1}(X_p \wedge (\partial \Delta^p/sk_{p-2}\Delta^p))$$

where in_i is the composite

$$\pi_q(X_p) \cong \pi_{p+q-1}(X_p \wedge S^{p-1}) \to \pi_{p+q-1}(X_p \wedge (\partial \Delta^p/sk_{p-2}\Delta^p))$$

induced by including the wedge summand corresponding to the ith face $d_i\iota_p$ of the top cell of Δ^p.

The composite

$$\pi_{p+q-1}(X_p\wedge S^{p-1}) \to \pi_{p+q-1}(X_p\wedge(\partial\Delta^p/sk_{p-2}\Delta^p)) \xrightarrow{\lambda_*} \pi_{p+q-1}(dX^{(p-1)}/dX^{(p-2)})$$

is induced by the string

$$X_p\ltimes\Delta^{p-1} \xrightarrow{1\ltimes d^i} X_p\ltimes\Delta^p \xrightarrow{\lambda} dX,$$

which in turn coincides with the composite

$$X_p\ltimes\Delta^{p-1} \xrightarrow{d_i\ltimes 1} X_{p-1}\ltimes\Delta^{p-1} \xrightarrow{\lambda} dX.$$

It follows that there is a commutative diagram

$$\begin{array}{ccc}
\bigoplus_{0\leq i\leq p}\pi_q(X_p) & \xrightarrow[\cong]{\sum in_i} & \pi_{p+q-1}(X_p\wedge(\partial\Delta^p/sk_{p-2}\Delta^p)) \\
{\scriptstyle\sum d_i}\downarrow & & \downarrow{\scriptstyle\lambda_*} \\
\pi_q(X_{p-1}) \xrightarrow[\cong]{} \pi_{p+q-1}(X_{p-1}\wedge S^{p-1}) & \xrightarrow{\lambda_*} & \pi_{p+q-1}(dX^{(p-1)}/dX^{(p-2)}).
\end{array} \qquad (4.19)$$

Lemma 4.15 implies that there is a commutative diagram

$$\begin{array}{ccc}
\pi_q(X_p) & \xrightarrow{\cong} & \pi_{p+q}(X_p\wedge S^p) \\
{\scriptstyle\text{can}}\downarrow & & \downarrow{\scriptstyle\lambda_*} \\
\pi_q(X_p)/s_{[p-1]}(\pi_q(X_{p-1})) & \xrightarrow{\cong} & \pi_{p+q}(dX^{(p)}/dX^{(p-1)}),
\end{array} \qquad (4.20)$$

where can is the canonical projection. Thus, appropriate pasting together of copies of the diagrams (4.17), (4.18), (4.19) and (4.20) proves

PROPOSITION 4.21. *The map*

$$\pi_q(X_p)/s_{[p-1]}(\pi_q(X_{p-1})) \to \pi_q(X_{p-1})/s_{[p-2]}(\pi_q(X_{p-2}))$$

which is induced by the composite

$$\pi_{p+q}(dX^{(p)}/dX^{(p-1)}) \xrightarrow{\partial} \pi_{p+q-1}(dX^{(p-1)}) \xrightarrow{p_*} \pi_{p+q-1}(dX^{(p-1)}/dX^{(p-2)})$$

and the natural isomorphisms

$$\pi_{p+q}(dX^{(p)}/dX^{(p-1)}) \cong \pi_q(X_p)/s_{[p-1]}(\pi_q(X_{p-1}))$$

coincides with the map induced by the boundary homomorphism

$$\sum_{i=0}^p(-1)^i d_i : \pi_q(X_p) \to \pi_q(X_{p-1})$$

coming from the simplicial abelian group $\pi_q(X_*)$.

COROLLARY 4.22. *Suppose that X is a simplicial spectrum. Then the filtration $dX^{(p)}$ of the diagonal spectrum dX gives rise to a spectral sequence, with*

$$E_2^{p,q} = H_p(\pi_q(X_*)) \Rightarrow \pi_{p+q}dX.$$

REMARK 4.23. Suppose that K is a pointed simplicial set, and associate to K the bisimplicial pointed set $\mathbf{n} \mapsto K(K_n, 0)$, where $K(K_n, 0)$ is the constant (pointed) simplicial set with vertices K_n. The the diagonal $d(X \wedge K(K_*, 0))$ of the simplicial spectrum $X \wedge K(K_*, 0)$ is canonically isomorphic to $X \wedge K$. In this way, one sees that the Atiyah-Hirzebruch-Whitehead spectral sequence

$$E_2^{p,q} = \tilde{H}_p(K, \pi_q X) \Rightarrow \pi_{p+q}(X \wedge K)$$

of Proposition 4.11 is a special case of the spectral sequence arising from a simplicial spectrum. The key point is really Lemma 4.9.   ∎

4.4. The Kan suspension

The ordinal number map $d^0 : \mathbf{n} \to \mathbf{n} + 1$ induces an inclusion $d^0 : \Delta^n \to \Delta^{n+1}$. Let the vertex 0 be a base point for Δ^{n+1}, and observe that any simplicial map $\theta : \Delta^n \to \Delta^m$ uniquely extends to a simplicial map $\theta_* : \Delta^{n+1} \to \Delta^{m+1}$, which is pointed in the sense that $\theta_*(0) = 0$, and satisfies the relation $\theta_* d^0 = d^0 \theta$.

The *cone CY* of a simplicial set Y is the pointed simplicial set

$$CY = \varinjlim_{\Delta^n \to Y} \Delta^{n+1},$$

where the colimit is indexed in the *simplex category* of all simplices $\Delta^n \to Y$, and is formed in the pointed simplicial set category.

If X is a pointed simplicial set, then the *pointed cone $C_* X$* is defined by the pushout

$$
\begin{array}{ccc}
C\Delta^0 & \xrightarrow{\;C*\;} & CX \\
\downarrow & & \downarrow \\
* & \longrightarrow & C_* X.
\end{array}
$$

Here, the map $C*$ is induced by the inclusion of the base point $* : \Delta^0 \to X$ in X.

The maps $d^0 : \Delta^n \to \Delta^{n+1}$ induce a natural pointed map $i : X \to C_* X$. The *Kan suspension ΣX* of X is defined to be the quotient

$$\Sigma X = C_* X / X.$$

This definition is the dual, in some sense, of the definition of Kan suspension that is given in [27]. The numbers have been changed here to get a comparison with chain complexes to work out properly below.

One sees directly from the definition that a pointed simplicial set map $\phi : \Sigma X \to Y$ consists of pointed functions

$$\phi_n : X_n \to Y_{n+1}$$

such that

(1) $d_1 \ldots d_{n+1}\phi_n(x) = *$, and $d_0\phi_n(x) = *$ for each $x \in X_n$, and
(2) for each ordinal number map $\theta : \mathbf{n} \to \mathbf{m}$, the diagram of pointed functions

$$
\begin{array}{ccc}
X_n & \xrightarrow{\phi_n} & Y_{n+1} \\
\theta* \downarrow & & \downarrow (\theta_*)^* \\
X_m & \xrightarrow{\phi_m} & Y_{m+1}
\end{array}
$$

commutes.

Pointed simplicial set maps $\psi : C_*X \to Y$ have a very similar characterization; one simply deletes the requirement that $d_0\psi_n(x) = *$.

It follows that the pointed cone and Kan suspension functors preserve colimits of pointed simplicial sets.

An equivalent description of C_*X starts from the observation that the pointed simplicial set X is a member of a coequalizer diagram

$$\bigvee_{\theta:\mathbf{n}\to\mathbf{m}} X_m \wedge \Delta_+^n \rightrightarrows \bigvee_{n\geq 0} X_n \wedge \Delta_+^n \to X,$$

where, for example, $X_m \wedge \Delta_+^n$ is the wedge of the pointed set of m-simplices X_m, thought of as a discrete pointed simplicial set, with Δ_+^n. Then C_*X is defined by the coequalizer diagram

$$\bigvee_{\theta:\mathbf{n}\to\mathbf{m}} X_m \wedge \Delta^{n+1} \rightrightarrows \bigvee_{n\geq 0} X_n \wedge \Delta^{n+1} \to C_*X.$$

The set of m-simplices of Δ^{n+1} is the set of ordinal number maps of the form $\gamma : \mathbf{m} \to \mathbf{n+1}$. Each such γ fits into a pullback diagram

$$
\begin{array}{ccc}
\mathbf{j} & \xrightarrow{\gamma_*} & \mathbf{n} \\
(d^0)^{n-j} \downarrow & & \downarrow d^0 \\
\mathbf{m} & \xrightarrow{\gamma} & \mathbf{n+1}
\end{array}
$$

in the ordinal number category, for some uniquely determined map $\gamma_* : \mathbf{j} \to \mathbf{n}$ if $\gamma^{-1}(\mathbf{n}) \neq \emptyset$. It follows that, as a pointed set, Δ_m^{n+1} has the form

$$\Delta_m^{n+1} = \Delta_m^n \sqcup \Delta_{m-1}^n \sqcup \cdots \sqcup \Delta_0^n \sqcup \{*\}$$
$$= (\Delta_+^n)_m \vee (\Delta_+^n)_{m-1} \vee \cdots \vee (\Delta_+^n)_0,$$

where the base point corresponds to the case $\gamma(\mathbf{m}) = 0$. Now take another map $\zeta : \mathbf{k} \to \mathbf{m}$; there is a pullback diagram of ordinal number maps

$$
\begin{array}{ccc}
\zeta^{-1}(\mathbf{j}) & \xrightarrow{\hat{\zeta}} & \mathbf{j} \\
\downarrow & & \downarrow {\scriptstyle (d^0)^{m-j}} \\
\mathbf{k} & \xrightarrow{\zeta} & \mathbf{m}
\end{array}
\qquad (4.24)
$$

in the case where $\mathbf{r} = \zeta^{-1}(\mathbf{j}) \neq \emptyset$. It follows that the restriction of $\zeta^* : \Delta_m^{n+1} \to \Delta_k^{n+1}$ to the summand $(\Delta_+^n)_j$ is the map

$$\hat{\zeta}^* : (\Delta_+^n)_j \to (\Delta_+^n)_r$$

if $\zeta^{-1}(\mathbf{j}) \neq \emptyset$, and is the map to the base point otherwise.

Suppose that X is a pointed simplicial set. There is a a pointed simplicial set $\tilde{C}_*(X)$ whose set of n-simplices is given by

$$\tilde{C}_*(X)_n = X_n \vee X_{n-1} \vee \cdots \vee X_0.$$

The map $\zeta^* : \tilde{C}_*(X)_m \to \tilde{C}_*(X)_k$ associated to $\zeta : \mathbf{k} \to \mathbf{m}$ is given on the summand X_j by the composite

$$X_j \xrightarrow{\hat{\zeta}^*} X_r \hookrightarrow \tilde{C}_*(X_k)$$

in the case where $\zeta^{-1}(\mathbf{j}) \neq \emptyset$, $\mathbf{r} = \zeta^{-1}(\mathbf{j})$, and the map $\hat{\zeta}$ is defined by the diagram (4.24). If $\zeta^{-1}(\mathbf{j}) = \emptyset$, then the restriction of ζ^* to X_j maps to the base point.

One checks that $\tilde{C}_*(X)$ is indeed a pointed simplicial set, and that the construction is functorial in X. Furthermore, the functor preserves colimits, so that the diagram

$$\bigvee_{\theta:\mathbf{n}\to\mathbf{m}} \tilde{C}_*(X_m \wedge \Delta_+^n) \rightrightarrows \bigvee_{n\geq 0} \tilde{C}_*(X_n \wedge \Delta_+^n) \to \tilde{C}_* X.$$

is a coequalizer. On the other hand, the definitions imply that there are isomorphisms

$$\tilde{C}_*(Y \wedge \Delta_+^n) \cong Y \wedge \tilde{C}_*(\Delta_+^n)$$
$$\cong Y \wedge \Delta^{n+1},$$

which are natural in the pointed sets Y and simplices Δ^n. This is enough to prove

LEMMA 4.25. *There is a pointed simplicial set isomorphism*

$$\tilde{C}_*(X) \cong C_*(X),$$

which is natural in X.

Observe that the composite

$$X \xrightarrow{i} C_*(X) \cong \tilde{C}_*(X),$$

in degree n is the inclusion of the wedge summand X_n. The canonical map $i : X \to C_*(X)$ is therefore an inclusion. Collapsing by X in each degree also gives a nice description of the Kan suspension ΣX.

There is a simplicial set map

$$\Delta^1 \times \Delta^n \xrightarrow{h} \Delta^{n+1} \qquad (4.26)$$

which is defined by the diagram

This map is natural in $\mathbf{n}$, and sends $\{0\} \times \Delta^n$ to the base point 0 of Δ^{n+1}. It follows, in particular, that h induces a pointed map

$$\Delta^1 \wedge \Delta^n_+ \xrightarrow{h} C_*\Delta^n_+,$$

or equivalently, a map

$$h : (\Delta^1 \times \Delta^n)/(\{0\} \times \Delta^n) \to \Delta^{n+1} \qquad (4.27)$$

which is natural in $\mathbf{n}$.

Comparing coequalizer diagrams therefore gives a pointed map

$$\Delta^1 \wedge X \xrightarrow{h} C_*X,$$

which is natural in X. Observe as well that there is a commutative diagram

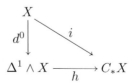

It follows that h induces a natural pointed map

$$h : S^1 \wedge X \to \Sigma X. \tag{4.28}$$

$\Delta^1 \wedge X$ and C_*X are both models for the pointed cone on X and are both contractible, so the map h of (4.28) is also a weak equivalence.

Write v_i for the vertex of the topological space $|\Delta^{n+1}|$ which corresponds to the number i. There is a pointed homeomorphism

$$H : |\Delta^1 \times \Delta^n| - |\{0\} \times \Delta^n| \to |\Delta^{n+1}| - \{v_0\}$$

which is defined by

$$(s, t_0 v_0 + \cdots + t_n v_n) \mapsto (1-s)v_0 + s(t_0 v_1 + \cdots + t_n v_{n+1}).$$

The homeomorphism H is natural in $\mathbf{n}$ in the sense that the diagram

$$
\begin{array}{ccc}
|\Delta^1 \times \Delta^n| - |\{0\} \times \Delta^n| & \xrightarrow{\;\;H\;\;} & |\Delta^{n+1}| - \{v_0\} \\
{\scriptstyle |1 \times \theta|}\Big\downarrow & & \Big\downarrow{\scriptstyle |\theta_*|} \\
|\Delta^1 \times \Delta^m| - |\{0\} \times \Delta^m| & \xrightarrow{\;\;H\;\;} & |\Delta^{m+1}| - \{v_0\}
\end{array}
$$

commutes, for every ordinal number map $\theta : \mathbf{n} \to \mathbf{m}$. Comparing compactifications therefore gives a natural pointed homeomorphism

$$H : |(\Delta^1 \times \Delta^n)/(\{0\} \times \Delta^n)| \xrightarrow{\;\cong\;} |\Delta^{n+1}| \tag{4.29}$$

The realization $|h|$ of the simplicial map h restricts to a continuous map

$$|h| : |\Delta^1 \times \Delta^n| - |\{0\} \times \Delta^n| \to |\Delta^{n+1}| - \{v_0\}$$

The space $|\Delta^{n+1}| - \{v_0\}$ is convex, so that there is a homotopy

$$g : (|\Delta^1 \times \Delta^n| - |\{0\} \times \Delta^n|) \times |\Delta^1| \to |\Delta^{n+1}| - \{v_0\}$$

from H to the restricted map $|h|$; this homotopy is defined by

$$g(z, s) = s|h|(z) + (1-s)H(z).$$

The homotopy g is natural in ordinal number maps $\theta : \mathbf{n} \to \mathbf{m}$, and it is constant on the subspace $|\{1\} \times \Delta^n|$. It therefore induces a natural pointed homotopy

$$g_* : |(\Delta^1 \times \Delta^n)/(\{0\} \times \Delta^n)| \times |\Delta^1| \to |\Delta^{n+1}|$$

from the homeomorphism H to the realized map $|h|$, and g_* restricts to the constant homotopy on the map

$$|\Delta^n| \xrightarrow{|d^0|} |\Delta^{n+1}|$$

on the subspace $|\{1\} \times \Delta^n|$.

It follows that there is a pointed homeomorphism

$$H : |\Delta^1 \wedge X| \xrightarrow{\cong} |C_*X|$$

which is natural in pointed simplicial sets X, and which fits into a commutative diagram

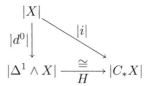

The homotopies g induce a natural pointed homotopy

$$g_* : |\Delta^1 \wedge X| \times |\Delta^1| \to |C_*X|$$

from H to $|h|$, which restricts along the map $|d^0|$ to the constant homotopy on the map

$$|X| \xrightarrow{|i|} |C_*X|.$$

Finally, one concludes that the homotopies g induce a natural pointed homotopy

$$g_* : |S^1 \wedge X| \times |\Delta^1| \to |\Sigma X|$$

from a homeomorphism

$$H_* : |S^1 \wedge X| \xrightarrow{\cong} |\Sigma X| \tag{4.30}$$

induced by the various maps H, to the map

$$|h| : |S^1 \wedge X| \to |\Sigma X|$$

which is induced by the simplicial homotopies h.

The homeomorphism H_* in (4.30) is the inverse of the Kan homeomorphism

$$|\Sigma X| \xrightarrow{\cong} |S^1 \wedge X|$$

(see [31], [8]).

Suppose that Y is a pointed topological space, and let S denote the singular functor (as always). There is a natural pointed simplicial set map

$$\nu : C_* SY \to S(|\Delta^1| \wedge Y),$$

which is best defined to be the adjoint of the composite

$$|C_* SY| \xrightarrow[\cong]{\tilde{H}} |\Delta^1| \wedge |SY| \xrightarrow{|\Delta^1| \wedge \epsilon} |\Delta^1| \wedge Y,$$

where $\epsilon : |SY| \to Y$ is the counit of the realization/singular functor adjunction, and $\tilde{H}$ is the composite homeomorphism

$$|C_* SY| \xrightarrow[\cong]{H^{-1}} |\Delta^1 \wedge SY| \cong |\Delta^1| \wedge |SY|.$$

In particular, the following diagram commutes:

$$\begin{array}{ccc}
|C_* SY| & \xrightarrow{\;|\nu|\;} & |S(|\Delta^1| \wedge Y)| \\
{\scriptstyle \tilde{H}}\big\downarrow{\scriptstyle \cong} & & \big\downarrow{\scriptstyle \epsilon} \\
|\Delta^1| \wedge |SY| & \xrightarrow{\;|\Delta^1| \wedge \epsilon\;} & |\Delta^1| \wedge Y
\end{array} \qquad (4.31)$$

The diagram

$$\begin{array}{ccc}
SY & & \\
{\scriptstyle i}\big\downarrow & \searrow{\scriptstyle S(d^0)} & \\
C_* SY & \xrightarrow{\;\nu\;} & S(|\Delta^1| \wedge Y)
\end{array}$$

commutes, and so there is an induced natural map

$$\nu_* : \Sigma SY \to S(S^1 \wedge Y).$$

One also sees, just by categorical diddling, that there is a commutative diagram

$$\begin{array}{ccc}
C_* X & \xrightarrow{\;\eta\;} & S|C_* X| \\
{\scriptstyle C_* \eta}\big\downarrow & & {\scriptstyle \cong}\big\| {\scriptstyle S\tilde{H}} \\
C_* S|X| & \xrightarrow{\;\nu\;} & S(|\Delta^1| \wedge |X|)
\end{array} \qquad (4.32)$$

for all pointed simplicial sets X. Finally, the commutativity of diagrams (4.31) and (4.32) implies that there is a commutative diagram

$$\begin{array}{ccc}
|\Sigma S Y| & \xrightarrow{\;|\nu_*|\;} & |S(S^1 \wedge Y)| \\
\tilde{H} \downarrow \cong & & \downarrow \epsilon \\
S^1 \wedge |SY| & \xrightarrow[\;S^1 \wedge \epsilon\;]{} & S^1 \wedge Y
\end{array} \tag{4.33}$$

of pointed continuous maps for all pointed spaces Y, and a commutative diagram of pointed simplicial set maps

$$\begin{array}{ccc}
\Sigma X & \xrightarrow{\;\eta\;} & S|\Sigma X| \\
\Sigma \eta \downarrow & & \cong \downarrow S\tilde{H} \\
\Sigma S|X| & \xrightarrow[\;\nu_*\;]{} & S(S^1 \wedge |X|)
\end{array} \tag{4.34}$$

for all pointed simplicial sets X.

A *Kan spectrum* X consists of pointed simplicial sets X^n and pointed maps $\sigma : \Sigma X^n \to X^{n+1}$. There is a category of such objects, which will be denoted by $\mathbf{Spt}_{Kan}$.

The realization functor induces a functor

$$|\cdot| : \mathbf{Spt}_{Kan} \to \mathbf{Spt}(\mathbf{Top}).$$

If X is a Kan spectrum with bonding maps $\sigma : \Sigma X^i \to X^{i+1}$, then the associated topological spectrum has bonding maps given by the composites

$$S^1 \wedge |X^i| \xrightarrow[\cong]{H_*} |\Sigma X^i| \xrightarrow{|\sigma|} |X^{i+1}|.$$

Similarly, the singular functor induces a functor

$$S : \mathbf{Spt}(\mathbf{Top}) \to \mathbf{Spt}_{Kan}.$$

If Y is topological spectrum with bonding maps $\sigma : S^1 \wedge Y^i \to Y^{i+1}$, then the associated Kan spectrum has bonding maps

$$\Sigma S Y^i \xrightarrow{\nu_*} S(S^1 \wedge Y^i) \xrightarrow{S\sigma} S Y^{i+1}.$$

Lemma 4.35.

(1) *The unit* $\eta : X^i \to S|X^i|$ *defines a natural strict weak equivalence of Kan spectra* $\eta : X \to S|X|$.

(2) *The counit* $\epsilon : |S(Y^i)| \to Y^i$ *defines a natural strict weak equivalence of topological spectra* $\epsilon : |S(Y)| \to Y$.

PROOF: The first statement is a consequence of diagram (4.34), while the second is a consequence of the commutativity of (4.33). ∎

Recall that the realization functor also induces a functor

$$|\cdot| : \mathbf{Spt} \to \mathbf{Spt}(\mathbf{Top}).$$

This functor is explicitly defined as follows: given a spectrum object (or just spectrum) X, the corresponding realized spectrum $|X|$ consists of the spaces $|X^i|$, with bonding maps

$$S^1 \wedge |X^i| \cong |S^1 \wedge X^i| \xrightarrow{|\sigma|} |X^{i+1}|.$$

The indicated isomorphism is induced by a canonical isomorphism

$$|K \wedge L| \xrightarrow[\cong]{\text{can}} |K| \wedge |L|,$$

valid for all pointed simplicial sets K and L.

REMARK 4.36. The map can arises from the fact that the realization functor preserves products and wedges, provided we agree that this functor takes values in the category of Kelly spaces (which we always do anyway). Even if one doesn't agree that all spaces should be Kelly spaces, the map can is nevertheless defined. Note finally that can is an isomorphism no matter what topological category one chooses to inhabit if either K or L is finite. ∎

The singular functor induces a functor

$$S : \mathbf{Spt}(\mathbf{Top}) \to \mathbf{Spt}.$$

Explicitly, if Y is a topological spectrum, then the object SY consists of the pointed simplicial sets $S(Y^i)$, and has bonding maps

$$S^1 \wedge S(Y^i) \xrightarrow{\eta \wedge 1} S(S^1) \wedge S(Y^i) \xrightarrow{c} S(S^1 \wedge Y^i) \xrightarrow{S(\sigma)} S(Y^{i+1}).$$

The map c is an instance of the pointed map

$$c : S(Z) \wedge S(W) \to S(Z \wedge W),$$

valid for all pointed spaces Z and W. This map is defined to be the adjoint of the composite

$$|S(Z) \wedge S(W)| \xrightarrow[\cong]{\text{can}} |S(Z)| \wedge |S(W)| \xrightarrow{\epsilon \wedge \epsilon} Z \wedge W,$$

so that the diagram

$$
\begin{array}{ccc}
|S(Z) \wedge S(W)| & \xrightarrow{\ |c|\ } & |S(Z \wedge W)| \\
\text{can} \downarrow \cong & & \downarrow \epsilon \\
|S(Z)| \wedge |S(W)| & \xrightarrow[\epsilon \wedge \epsilon]{} & Z \wedge W
\end{array}
\tag{4.37}
$$

commutes. Here, ϵ is the counit of the realization/singular functor adjunction.

Dually, if K and L are pointed simplicial sets, then there is a commutative diagram

$$
\begin{array}{ccc}
K \wedge L & \xrightarrow{\ \eta \wedge \eta\ } & S|K| \wedge S|L| \\
\eta \downarrow & & \downarrow c \\
S|K \wedge L| & \xrightarrow[S(\text{can})]{\cong} & S(|K| \wedge |L|)
\end{array}
\tag{4.38}
$$

This diagram is obtained from the diagram (4.37) by fooling around with triangle identities.

Lemma 4.39.

(1) The unit $\eta : X^i \to S|X^i|$ defines a natural strict weak equivalence of spectra $\eta : X \to S|X|$.

(2) The counit $\epsilon : |S(Y^i)| \to Y^i$ defines a natural strict weak equivalence of topological spectra $\epsilon : |S(Y)| \to Y$.

Proof: The first statement is a consequence of diagram (4.38), while the second is a consequence of diagram (4.37). ∎

The natural comparison map

$$
h : S^1 \wedge X \to \Sigma X
$$

induces a functor

$$
h_* : \mathbf{Spt}_{Kan} \to \mathbf{Spt},
$$

which is defined by associating to a Kan spectrum X, the spectrum $h_* X$ having the same "spaces" as X, and with bonding maps of the form

$$
S^1 \wedge X^i \xrightarrow{h} \Sigma X^i \xrightarrow{\sigma} X^{i+1}.
$$

The natural pointed homotopies

$$g_* : |S^1 \wedge X^i| \times |\Delta^1| \to |\Sigma X^i|$$

induce natural pointed homotopies from the bonding maps of the topological spectrum $|X|$ to the bonding maps of $|h_* X|$. The telescope construction of Chapter 1 (specifically, topological analogues of Lemma 1.13 and its corollaries) therefore implies that the topological spectra $|X|$ and $|h_* X|$ are strictly weakly equivalent, and that this equivalence is natural in Kan spectra X. This essentially proves

PROPOSITION 4.40. *The functor*

$$h_* : \mathbf{Spt}_{Kan} \to \mathbf{Spt}$$

is canonically strictly equivalent to the composite functor

$$\mathbf{Spt}_{Kan} \xrightarrow{|\cdot|} \mathbf{Spt}(\mathbf{Top}) \xrightarrow{S} \mathbf{Spt}.$$

In particular, h_* induces an equivalence of strict homotopy categories.

This result means that h_* induces the *standard* equivalence between the respective strict homotopy categories.

4.5. Simplicial abelian group spectra

Suppose that K is a pointed simplicial set, and let $\mathbb{Z}(K)$ denote the corresponding free simplicial abelian group. The *reduced part* $\tilde{\mathbb{Z}}(K)$ of $\mathbb{Z}(K)$ is defined to be the cokernel of the map

$$\mathbb{Z}(*) \to \mathbb{Z}(K)$$

which is induced by the inclusion of the base point. One sees, for example, that $\tilde{\mathbb{Z}}(\Delta^n_+)$ is isomorphic to $\mathbb{Z}(\Delta^n)$, and that the isomorphism is natural in simplices Δ^n.

Let A be a simplicial abelian group. There is a natural coequalizer diagram

$$\bigoplus_{\theta:\mathbf{n}\to\mathbf{m}} A_m \otimes \mathbb{Z}(\Delta^n) \rightrightarrows \bigoplus_{n\geq 0} A_n \otimes \mathbb{Z}(\Delta^n) \to A,$$

where $A_m \otimes \mathbb{Z}(\Delta^n)$ is the degreewise tensor product of the abelian group A_m with the simplicial abelian group $\mathbb{Z}(\Delta^n)$. Notice that this diagram may also be written in the form

$$\bigoplus_{\theta:\mathbf{n}\to\mathbf{m}} A_m \otimes \tilde{\mathbb{Z}}(\Delta^n_+) \rightrightarrows \bigoplus_{n\geq 0} A_n \otimes \tilde{\mathbb{Z}}(\Delta^n_+) \to A. \tag{4.41}$$

I define the *cone CA* on A by the coequalizer

$$\bigoplus_{\theta:\mathbf{n}\to\mathbf{m}} A_m \otimes \tilde{\mathbb{Z}}(\Delta^{n+1}) \rightrightarrows \bigoplus_{n\geq 0} A_n \otimes \tilde{\mathbb{Z}}(\Delta^{n+1}) \to CA,$$

where, as before, one assumes that Δ^{n+1} is pointed by 0. The pointed maps $d^0 : \Delta^n_+ \to \Delta^{n+1}$ define a natural homomorphism of simplicial abelian groups $i : A \to CA$, and one can define the *suspension* ΣA *of* A to be the cokernel CA/A.

There is another way to describe ΣA, which starts with a description of CA analogous to the wedge decomposition of cones of pointed simplicial sets that we saw earlier.

By analogy with the construction of $\tilde{C}_*(X)$ for pointed simplicial sets X, there is a simplicial abelian group $\tilde{C}A$ which is naturally associated to A, with

$$\tilde{C}A_n = A_n \oplus A_{n-1} \oplus \cdots \oplus A_0.$$

The map $\zeta^* : \tilde{C}A_m \to \tilde{C}A_k$ associated to $\zeta : \mathbf{k} \to \mathbf{m}$ is given on the summand A_j by the composite

$$A_j \xrightarrow{\hat{\zeta}^*} A_r \hookrightarrow \tilde{C}A_k$$

in the case where $\zeta^{-1}(\mathbf{j}) \neq \emptyset$, $\mathbf{r} = \zeta^{-1}(\mathbf{j})$ and $\hat{\zeta}$ is defined by the diagram (4.28). Otherwise the restriction of ζ^* to A_j is the 0 map.

There is a natural isomorphism

$$\tilde{\mathbb{Z}}(\tilde{C}_*(X)) \cong \tilde{C}(\tilde{\mathbb{Z}}(X))$$

for pointed simplicial sets X. Applying this observation to the definition of CA gives

LEMMA 4.42. *There is an natural isomorphism*

$$\tilde{C}A \cong CA$$

of simplicial abelian groups.

PROOF: Apply $\tilde{C}$ to the coequalizer (4.41). Then there are isomorphisms

$$\begin{aligned}
\tilde{C}(A_m \otimes \tilde{\mathbb{Z}}(\Delta^n_+)) &\cong A_m \otimes \tilde{C}(\tilde{\mathbb{Z}}(\Delta^n_+)) \\
&\cong A_m \otimes \tilde{\mathbb{Z}}(\tilde{C}_* \Delta^n_+) \\
&\cong A_m \otimes \tilde{\mathbb{Z}}(\Delta^{n+1})
\end{aligned}$$

which are natural in $\mathbf{m}$ and $\mathbf{n}$. ■

The composite map

$$A \xrightarrow{i} CA \cong \tilde{C}A,$$

on the level of n-simplices, corresponds to the inclusion of the wedge summand A_n in $A_n \oplus \cdots \oplus A_0$; this map is, in particular, a monomorphism.

To understand the actual face and degeneracy maps of $\check{C}A$ a little better, observe that there are commutative diagrams of ordinal number morphisms

$$ (4.43) $$

and

$$ (4.44) $$

in which the squares are pullbacks. By definition, a typical element of $\check{C}A_n$ can be written $(a_n, a_{n-1}, \ldots, a_0)$, with $a_i \in A_i$. The commutativity of diagram (4.43) implies that

$$ d_i(a_n, \ldots, a_0) = (d_i a_n, \ldots, d_1 a_{n-i+1}, d_0 a_{n-i} + a_{n-i-1}, a_{n-i-2}, \ldots, a_0), $$

while the commutativity of diagram (4.44) implies that

$$ s_i(a_n, \ldots, a_0) = (s_i a_n, \ldots, s_0 a_{n-i}, 0, a_{n-i-1}, \ldots, a_0). $$

The moral is that the cone construction $\check{C}A$ has been known from the dawn of time as the Eilenberg-Mac Lane complex WA, while the suspension ΣA is canonically isomorphic to the complex $\overline{W}A$. We shall use the original Eilenberg-Mac Lane notation for the cone and suspension of a simplicial abelian group henceforth.

In general, if K is a pointed simplicial set and A is a simplicial abelian group, define a simplicial abelian group $K \otimes A$ by

$$ K \otimes A = (\mathbb{Z}(K) \otimes A)/(\mathbb{Z}(*) \otimes A) \cong \tilde{\mathbb{Z}}(K) \otimes A. $$

Note that there is a natural isomorphism

$$ \tilde{\mathbb{Z}}(K \wedge L) \cong K \otimes \tilde{\mathbb{Z}}(L) $$

for arbitrary pointed simplicial sets K and L.

There is a second set of natural candidates for cone and suspension functors of simplicial abelian groups A. These are $\Delta^1 \otimes A$ and $S^1 \otimes A$, respectively (where Δ^1 is pointed by 0, as above). The natural isomorphisms

$$\Delta^1 \otimes (B \otimes \tilde{\mathbb{Z}}(\Delta_+^n)) \cong B \otimes \tilde{\mathbb{Z}}(\Delta^1 \wedge \Delta_+^n)$$

associated to any abelian group B imply that, for any simplicial abelian group A, there is a coequalizer diagram

$$\bigoplus_{\theta:\mathbf{n}\to\mathbf{m}} A_m \otimes \tilde{\mathbb{Z}}(\Delta^1 \wedge \Delta_+^n) \rightrightarrows \bigoplus_{n \geq 0} A_n \otimes \tilde{\mathbb{Z}}(\Delta^1 \wedge \Delta_+^n) \to \Delta^1 \otimes A.$$

Of course, we also needed the exactness of the functors $A \mapsto K \otimes A$. From this point of view, the maps

$$h : \Delta^1 \wedge \Delta_+^n \to C_*(\Delta_+^n) \cong \Delta^{n+1}$$

induce a natural map

$$h : \Delta^1 \otimes A \to WA$$

which fits into a commutative diagram

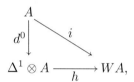

and where the maps defined on A are the respective canonical inclusions. It follows that there is an induced natural simplicial abelian group homomorphism

$$h : S^1 \otimes A \to \overline{W}A. \tag{4.45}$$

The complexes $\Delta^1 \otimes A$ and WA are both acyclic, and so the map (4.45) is a weak equivalence. Something prettier is actually afoot in the constant case:

LEMMA 4.46. *The maps* $h : \Delta^1 \otimes B \to WB$ *and* $h : S^1 \otimes B \to \overline{W}B$ *are isomorphisms if* B *is a constant simplicial object* $K(A,0)$ *for some abelian group* A.

PROOF: The canonical maps

$$A \otimes \tilde{\mathbb{Z}}(\Delta^1 \wedge \Delta_+^0) \to \Delta^1 \otimes K(A,0)$$

and

$$A \otimes \tilde{\mathbb{Z}}(\Delta^1) \to WK(A,0)$$

corresponding to the degree 0 summands in the coequalizer descriptions are isomorphisms, and the pointed simplicial set map

$$h : \Delta^1 \wedge \Delta_+^0 \to \Delta^1$$

is an isomorphism. ∎

COROLLARY 4.47.

(1) *The simplicial abelian group* $S^1 \otimes K(A, 0)$ *is naturally isomorphic to* BA *if* A *is an abelian group.*

(2) *The simplicial abelian group* $S^1 \otimes A$ *is naturally isomorphic to the diagonal of the bisimplicial abelian group* BA *if* A *is an arbitrary simplicial abelian group.*

PROOF: BA is $\overline{W} K(A, 0)$. ∎

The natural map

$$h : S^1 \otimes A \to \overline{W} A$$

is a weak equivalence, but, the map h is even a natural *homotopy* equivalence of simplicial abelian groups with respect to the most naive notion of homotopy in this category. The proof of this statement requires a change of gears: one could think that the method of acyclic models is involved, but the Bousfield-Kan theory of cosimplicial spaces is used instead.

Suppose that X is a pointed simplicial set. Then there is a canonical pointed map $\eta_* : X \to \tilde{\mathbb{Z}} X$, which is defined to be the composite

$$X \xrightarrow{\eta} \mathbb{Z} X \xrightarrow{\pi} \tilde{\mathbb{Z}} X.$$

Write $\tilde{\Delta}_+$ for the pointed cosimplicial space

$$\mathbf{n} \mapsto \Delta_+^n.$$

Then applying the cone functor gives a pointed cosimplicial space $C_* \tilde{\Delta}_+$ and a levelwise inclusion of cosimplicial spaces

$$\tilde{\Delta}_+ \xrightarrow{i} C_* \tilde{\Delta}_+.$$

The maximal augmentation for each of these objects is a point (ie. copy of Δ^0), so that the map i is a cofibration of pointed cosimplicial spaces in the sense of Bousfield and Kan [9, p.273]. Similarly, one sees that the maps $d^0 \times 1$ induce a pointed cofibration of cosimplicial spaces of the from

$$d^0 : \tilde{\Delta}_+ \to \Delta^1 \wedge \tilde{\Delta}_+.$$

On the other hand, the cosimplicial simplicial abelian groups $\tilde{\mathbb{Z}}(\Delta^1 \wedge \tilde{\Delta}_+)$ and $\tilde{\mathbb{Z}}(C_* \tilde{\Delta}_+)$ are levelwise contractible. All cosimplicial simplicial abelian groups are fibrant cosimplicial spaces, so that the Bousfield-Kan closed model structure on the category of cosimplicial spaces [9] implies that there is a dotted arrow making the diagram

$$
\begin{array}{ccc}
\tilde{\Delta}_+ & \xrightarrow{\;\;\eta_*\;\;} & \tilde{\mathbb{Z}}(\tilde{\Delta}_+) \\
\Big\downarrow{\scriptstyle d^0} & & \Big\downarrow{\scriptstyle i_*} \\
\Delta^1 \wedge \tilde{\Delta}_+ & \dashrightarrow & \tilde{\mathbb{Z}}(C_*\tilde{\Delta}_+)
\end{array}
$$

commute. Furthermore, any two such extensions are pointed homotopic, in such a way that the homotopy restricts to a constant homotopy on $\tilde{\Delta}_+$. Similarly, there is an arrow making the diagram

$$
\begin{array}{ccc}
\tilde{\Delta}_+ & \xrightarrow{\;\;\eta_*\;\;} & \tilde{\mathbb{Z}}(\tilde{\Delta}_+) \\
\Big\downarrow{\scriptstyle i_*} & & \Big\downarrow{\scriptstyle d^0_*} \\
C_*\tilde{\Delta}_+ & \dashrightarrow & \tilde{\mathbb{Z}}(\Delta^1 \wedge \tilde{\Delta}_+)
\end{array}
$$

of pointed cosimplicial maps commute, and any two such are pointed homotopic, via a homotopy which restricts to the constant homotopy on $\tilde{\Delta}_+$. Finally, any cosimplicial map

$$
C_*\tilde{\Delta}_+ \to \tilde{\mathbb{Z}}(C_*\tilde{\Delta}_+)
$$

which extends $\eta_* : \tilde{\Delta}_+ \to \tilde{\mathbb{Z}}(\tilde{\Delta}_+)$ must be pointed homotopic to

$$
\eta_* : C_*\tilde{\Delta}_+ \to \tilde{\mathbb{Z}}(C_*\tilde{\Delta}_+)
$$

rel $\tilde{\Delta}_+$. A corresponding statement holds for maps of the form

$$
\Delta^1 \wedge \tilde{\Delta}_+ \to \tilde{\mathbb{Z}}(\Delta^1 \wedge \tilde{\Delta}_+).
$$

These observations imply

LEMMA 4.48.

(1) The cosimplicial simplicial abelian groups $\tilde{\mathbb{Z}}(C_*\tilde{\Delta}_+)$ and $\tilde{\mathbb{Z}}(\Delta^1 \wedge \tilde{\Delta}_+)$ are simplicially homotopy equivalent rel $\tilde{\Delta}_+$ in the category of cosimplicial simplicial abelian groups.

(2) The cosimplicial abelian groups $\tilde{\mathbb{Z}}(\Sigma\tilde{\Delta}_+)$ and $\tilde{\mathbb{Z}}(S^1 \wedge \tilde{\Delta}_+)$ are simplicially homotopy equivalent in the category of cosimplicial simplicial abelian groups.

COROLLARY 4.49. *The functors* $A \mapsto \overline{W}A$ *and* $A \mapsto S^1 \otimes A$ *are naturally homotopy equivalent in the category of simplicial abelian groups, and this equivalence is induced by the natural map*

$$h : S^1 \otimes A \to \overline{W}A.$$

The proof of the corollary uses the characterization of $\overline{W}A$ and $S^1 \otimes A$ as coends, keeping in mind that a simplicial homotopy in the category of simplicial abelian groups is a map $A \otimes \Delta^1 \to B$.

A *spectrum object* B in the category of simplicial abelian groups consists of simplicial abelian groups B^i, $i \geq 0$, and bonding homomorphisms $\sigma : S^1 \otimes B^i \to B^{i+1}$. The category of such things will be denoted by $\mathbf{Spt}(Ab)$.

Suppose that X is a pointed set and that B is an abelian group. There is a canonical map

$$X \wedge B \xrightarrow{\ \mathrm{can}\ } \tilde{\mathbb{Z}}(X) \otimes B,$$

natural in X and B, which is induced by the composite function

$$X \times A \xrightarrow{\ \eta \times 1\ } \mathbb{Z}(X) \times A \xrightarrow{\ p\ } \mathbb{Z}(X) \otimes A.$$

η is the universal map to the free abelian group, and p is the universal bilnear map. Applying this map degreewise to pointed simplicial sets K and simplicial abelian groups A gives a canonical map

$$K \wedge A \xrightarrow{\ \mathrm{can}\ } K \otimes A.$$

This map has several variants, all of which will have the same notation.

Note in particular that the maps

$$A_n \wedge \Delta^{n+1} \xrightarrow{\ \mathrm{can}\ } A_n \otimes \tilde{\mathbb{Z}}(\Delta^{n+1})$$

induce a canonical map

$$\mathrm{can} : C_*(A) \to WA$$

between the set-theoretic and group-theoretic cones of A, and that this map respects the usual inclusions of A into both objects. It follows that there is an induced map

$$\mathrm{can} : \Sigma A \to \overline{W}A \tag{4.50}$$

relating $\overline{W}A$ to the Kan suspension ΣA of the pointed simplicial set underlying the simplicial abelian group A.

Suppose that B is an abelian group. There is a commutative diagram of pointed simplicial set maps

$$
\begin{array}{ccc}
\Delta^1 \wedge B \wedge \Delta_+^n & \xrightarrow{\text{can}} & \tilde{\mathbb{Z}}(\Delta^1) \otimes B \otimes \tilde{\mathbb{Z}}(\Delta_+^n) \\
\cong \downarrow & & \downarrow \cong \\
B \wedge (\Delta^1 \wedge \Delta_+^n) & \xrightarrow{\text{can}} & B \otimes \tilde{\mathbb{Z}}(\Delta^1 \wedge \Delta_+^n) \\
B \wedge h \downarrow & & \downarrow B \otimes \tilde{\mathbb{Z}}(h) \\
B \wedge \Delta^{n+1} & \xrightarrow[\text{can}]{} & B \otimes \tilde{\mathbb{Z}}(\Delta^{n+1})
\end{array}
$$

It follows that there are commutative diagrams of pointed simplicial sets

$$
\begin{array}{ccc}
\Delta^1 \wedge A & \xrightarrow{\text{can}} & \Delta^1 \otimes A \\
h \downarrow & & \downarrow h \\
C_*(A) & \xrightarrow[\text{can}]{} & WA
\end{array}
$$

and

$$
\begin{array}{ccc}
S^1 \wedge A & \xrightarrow{\text{can}} & S^1 \otimes A \\
h \downarrow & & \downarrow h \\
\Sigma A & \xrightarrow[\text{can}]{} & \overline{W} A,
\end{array}
\tag{4.51}
$$

for all simplicial abelian groups A.

The map can : $S^1 \wedge A \to S^1 \otimes A$ is the gadget that allows one to extract an ordinary spectrum from a spectrum object in simplicial abelian groups. This transport of structure gives rise to notions of strict and stable weak equivalence for maps of such objects. In particular, a morphism $f : A \to B$ of spectrum objects of simplicial abelian groups is a *strict* (respectively stable) *weak equivalence* if it induces a strict (respectively stable) map of spectra when one forgets the abelian group structure.

A *Kan spectrum object* C in the category of simplicial abelian groups consists of simplicial abelian groups C^i, $i \geq 0$, and bonding maps $\sigma : \overline{W} C^i \to C^{i+1}$. Every such Kan spectrum object gives rise to, variously, a spectrum object in simplicial abelian groups, a spectrum, and a Kan spectrum, in view of the comparison maps can : $\Sigma C^i \to \overline{W} C^i$, $h : S^1 \otimes C^i \to \overline{W} C^i$, and can : $S^1 \wedge C^i \to S^1 \otimes C^i$. Furthermore, the commutativity of diagram (4.51) means that these objects are related to each other in the expected way.

Write $\mathbf{Spt}_{Kan}(Ab)$ for the category of Kan spectrum objects in simplicial abelian groups. Note in particular that the comparison map

$$h : S^1 \otimes A \to \overline{W} A$$

gives rise to a functor

$$h_* : \mathbf{Spt}_{Kan}(Ab) \to \mathbf{Spt}(Ab).$$

This functor is defined, at an object C with bonding homomorphisms $\sigma : \overline{W} C^i \to C^{i+1}$, by specifying that

$$h_*(C)^i = C^i,$$

and by defining the bonding map $S^1 \otimes h_*(C)^i \to h_*(C)^{i+1}$ to be the composite

$$S^1 \otimes C^i \xrightarrow{h} \overline{W} C^i \xrightarrow{\sigma} C^{i+1}.$$

THEOREM 4.52. *The functor*

$$h_* : \mathbf{Spt}_{Kan}(Ab) \to \mathbf{Spt}(Ab)$$

induces an equivalence of strict homotopy categories.

A map $f : A \to B$ of Kan spectrum objects is a *strict weak equivalence* if each of the constituent simplicial abelian group homomorphisms $f^i : A^i \to B^i$ is a weak equivalence. The *strict homotopy categories* associated to $\mathbf{Spt}_{Kan}(Ab)$ and $\mathbf{Spt}(Ab)$ are formed by formally inverting the strict weak equivalences in each case.

PROOF: The existence of a natural simplicial abelian group map

$$f : \overline{W} A \to S^1 \otimes A$$

is shown in Corollary 4.49. This map is an inverse for

$$h : S^1 \otimes A \to \overline{W} A,$$

up to natural naive homotopy of simplicial abelian group homomorphisms. There is therefore an induced functor

$$f_* : \mathbf{Spt}(Ab) \to \mathbf{Spt}_{Kan}(Ab),$$

which is defined by analogy with h_*.

Observe that, if A is a Kan spectrum object, with bonding homomorphisms $\sigma : \overline{W}A^i \to A^{i+1}$, then $f_* h_* A$ has the same constituent simplicial abelian groups as A, but with bonding homomorphisms given by the composites

$$\overline{W}A^i \xrightarrow{f} S^1 \otimes A^i \xrightarrow{h} \overline{W}A^i \xrightarrow{\sigma} A^{i+1}.$$

Corollary 4.49 implies that there is a natural homotopy

$$H : \overline{W}A^i \otimes \Delta^1 \to A^{i+1}$$

in the category of simplicial abelian groups from σ to $\sigma h f$.

Recall from [46] that the category of simplicial abelian groups carries a simplicial closed model structure in which the fibrations (respectively weak equivalences) are those simplicial abelian group homomorphisms which are fibrations (respectively weak equivalences) as maps of simplicial sets. In particular, a map $f : A \to B$ of simplicial abelian groups is a fibration if and only if the associated map $Nf : NA \to NB$ of normalized chain complexes (see the next section) is surjective in degrees above 0.

The normalized complex $N\overline{W}A$ is naturally isomorphic to the shifted complex $NA[-1]$ given by $NA[-1]_i = NA_{i-1}$. It therefore follows from the Dold-Kan categorical equivalence of simplicial abelian groups with chain complexes that the functor $\overline{W}$ has a right adjoint which preserves fibrations and trivial fibrations. It follows that the functor $\overline{W}$ preserves cofibrations and trivial cofibrations. The functor $A \mapsto S^1 \otimes A$ also preserves cofibrations and trivial cofibrations; in this case the right adjoint is the ordinary loop space functor $B \mapsto \mathbf{hom}_*(S^1, B)$.

Every Kan spectrum object A may be replaced up to strict weak equivalence by a Kan spectrum object which is levelwise cofibrant in the category of simplicial abelian groups. In effect, factorize the map $0 \to A^i$ as a composite

$$0 \to B^i \xrightarrow{\pi} A^i,$$

where B^i is cofibrant and π is a trivial fibration. Then $\overline{W}B^i$ is cofibrant, and so there is a dotted arrow in the category of simplicial abelian groups making the following diagram commute:

$$\begin{array}{ccc}
\overline{W}B^i & \dashrightarrow & B^{i+1} \\
{\scriptstyle \overline{W}\pi} \downarrow & & \downarrow {\scriptstyle \pi} \\
\overline{W}A^i & \xrightarrow{\sigma} & A^{i+1}
\end{array}$$

There is a completely analogous statement and proof for ordinary spectrum objects of simplicial abelian groups. It is therefore harmless to replace the full strict homotopy categories in the statement of the theorem by the full subcategories on objects which are levelwise cofibrant: the functors h_* and f_* preserve them.

But then there's a telescope construction for levelwise cofibrant Kan spectrum objects B, yielding strict natural weak equivalences

$$B \overset{\simeq}{\leftarrow} TB \overset{H}{\underset{\simeq}{\longrightarrow}} f_* h_* B.$$

The construction is by analogy to the telescope construction given in the first chapter, keeping in mind that each map

$$B^i \overset{d^0}{\longrightarrow} B^i \otimes \Delta^1$$

is a trivial cofibration since B^i is cofibrant. Note that the telescope TB is levelwise cofibrant.

A similar story obtains for levelwise cofibrant spectrum objects A: there is a telescope construction within the category, giving strict natural weak equivalences

$$A \overset{\simeq}{\leftarrow} TA \overset{\simeq}{\longrightarrow} h_* f_* A. \qquad \blacksquare$$

We are entitled to construct suspension spectrum objects for simplicial abelian groups A, from two points of view. Theorem 4.52 will imply that the two constructions are equivalent.

In particular, there is a *suspension spectrum object* $\Sigma_{ab}^\infty A$ associated to any simplicial abelian group A, in the category of spectrum objects in simplicial abelian groups. The definition is the following:

$$\Sigma_{ab}^\infty A^n = S^1 \otimes \ldots S^1 \otimes A \cong S^n \otimes A.$$

The spectrum associated to $\Sigma_{ab}^\infty A$ is an Ω-spectrum, in view of

LEMMA 4.53. *Suppose that A is an arbitrary simplicial abelian group. Then the canonical map* can : $S^1 \wedge A \to S^1 \otimes A$ *induces a weak equivalence*

$$\mathrm{can}_* : A \to \mathbf{hom}_*(S^1, S^1 \otimes A).$$

PROOF: The map can_* is the pointed simplicial set theoretic adjoint of the map can, and it is a natural homomorphism of simplicial abelian groups. Furthermore, the functors on both sides of the natural transformation can_* preserve fibre sequences. The path-loop sequence

$$0 \to \Omega A \to PA \to A$$

is such a fibre sequence, so that the map

$$\pi_1 A \xrightarrow{\;\text{can}_*\;} \pi_1 \mathbf{hom}_*(S^1, S^1 \otimes A)$$

which is induced by can_* is isomorphic to the map induced on the π_0 level for some other simplicial abelian group, namely

$$\Omega A = \mathbf{hom}_*(S^1, A).$$

This technique can be iterated, so it suffices to show that can_* induces an isomorphism in π_0 for all simplicial abelian groups A.

Now consider the diagram

$$
\begin{array}{ccc}
A & \xrightarrow{\;\text{can}_*\;} & \mathbf{hom}_*(S^1, S^1 \otimes A) \\
\Big\downarrow{\scriptstyle p} & & \Big\downarrow{\scriptstyle p_*} \\
K(\pi_0 A, 0) & \xrightarrow[\;\text{can}_*\;]{} & \mathbf{hom}_*(S^1, S^1 \otimes K(\pi_0 A, 0)),
\end{array}
$$

where p is the canonical map. Both vertical maps are isomorphisms in π_0, so it suffices to prove that can_* induces a π_0 isomorphism for constant simplicial abelian groups.

The image of $a \in \pi_0 A = K(\pi_0 A, 0)_0$ under can_* is the composite map

$$S^1 \cong S^1 \wedge \Delta^0_+ \xrightarrow{\;S^1 \wedge a\;} S^1 \wedge K(\pi_0 A, 0) \xrightarrow{\;\text{can}\;} S^1 \otimes K(\pi_0 A, 0) \cong B(\pi_0 A),$$

which is the loop corresponding to $a \in B(\pi_0 A)_1$. It follows that the π_0 level map induced by can_* in this case is the the canonical isomorphism

$$\pi_0 A \cong \pi_1 B(\pi_0 A). \qquad \blacksquare$$

Any simplicial abelian group A give rises to a suspension object

$$A, \; \overline{W}A, \; \overline{W}^2 A, \; \ldots,$$

in the category of Kan spectrum objects in simplicial abelian groups, which will be denoted by $H(A)$. In the case where B is an abelian group, the notation $H(B)$ will also denote the Kan spectrum object $H(K(B, 0))$, since the associated spectrum (along with the notation for it) is an old friend, namely the *Eilenberg-Mac Lane spectrum* associated to the abelian group B.

Lemma 4.54. *There is a natural strict weak equivalence*

$$\Sigma^\infty A \xrightarrow{\alpha} h_* H(A),$$

for arbitrary simplicial abelian groups A.

Proof: The map α is defined levelwise inductively by the requirement that the diagram

$$
\begin{array}{ccc}
S^1 \otimes S^n \otimes A & \xrightarrow{\;\;\sigma\;\;}_{\cong} & S^{n+1} \otimes A \\
{\scriptstyle S^1 \otimes \alpha} \downarrow & & \downarrow {\scriptstyle \alpha} \\
S^1 \otimes \overline{W}^n A & \xrightarrow{\;\;h\;\;} & \overline{W}^{n+1} A
\end{array}
$$

commutes, where we note that

$$h : S^1 \otimes \overline{W}^n A \to \overline{W}^{n+1} A$$

is the bonding map for $h_* H(A)$. h is a weak equivalence of simplicial abelian groups, and the functor $B \mapsto S^1 \otimes B$ preserves weak equivalences of simplicial abelian groups, so α is a weak equivalence at all levels. ∎

Corollary 4.55. *The spectrum associated to the Kan suspension object $H(A)$ is an Ω-spectrum, for all simplicial abelian groups A.*

Remark 4.56. The natural map $f : \overline{W} A \to S^1 \otimes A$ which appears in the proof of Theorem 4.52 can be used to construct a natural strict weak equivalence of Kan spectrum objects

$$H(A) \xrightarrow{\beta} f_* \Sigma^\infty_{ab} A.$$

The proof is the same as that for Lemma 4.54. ∎

4.6. Stable Dold-Kan theory

Suppose that A is a simplicial abelian group, and recall that the *normalized chain complex NA* has

$$NA_n = \bigcap_{i=0}^{n-1} ker(d_i) \subset A_n,$$

and differentials defined by

$$NA_n \xrightarrow{(-1)^n d_n} NA_{n-1}.$$

The assignment $A \mapsto NA$ is a functor from the category $\mathbf{S}Ab$ of simplicial abelian groups to the category Ch_+ of chain complexes.

Every simplicial structure map $d^* : A_n \to A_m$ corresponding to a monomorphism $d : \mathbf{m} \hookrightarrow \mathbf{n}$ of ordinal numbers takes NA_n into NA_k. In fact, such maps are 0 unless d is of the form $d = d^n : \mathbf{n} - \mathbf{1} \to \mathbf{n}$. Put a different way, suppose given a collection of abelian group homomorphisms

$$\partial : C_n \to C_{n-1}, \ \ n \geq 0.$$

Associate to each ordinal number $\mathbf{n}$ the group C_n, and map each ordinal number monomorphism to an abelian group homomorphisms by the rule

$$d \mapsto \begin{cases} 0 & \text{if } d \text{ is not some } d^n, \text{ and} \\ C_n \xrightarrow{(-1)^n \partial} C_{n-1} & \text{if } d = d^n. \end{cases}$$

Then we get a contravariant functor on the category of ordinal number monomorphisms from such an assignment if and only if we started with a chain complex.

There is a simplicial abelian group whose n-simplices have the form

$$\bigoplus_{\mathbf{n} \twoheadrightarrow \mathbf{k}} NA_k.$$

Note that the direct sum is indexed over all ordinal number epimorphisms whose source is $\mathbf{n}$. The map

$$\theta^* : \bigoplus_{\mathbf{n} \twoheadrightarrow \mathbf{k}} NA_k \to \bigoplus_{\mathbf{m} \twoheadrightarrow \mathbf{r}} NA_r$$

associated to the ordinal number map $\theta : \mathbf{m} \to \mathbf{n}$ is given on the summand corresponding to $\sigma : \mathbf{n} \to \mathbf{k}$ by the composite

$$NA_k \xrightarrow{d^*} NA_s \xrightarrow{in_t} \bigoplus_{\mathbf{m} \twoheadrightarrow \mathbf{r}} NA_r,$$

where

$$\mathbf{m} \xrightarrow{t} \mathbf{s} \xrightarrow{d} \mathbf{k}$$

is the (unique) epi-monic factorization of the composite

$$\mathbf{m} \xrightarrow{\theta} \mathbf{n} \xrightarrow{\sigma} \mathbf{k}.$$

Note as well that there is a morphism of simplicial abelian groups which is given in degree n by the map

$$\Psi : \bigoplus_{\mathbf{n} \twoheadrightarrow \mathbf{k}} NA_k \to A_n,$$

which is defined at the summand corresponding to $\sigma : \mathbf{n} \to \mathbf{k}$ by the composite

$$NA_k \hookrightarrow A_k \xrightarrow{\sigma^*} A_n.$$

More generally, there is a functor

$$\Gamma : Ch_+ \to \mathbf{S}Ab$$

from chain complexes to simplicial abelian groups, with

$$\Gamma(C)_n = \bigoplus_{\mathbf{n} \to \mathbf{k}} C_k$$

for a chain complex C, and with simplicial structure maps given by the recipe above. Also, the map Ψ defines a natural transformation

$$\Psi : \Gamma N A \to A,$$

defined on simplicial abelian groups A.

The following result is the well known theorem of Dold and Kan which relates chain complexes to simplicial abelian groups [37]:

THEOREM 4.57 DOLD-KAN. *The functors $N : \mathbf{S}Ab \to Ch_+$ and $\Gamma : Ch_+ \to \mathbf{S}Ab$ are part of the data for an equivalence of categories.*

This result is proved, in part, by showing that $\Psi : \Gamma N A \to A$ is a natural isomorphism.

There are natural isomorphisms

$$N\overline{W}A_n \cong NA_{n-1}.$$

Furthermore, these isomorphisms fit into a commutative diagram

$$
\begin{array}{ccc}
N\overline{W}A_n & \xrightarrow{\cong} & NA_{n-1} \\
\partial \downarrow & & \downarrow (-1)^n d_{n-1} \\
N\overline{W}A_{n-1} & \xrightarrow{\cong} & NA_{n-2}
\end{array}
$$

It follows that there is a natural isomorphism of chain complexes

$$N\overline{W}A \cong NA[-1], \tag{4.58}$$

where $NA[-1]$ is the chain complex which is 0 in degree 0 and is otherwise defined by $NA[-1]_i = NA_{i-1}$ for $i > 0$.

The category Ch_+ of chain complexes imbeds fully faithfully in the category Ch of $\mathbb{Z}$-graded chain complexes: one simply identifies a chain complex C_* with the $\mathbb{Z}$-graded object

$$\cdots \xrightarrow{\partial} C_1 \xrightarrow{\partial} C_0 \to 0 \to 0 \to \cdots .$$

Observe that any $\mathbb{Z}$-graded chain complex D can be translated by any integer n, giving a complex $D[n]$ with

$$D[n]_i = D_{n+i},$$

and that the inclusion of the ordinary chain complex category Ch_+ into the $\mathbb{Z}$-graded category Ch respects translation by negative integers.

A *spectrum object C in chain complexes* consists of ordinary chain complexes C^i, $i \geq 0$, (ie. members of Ch_+) and chain complex maps

$$\sigma : C^i[-1] \to C^{i+1}.$$

A map $f : C \to D$ of spectrum objects in chain complexes consists of chain complex morphisms $f^i : C^i \to D^i$ which preserve structure. The resulting category will be denoted by $\mathbf{Spt}(Ch_+)$. From what we have seen already, the Dold-Kan functors N and Γ induce functors

$$N : \mathbf{Spt}_{Kan}(Ab) \to \mathbf{Spt}(Ch_+),$$

and

$$\Gamma : \mathbf{Spt}(Ch_+) \to \mathbf{Spt}_{Kan}(Ab),$$

giving an equivalence of categories between Kan spectrum objects in simplicial abelian groups and spectrum objects in chain complexes.

Write C for both an ordinary chain complex C and its associated $\mathbb{Z}$-graded complex. Now suppose that D is a spectrum object in Ch_+. Then the associated maps

$$D^i[-1] \xrightarrow{\sigma} D^{i+1}$$

of $\mathbb{Z}$-graded chain complexes can be identified with (adjoint) maps

$$D^i \xrightarrow{\sigma} D^{i+1}[1],$$

and we can form the $\mathbb{Z}$-graded chain complex QD, which is defined to be the colimit in Ch of the diagram

$$D^0 \to D^1[1] \to D^2[2] \to \cdots .$$

This construction is natural in spectrum objects D, and gives a functor

$$Q : \mathbf{Spt}(Ch_+) \to Ch.$$

The functor Q leads to a notion of stable equivalence for spectrum objects in Ch_+: a map $f : C \to D$ of spectrum objects in Ch_+ is a *stable equivalence* if the associated map

$$Qf : QC \to QD$$

of $\mathbb{Z}$-graded chain complexes is a homology isomorphism.

Suppose that E is a $\mathbb{Z}$-graded chain complex, and let n be an integer. The complex $G_n E$ is the complex defined by setting

$$G_n E_i = \begin{cases} E_i & \text{if } i > n, \\ ker\partial & \text{if } i = n, \text{ and} \\ 0 & \text{if } i < n. \end{cases}$$

Plainly, there are canonical maps $\tau : G_n E \to E$ and $\sigma : G_n E \to G_{n-1} E$ such that the diagrams

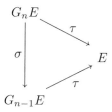

commute. Furthermore, the induced map

$$\tau_* : \varinjlim_{n \in \mathbb{Z}} G_n E \to E$$

is a natural isomorphism.

There is a functor $G_* : Ch \to \mathbf{Spt}(Ch_+)$, which is defined by setting

$$G_* E^i = G_{-i} E[-i],$$

for $i \geq 0$. The bonding homomorphisms of $G_* E$ are the maps

$$G_{-i} E[-i][-1] = G_{-i} E[-i-1] \xrightarrow{\sigma[-i-1]} G_{i-1} E[-i-1].$$

Observe that this construction is rigged in such a way that the maps τ induce a natural isomorphism

$$\tau_* : QG_* E \xrightarrow{\cong} E,$$

for all $\mathbb{Z}$-graded chain complexes E.

Suppose that C is a spectrum object in Ch_+. Then the canonical maps

$$C^i[i] \to QC$$

of $\mathbb{Z}$-graded chain complexes induce maps

$$C^i[i] \to G_{-i}QC,$$

giving maps

$$\eta^i : C^i \to G_{-i}QC[-i]$$

of ordinary chain complexes. These maps are the components of a map of spectrum objects

$$\eta : C \to G_*QC,$$

which map is a natural stable equivalence, since $Q\eta$ is an isomorphism of $\mathbb{Z}$-graded chain complexes.

The stable homotopy category of spectrum objects in Ch_+ is obtained from $\mathbf{Spt}(Ch_+)$ by formally inverting the stable equivalences, while the homotopy category (aka. derived category) of $\mathbb{Z}$-graded chain complexes is constructed by formally inverting the homology isomorphisms of Ch. We have shown

THEOREM 4.59. *The functors Q and G_* induce an equivalence of the stable homotopy category of spectrum objects in Ch_+ with the homotopy category of $\mathbb{Z}$-graded chain complexes.*

Putting this result together with the Dold-Kan equivalence between Kan spectrum objects in simplicial abelian groups and spectrum objects in ordinary chain complexes, and with Theorem 4.52 gives

COROLLARY 4.60. *The stable homotopy category associated to the category $\mathbf{Spt}(Ab)$ of spectrum objects in simplicial abelian groups is equivalent to the homotopy category associated to $\mathbb{Z}$-graded chain complexes.*

4.7. Postnikov towers

LEMMA 4.61. *Suppose that X is a pointed simplicial set. Then there is a natural pushout diagram*

$$
\begin{array}{ccc}
sk_kX & \xrightarrow{\;\;i\;\;} & C_*sk_kX \\
{\scriptstyle j}\big\downarrow & & \big\downarrow \\
sk_{k+1}X & \xrightarrow[sk_{k+1}i]{} & sk_{k+1}C_*X,
\end{array}
$$

where j is the canonical inclusion of skeleta.

PROOF: Suppose that $s : \mathbf{r} \twoheadrightarrow \mathbf{t}$ is a surjective ordinal number map, and that $r < n$. Then the composite

$$\mathbf{r} \xrightarrow{s} \mathbf{t} \xrightarrow{d^0} \mathbf{t} + \mathbf{1}$$

extends uniquely to a surjective ordinal number map $\tilde{s} : \mathbf{n} \twoheadrightarrow \mathbf{t} + \mathbf{1}$ such that $\tilde{s}(i) = 0$ for $0 \leq i \leq n - r - 1$. Furthermore, the square of ordinal number maps

$$
\begin{array}{ccc}
\mathbf{r} & \xrightarrow{\;s\;} & \mathbf{t} \\
{\scriptstyle (d^0)^{n-r}} \downarrow & & \downarrow {\scriptstyle d^0} \\
\mathbf{n} & \xrightarrow[\;\tilde{s}\;]{} & \mathbf{t} + \mathbf{1}
\end{array}
$$

is a pullback. One therefore has a commutative diagram

$$
\begin{array}{ccc}
X_t & \hookleftarrow & C_* X_{t+1} \\
{\scriptstyle s^*} \downarrow & & \downarrow {\scriptstyle \tilde{s}^*} \\
X_r & \hookleftarrow & C_* X_n
\end{array}
$$

in which the horizontal maps are canonical inclusions of the respective wedge summands. The image of $C_* sk_k X$ in $C_* X$ is therefore contained in $sk_{k+1} C_* X$, so the statement of the Lemma makes sense.

Suppose that $s : \mathbf{n} \twoheadrightarrow \mathbf{r}$ is a surjective ordinal number morphism, with $r \leq k + 1$. The $s^* : C_* X_r \to C_* X_n$ is determined on the wedge summands X_i of $C_* X_r$ by the diagrams

$$
\begin{array}{ccc}
X_i & \xrightarrow{\;t^*\;} & X_j \\
\uparrow & & \uparrow \\
C_* X_r & \xrightarrow[\;s^*\;]{} & C_* X_n
\end{array}
$$

which are induced by the pullback diagrams

$$
\begin{array}{ccc}
\mathbf{j} & \xrightarrow{\;t\;} & \mathbf{i} \\
{\scriptstyle (d^0)^{n-j}} \downarrow & & \downarrow {\scriptstyle (d^0)^{r-i}} \\
\mathbf{n} & \xrightarrow[\;s\;]{} & \mathbf{r}
\end{array}
$$

in the ordinal number category. In particular s^* takes values in

$$sk_{k+1}X_n \vee sk_k X_{n-1} \vee \cdots \vee sk_k X_0,$$

so that

$$sk_{k+1}C_*X \subset sk_{k+1}X \cup C_* sk_k X$$

in C_*X. ∎

COROLLARY 4.62. *Suppose that X is a pointed simplicial set. Then the inclusion $C_* sk_k X \hookrightarrow sk_{k+1}C_*X$ induces a natural isomorphism*

$$\Sigma sk_k X \cong sk_{k+1}\Sigma X$$

of pointed simplicial sets.

Suppose that Y is an arbitrary simplicial set. The nth coskeleton $cosk_n Y$ is defined to be the simplicial set having m-simplices

$$cosk_n Y_m = \hom(sk_n \Delta^m, Y).$$

There is a natural restriction map

$$\mathrm{res} : Y \to cosk_n Y,$$

which is defined on the level of m-simplices by sending a simplex $x : \Delta^m \to Y$ to the composite

$$sk_n \Delta^m \subset \Delta^m \xrightarrow{x} Y.$$

Form the pullback diagram

$$
\begin{array}{ccc}
R_n Y & \xrightarrow{\;pr_R\;} & Y \\
{\scriptstyle pr_L}\downarrow & & \downarrow{\scriptstyle \mathrm{res}} \\
Y & \xrightarrow[\mathrm{res}]{} & cosk_n Y.
\end{array}
$$

Then $R_n Y$ is the subcomplex of $Y \times Y$ consisting of all pairs of simplices (x, y) such that x and y restrict to the same map on n-skeleta, and the maps pr_L and pr_R are the restrictions of projection onto the left and right factors, respectively, of $Y \times Y$.

The simplicial set $P_n Y$ is defined by requiring that the following diagram is a coequalizer in the simplicial set category:

$$R_n Y \xrightarrow[\;pr_R\;]{\;pr_L\;} Y \xrightarrow{\;\pi\;} P_n Y.$$

$P_n Y$ is the nth *Postnikov section* of the simplicial set Y [37, p.32]. The construction just given demonstrates (in categorical terms) that the map $\pi : Y \to P_n Y$ is the coequalizer of the kernel pair associated to the restriction map $\mathrm{res} : Y \to cosk_n Y$. The main features of Postnikov sections can be summarized as follows:

LEMMA 4.63. *Suppose that Y is a Kan complex.*

(1) *The map $\pi : Y \to P_n Y$ is a fibration, and $P_n Y$ is a Kan complex.*
(2) *The map π induces isomorphisms*

$$\pi_j(Y, y) \cong \pi_j(P_n Y, y),$$

for $j \leq n$ and for any choice of base point y of Y, and $\pi_j(P_n Y, y) = 0$ for $j > n$ and all choices of base points.

(3) *There is a commutative diagram*

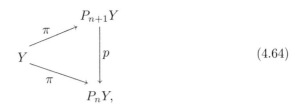

$$(4.64)$$

and the map p is a fibration.

The collection of maps

$$\cdots \xrightarrow{p} P_2 Y \xrightarrow{p} P_1 Y \xrightarrow{p} Y$$

is usually called the *Postnikov tower* of the simplicial set Y. If Y is a pointed simplicial set, then the entire construction is pointed in a natural way. The purpose of this section is to extend this tower to a construction for Kan spectra, essentially following the methods of [27].

Suppose that $x : \Delta^m \to X$ is a simplex of a pointed simplicial set X. Define the *suspension* Σx of x to be the composite

$$\Delta^{m+1} \cong C_* \Delta^m_+ \to \Sigma \Delta^m_+ \xrightarrow{\Sigma x_+} \Sigma X.$$

Suppose now that x and y are two m-simplices of X which have the same restriction to n-skeleta, so that the diagram

$$
\begin{array}{ccc}
sk_n \Delta^m & \hookrightarrow & \Delta^m \\
\uparrow & & \downarrow x \\
\Delta^m & \xrightarrow{\quad y \quad} & X
\end{array}
$$

commutes. Then it follows from Lemma 4.61 that the diagram

$$
\begin{array}{ccc}
sk_{n+1}\Delta^{m+1} & \lhook\joinrel\longrightarrow & \Delta^{m+1} \\
\downarrow & & \downarrow{\scriptstyle \Sigma x} \\
\Delta^{m+1} & \xrightarrow{\ \Sigma y\ } & \Sigma X
\end{array}
$$

commutes, and so the assignment

$$(x, y) \mapsto (\Sigma x, \Sigma y)$$

defines a pointed map

$$\Sigma R_n X \xrightarrow{\ \Psi\ } R_{n+1}\Sigma X$$

such that $pr_L \Psi = \Sigma pr_L$ and $pr_R \Psi = \Sigma pr_R$. It follows that there is a pointed natural map

$$\Sigma P_n X \xrightarrow{\ \Psi_*\ } P_{n+1}\Sigma X,$$

such that the diagrams

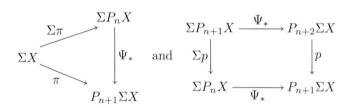

commute, for each n. Note finally that the Kan suspension ΣX has only one vertex, whereas the simplices of $P_0 Y$ for any simplicial set Y are determined by their vertices. It follows that

$$P_0 \Sigma X = *,$$

for all pointed simplicial sets X. For this reason, one decrees that, for pointed simplicial sets X, the Postnikov sections $P_n X$ for $n < 0$ are copies of the one point simplicial set $* = \Delta^0$. This is enough to prove

PROPOSITION 4.65. *Suppose that X is a Kan spectrum, and let n be an integer. There is a Kan spectrum $P_n X$ with space at level i given by*

$$(P_n X)^i = P_{n+i} X^i,$$

and with bonding maps defined in terms of the bonding maps $\sigma : \Sigma X^n \to X^{n+1}$ by the composites

$$\Sigma P_{n+i} X^i \xrightarrow{\Psi_*} P_{n+i+1} \Sigma X^i \xrightarrow{P_{n+i+1}\sigma} P_{n+i+1} X^{i+1}.$$

The pointed maps $\pi : X^i \to P_{n+i} X^i$ define a map of Kan spectra $\pi : X \to P_n X$. This map π is a strict fibration if X is strictly fibrant and induces isomorphisms in stable homotopy groups

$$\pi_j X \cong \pi_j P_n X, \quad j \le n,$$

whereas

$$\pi_j P_n X = 0 \quad \text{for } j > n.$$

The maps $P_{n+1+i} X^i \xrightarrow{p} P_{n+i} X^i$ induce a map of Kan spectra

$$p : P_{n+1} X \to P_n X,$$

and the diagrams

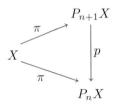

commute.

The Postnikov section construction also makes homotopical sense for simplicial abelian groups. Suppose that A is a simplicial abelian group, and let $K_n A$ be the kernel of the simplicial abelian group homomorphism res : $A \to cosk_n A$. Let $i : K_n A \to A$ denote the inclusion of $K_n A$ in A. Then there is a short exact sequence of simplicial abelian groups

$$0 \to K_n A \xrightarrow{i} A \xrightarrow{\pi} P_n A \to 0,$$

which gives a definition of $P_n A$ that is internal to the category. Applying the normalized chains construction gives

$$NK_n A_i = \begin{cases} 0 & \text{if } i \le n, \\ ZNA_{n+1} & \text{if } i = n+1, \text{ and} \\ NA_i & \text{if } i > n+1. \end{cases}$$

The group ZNA_{n+1} is the kernel of the boundary homomorphism

$$(-1)^{n+1}d_{n+1} : NA_{n+1} \to NA_n.$$

The normalized chains functor is exact, and so

$$NP_nA_i = \begin{cases} NA_i & \text{if } i \leq n, \\ NA_{n+1}/ZNA_{n+1} & \text{if } i = n+1, \text{ and} \\ 0 & \text{if } i > n+1. \end{cases}$$

The Postnikov tower construction therefore specializes to the first thing that one would think of as an analogue for chain complexes. The category of chain complexes is the right place to construct Postnikov sections for Kan spectrum objects in simplicial abelian groups, via the Dold-Kan equivalence for these objects.

Suppose that X is a strictly fibrant Kan spectrum with one non-trivial stable homotopy group $A = \pi_n X$. There is a natural isomorphism

$$\tilde{\mathbb{Z}}\Sigma Y \cong \overline{W}\tilde{\mathbb{Z}}Y,$$

valid for all pointed simplicial sets Y, which implies that the free abelian group functor associates to X a Kan spectrum object in simplicial abelian groups $\tilde{\mathbb{Z}}X$. Furthermore, the canonical map

$$\eta_* : X \to \tilde{\mathbb{Z}}X$$

induces an isomorphism $\pi_n X \cong \pi_n \tilde{\mathbb{Z}}X$, by the Hurewicz theorem. The abelian category Postnikov section map

$$\tilde{\mathbb{Z}}X \xrightarrow{\pi} P_n\tilde{\mathbb{Z}}X$$

therefore induces a stable equivalence, namely the composite

$$X \xrightarrow{\eta_*} \tilde{\mathbb{Z}}X \xrightarrow{\pi} P_n\tilde{\mathbb{Z}}X,$$

of X with a Kan spectrum object in simplicial abelian groups that has one non-vanishing homotopy group.

Any $\mathbb{Z}$-graded chain complex C with one non-trivial homology group $A = H_n C$ may be replaced up to quasi-isomorphism by the complex $A[n]$ which consists of the group A concentrated in degree n. In effect, C is weakly equivalent, via a canonical inclusion, to the complex $K_{n-1}C$, which is given by

$$\cdots \xrightarrow{\partial} C_{n+1} \xrightarrow{\partial} Z_n \to 0 \to \cdots,$$

but then there is a homology equivalence of chain complexes given by the map

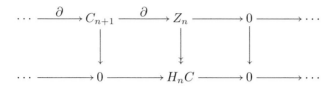

Theorem 4.59 therefore implies that $P_n\tilde{\mathbb{Z}}X$ is stably equivalent, in the category of Kan spectrum objects in simplicial abelian groups, to the shifted Eilenberg-Mac Lane spectrum $H(A)[n]$. We have therefore proved

PROPOSITION 4.66. *If X is a strictly fibrant Kan spectrum which has only one non-vanishing stable homotopy group $\pi_n X$, then X is stably equivalent to a shifted Eilenberg-Mac Lane spectrum $H(\pi_n X)[n]$.*

COROLLARY 4.67. *A strictly fibrant spectrum Z having one non-vanishing stable homotopy group is stably equivalent to a shifted Eilenberg-Mac Lane spectrum.*

PROOF: Use the fact that Z is naturally strictly equivalent to the spectrum $h_* S|Z|$, by Proposition 4.40. ∎

The Postnikov tower construction has been defined up to now only for Kan spectra. The nth *Postnikov section* $P_n Z$ is defined for an ordinary strictly fibrant spectrum Z by setting

$$P_n Z = h_* P_n S|Z|.$$

More generally the nth Postnikov section $P_n Y$ of an arbitrary spectrum Y is defined to be the nth Postnikov section $P_n Y_{Kan}$ of the strictly fibrant model of Y. This construction has all of the properties that we shall need:

LEMMA 4.68.

(1) $P_n Z$ *is a strictly fibrant spectrum with $\pi_j P_n Z = 0$ for $j > n$.*

(2) *There is a natural map $\pi : Z \to P_n Z$ in the strict homotopy category, which induces isomorphisms in stable homotopy groups*

$$\pi_j Z \cong \pi_j P_n Z$$

for $j \leq n$.

(3) *There is a canonical map* $p : P_{n+1}Z \to P_n Z$ *which fits into a commutative triangle*

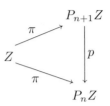

Furthermore all of these constructions are natural in Z.

Another application of the theory arises from a relation between the Postnikov section construction and smash products of spectra, via the following result:

LEMMA 4.69. *Suppose that* X *and* Y *are strictly fibrant spectra, and that* Y *is connective. Then the map* $\pi : X \to P_n X$ *induces a stable equivalence of spectra*

$$P_n(X \wedge Y) \xrightarrow[\simeq]{P_n(\pi \wedge Y)} P_n(P_n X \wedge Y).$$

The nth *Postnikov section* $P_n Z$ of an n-fold spectrum Z is defined to be the nth Postnikov section $P_n d(Z)$ of the associated diagonal spectrum $d(Z)$.

PROOF: Let $F_n X$ denote the strict (hence stable) homotopy fibre of the restriction map $r : X \to P_n X$, and use Lemma 4.1 to identify the fibre sequence

$$F_n X \xrightarrow{i} X \xrightarrow{r} P_n X$$

up to stable equivalence with a cofibre sequence. Then Lemma 1.28 and Proposition 4.11 (or Lemma 2.20) together imply that there is a cofibre sequence of bispectra of the form

$$F_n X \wedge Y \xrightarrow{i \wedge Y} X \wedge Y \xrightarrow{r \wedge Y} P_n X \wedge Y.$$

It is enough to show that the bispectrum $F_n X \wedge Y$ is n-connected, for then the map

$$r \wedge Y : X \wedge Y \to P_n X \wedge Y$$

induces an isomorphism in stable homotopy groups up to degree n.
    The space F_n^i sits in a fibre sequence

$$F_n^i \to X^i \xrightarrow{\pi} P_{n+i} X^i,$$

and is therefore $(n+i)$-connected. One is assuming that Y is connective, so the spectral sequence

$$E_2^{p,q} = \tilde{H}_p(F_n^i, \pi_q Y) \Rightarrow \pi_{p+q}(F_n^i \wedge Y)$$

of Lemma 4.11 can be used to show that the spectrum $F_n^i \wedge Y$ is $(n+i)$-connected. The proof of Lemma 1.28 implies that the stable homotopy groups of the spectrum $F_n X \wedge Y$ have the form

$$\pi_j(F_n X \wedge Y) = \varinjlim_i \pi_{j+i}(F_n X^i \wedge Y),$$

and so

$$\pi_j(F_n X \wedge Y) = 0$$

if $j \le n$. ∎

COROLLARY 4.70. *Suppose that X and Y are spectra, Y is connective, and that*

$$\phi : X \wedge Y \to Z$$

is a map of bispectra. Then ϕ naturally induces a map

$$\phi_* : P_n X \wedge Y \to P_n Z,$$

in the ordinary stable category, which fits into a commmutative diagram

$$
\begin{array}{ccc}
X \wedge Y & \xrightarrow{\phi} & Z \\
{\scriptstyle \pi \wedge Y}\downarrow & & \downarrow{\scriptstyle \pi} \\
P_n X \wedge Y & \xrightarrow[\phi_*]{} & P_n Z
\end{array}
$$

in the stable category.

PROOF: Use the diagram

$$
\begin{array}{ccccc}
P_n X \wedge Y & \xleftarrow{\pi \wedge Y} & X \wedge Y & \xrightarrow{\phi} & Z \\
{\scriptstyle \pi}\downarrow & & {\scriptstyle \pi}\downarrow & & \downarrow{\scriptstyle r} \\
P_n(P_n X \wedge Y) & \xleftarrow[\simeq]{} & P_n(X \wedge Y) & \xrightarrow[P_n \phi]{} & P_n Z
\end{array}
$$

The map ϕ_* is the composite

$$P_n X \wedge Y \xrightarrow{\pi} P_n(P_n X \wedge Y) \xleftarrow{\simeq} P_n(X \wedge Y) \xrightarrow{P_n \phi} P_n Z$$

in the stable category. ∎

COROLLARY 4.71. *Suppose that X and Y are spectra such that X is n-connected and Y is m-connected. Then the smash product $X \wedge Y$ is $(n+m+1)$-connected.*

PROOF: This is a corollary of the proof of Lemma 4.69, in which the current statement is demonstrated for the case $m = -1$. It follows that

$$X \wedge (Y[-m-1]) \simeq (X \wedge Y)[-m-1]$$

is n-connected, so that $X \wedge Y$ is $(n + m + 1)$-connected. ∎

Chapter 5. K-theory presheaves

The first part of this chapter addresses the problem of explicitly constructing smash product pairings of K-theory spectra which arise from tensor products over all small diagrams of schemes. The existence of cup product structures for K-theory presheaves of spectra is a consequence, as are the cup product structures on the associated generalized étale cohomological invariants that we shall meet in subsequent chapters.

The main technical problem to overcome is that K-theory is not functorial on schemes. It does, however, arise from a pseudo-functor at the fundamental categorical level of vector bundles on schemes, and this structure can be analysed successfully with supercoherence theory [28]. This analysis must be combined with Waldhausen's multiple $S.$-construction and a suitable notion of bilinear map of symmetric monoidal categories to achieve the desired effect.

Supercoherence and Waldhausen's theory both seem to come equipped with an irreducible large amount of verbiage, and this is reflected in the length of this chapter. The extreme generality of the end, however, justifies the means: any biexact pairing

$$A \times B \to C$$

(like tensor product) induces a smash product pairing of spectra

$$KA \wedge KB \to KC.$$

More generally, any pseudo-natural biexact pairing

$$A_i \times B_i \to C_i$$

defined for i in some index category I gives rise to a functorial cup product pairing

$$KA_i \wedge KB_i \to KC_i,$$

once we've agreed that homotopy coherent diagrams like $i \mapsto KA_i$ have been straightened out first on the categorical level with supercoherence theory. It is a general rule of thumb that homotopy coherence problems are really categorical coherence problems in this game, "the game" being the chain of reasoning leading to the theorems in the last chapter of this book.

These results appear in the third section of this chapter, along with their consequences for K-theory presheaves of spectra. The first section contains a construction of the K-theory presheaf of spectra and its Waldhausen-style deloopings. The second section is a general description of the smash product pairings of spectra which arise from bilinear maps of symmetric monoidal categories, and their n-fold and pseudo-functorial analogues.

Suppose that L/k is a finite Galois extension with Galois group G, and let i denote the inclusion $k \subset L$. Restriction of scalars along i defines an exact functor $i_* : \mathcal{P}(L) \to \mathcal{P}(k)$, which induces the K-theory transfer $i_* : K(L) \to K(k)$. The composite

$$K(L) \xrightarrow{i_*} K(k) \xrightarrow{i^*} K(L)$$

is what I call the K-*theory norm*. It is well known that this map coincides in the stable category with the map which is the sum over all $g \in G$ of the induced maps $g^* : K(L) \to K(L)$ — in fact, this is evidently true on the categorical level on account of the well known L-algebra isomorphism

$$L \otimes_k L \cong \prod_{g \in G} L.$$

The purpose of the last two sections of this chapter is to establish the deeper G-equivariance properties of this map.

The fourth section contains an investigation of various functoriality properties of the K-theory transfer. A transfer $\pi_* : K(B) \to K(A)$ is, more generally, defined by a restriction of scalars functor $\pi_* : \mathcal{P}(B) \to \mathcal{P}(A)$ for any ring homomorphism $\pi : A \to B$ which gives B the structure of a finitely generated projective A-module. The basic point of the first section is that π_* is pseudofunctorial in two directions with respect to pushouts of rings, up to canonical homotopy given by the standard base change isomorphism. These directions correspond to horizontal and vertical composition of commutative squares.

Applying this principle to the pushout diagrams

$$
\begin{array}{ccc}
k & \xrightarrow{\;1\;} & k \\
\downarrow{\scriptstyle i} & & \downarrow{\scriptstyle i} \\
L & \xrightarrow{\;g\;} & L
\end{array}
$$

that arise from the various $g \in G$ establishes that the transfer $i_* : K(L) \to K(k)$ is G-equivariant. Other consequences include the fact that this G-equivariant map is natural with respect to pushout diagrams of the form

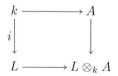

arising from k-algebras A, for the induced action of G on $L \otimes_k A$ and the trivial action on A. The same techniques are used to show that the projection formula is G-equivariant.

The K-theory norm

$$K(L) \xrightarrow{i_*} K(k) \xrightarrow{i^*} K(L)$$

is therefore $(G \times G)$-equivariant in the sense that any pair (g, h) of elements in the Galois group induces a commutative diagram

$$
\begin{array}{ccccc}
K(L) & \xrightarrow{\ i_* \ } & K(k) & \xrightarrow{\ i^* \ } & K(L) \\
{\scriptstyle g^*}\downarrow & & & & \downarrow{\scriptstyle h^*} \\
K(L) & \xrightarrow[\ i_* \ ]{} & K(k) & \xrightarrow[\ i^* \ ]{} & K(L).
\end{array}
$$

In other words, the K-theory norm is equivariant for the $(G \times G)$-action on the source which factors through projection on the left, and for the $(G \times G)$-action on the target which factors through projection on the right.

I call maps which behave this way join transformations. The abstract norm homomorphism

$$N : K(L) \to K(L)$$

that was introduced in Section 3.3 for the G-spectrum $K(L)$ is also a join transformation, and the point of the last section of this chapter is to show (Theorem 5.72) that the K-theory norm represents the same map as the abstract norm in the $(G \times G)$-equivariant stable category. If you forget about the equivariance, this is obvious, because the direct sum in the symmetric monoidal category $\mathcal{P}(L)$ induces the addition operation on the spectrum $K(L)$ by standard arguments. The $(G \times G)$-equivariance is, however, crucial to the applications of Chapter 7.

5.1. The K-theory presheaf of spectra and its deloopings

We shall begin by reprising some of the notation and results of [28]. Suppose that $X : I \to Sch$ is a functor from an index category I to the category Sch of schemes. Then each morphism $X(\alpha) : X(i) \to X(j)$ induces a pullback functor $\alpha^* : Mod\ X(j) \to Mod\ X(i)$ from the category of $O_{X(j)}$-modules to the category of $O_{X(i)}$-modules. The category of sheaves of $O_{X(j)}$-modules is a symmetric monoidal category under direct sum, and each α^* preserves finite direct sums and zero objects up to unique natural isomorphism, since α^* has a right adjoint, namely the direct image functor α_*. If

$$i \xrightarrow{\alpha} j \xrightarrow{\beta} k$$

is a pair of composeable arrows in I, then there is a canonical isomorphism $\alpha^* \beta^* \cong (\beta\alpha)^*$ — this is a consequence of adjointness and the functoriality of direct image. More generally, the same kind of argument implies that these canonical isomomorphisms fit together to define an I^{op}-indexed pseudo-functor $i \mapsto Mod\ X(i)$ which takes values in the category of symmetric monoidal categories [28, p.65]. This pseudo-functor restricts to a pseudo-functor $i \mapsto \mathcal{P}X(i)$ which takes values in the symmetric monoidal categories $\mathcal{P}X(i)$ of vector bundles on the schemes $X(i)$, and then applying the Quillen Q-construction yields a pseudo-functor $i \mapsto Q\mathcal{P}X(i)$, which I shall denote by $Q\mathcal{P}X$.

As in [28], Γ^o is the category of finite pointed sets and base point preserving functions, and $\mathbf{n}^+$ denotes the set $\{0, 1, \ldots n\}$, pointed by 0. It is a consequence of the Γ^o-supercoherence theorem [28, 2.11, also p.66] that any J-indexed pseudo-functor S in the category of symmetric monoidal categories gives rise to a pseudo-functor $\Gamma^o S : J \times \Gamma^o \dashrightarrow cat$. This pseudo-functor has the form

$$\Gamma^o S(i, \mathbf{n}^+) = \overbrace{S(i) \times \cdots \times S(i)}^{n \text{ factors}}.$$

Suppose in particular that T is a symmetric monoidal category. Although it's confusing in some cases, let 0 denote the identity object of T, and let $\oplus$ denote addition. Then [28, p.34] the category Γ^o is generated by the coface maps

$$d^i : \mathbf{n}^+ \to \mathbf{n+1}^+, \qquad 0 < i \le n+1,$$

the codegeneracies

$$s^j : \mathbf{n+1}^+ \to \mathbf{n}^+, \qquad 0 \le j \le n,$$

and the permutations

$$\omega : \mathbf{n}^+ \to \mathbf{n}^+, \qquad n \ge 0.$$

The pseudo-functor $\Gamma^o T$ is completely determined by its action on these maps, along with the natural isomorphisms intrinisic to the pseudo-functor structure. Furthermore, the corresponding functors in $\Gamma^o T$ have a particularly agreeable form. Suppose that $a_1, \ldots a_n$ are objects of of T; then the generating functors for $\Gamma^o T$ are defined by

$$d^i(a_n, \ldots, a_1) = (a_n, \ldots, a_i, 0, a_{i-1}, \ldots, a_1), \qquad 1 \le i \le n+1,$$

$$s^j(a_{n+1}, \ldots, a_1) = (a_{n+1}, \ldots, a_{j+1} \oplus a_j, \ldots, a_1) \qquad 1 \le j \le n,$$

and

$$s^0(a_{n+1}, \ldots a_1) = (a_{n+1}, \ldots, a_2),$$

while a permutation $\omega \in \Sigma_n$ induces the functor

$$\omega : T^{\times n} \to T^{\times n}$$

which permutes factors. It's even more good news that the apparent generalization of these definitions to diagrams of symmetric monoidal categories actually works.

Suppose that S is a J-indexed pseudo-functor in the category of symmetric monoidal categories as above, and recall from [28], [39] and elsewhere that the pseudo-functor $\Gamma^o S$ has associated to it a category $[\Gamma^o S]$ and a functor

$$\pi_{\Gamma^o S} : [\Gamma^o S] \to J \times \Gamma^o.$$

This is a special case of the *Grothendieck construction*. The objects of the category $[\Gamma^o S]$ are pairs $((i, \mathbf{n}^+), t)$, where $(i, \mathbf{n}^+)$ is an object of $J \times \Gamma^o$ and t is an object of the category $\Gamma^o S(i, \mathbf{n}^+)$. A morphism

$$((i, \mathbf{n}^+), t) \xrightarrow{((\alpha, f), \omega)} ((j, \mathbf{m}^+), s)$$

consists of morphisms

$$\begin{cases} (\alpha, f) : (i, \mathbf{n}^+) \to (j, \mathbf{m}^+) & \text{in } J \times \Gamma^o, \text{ and} \\ \omega : \Gamma^o S(\alpha, f)(t) \to s & \text{in } S(j, \mathbf{m}^+). \end{cases}$$

Composition of such morphisms is accomplished by using the isomorphisms that one encounters in the structure of a pseudo-functor.

The usual *rectification* of a pseudo-functor $Y : J \dashrightarrow cat$ is the functor $j \mapsto \pi_Y \downarrow j$, but this has to be altered for the purposes at hand (which involve getting pointed simplicial sets out of $\Gamma^o S$). More precisely, let e_i denote the identity element of the symmetric monoidal category $S(i)$, and observe that the assignments $* \mapsto (e_i, \ldots, e_i) \in \Gamma^o S(i, \mathbf{n}^+)$ determine a pseudo-natural transformation which gives rise to a monomorphism of simplicial sets

$$B((J \times \Gamma^o) \downarrow (i, \mathbf{n}^+)) \hookrightarrow B(\pi_{\Gamma^o S} \downarrow (i, \mathbf{n}^+))$$

that is natural with respect to morphisms of $J \times \Gamma^o$. It follows that one can specify a functor

$$\Gamma^o S_* : J \times \Gamma^o \to \mathbf{S}_*$$

which takes values in the category $\mathbf{S}_*$ of pointed simplicial sets by setting

$$\Gamma^o S_*(i, \mathbf{n}^+) = B(\pi_{\Gamma^o S} \downarrow (i, \mathbf{n}^+))/B((J \times \Gamma^o) \downarrow (i, \mathbf{n}^+)).$$

Note that the simplicial set $\Gamma^o S_*(i, \mathbf{n}^+))$ is weakly equivalent to $B(\Gamma^o S(i, \mathbf{n}^+))$, since the space $B((J \times \Gamma^o) \downarrow (i, \mathbf{n}^+))$ is contractible.

Recall that a Γ-*space* is a functor which is defined on the pointed ordinal number category Γ^o, and takes values in the category of pointed simplicial sets. Letting the $\mathbf{n}^+$ vary gives Γ-spaces $\Gamma^o S_*(i, *)$, and the assignment

$$i \mapsto \Gamma^o S_*(i, *)$$

determines a functor from J to the category of Γ-spaces, which is also denoted by $\Gamma^o S_*$.

Write $Spt(S)$ for the *diagram of spectra* (perhaps more properly denoted by $Spt(\Gamma^o S_*)$) which is associated to the diagram $\Gamma^o S_*$ of Γ-spaces, by the methods of Bousfield and Friedlander [8].

Explicitly, if X is a Γ-space, and K and L are finite pointed sets, then there is a canonical map

$$\sigma : K \wedge X(L) \to X(K \wedge L). \tag{5.1}$$

The map σ is universally determined by the case $K = \mathbf{1}^+$, in which case it is a composite of canonical isomorphisms

$$\mathbf{1}^+ \wedge X(L) \xrightarrow[\cong]{c^{-1}} X(L) \xrightarrow[\cong]{X(c)} X(\mathbf{1}^+ \wedge L),$$

where the bijection $c : L \to \mathbf{1}^+ \wedge L$ is induced by the function $L \to L \times \mathbf{1}^+$ which takes an element x to the element $(x, 1)$. The canonical map σ induces a map of pointed trisimplicial sets

$$\sigma : S^1 \wedge X((S^1)^{\wedge n}) \to X(S^1 \wedge (S^1)^{\wedge n}). \tag{5.2}$$

One therefore defines the nth space $Spt(X)^n$ of the associated spectrum $Spt(X)$ to be the diagonal of the $(n+1)$-fold pointed simplicial set $X((S^1)^{\wedge n})$. Then the maps (5.2) induce bonding maps $S^1 \wedge Spt(X)^n \to Spt(X)^{n+1}$ after taking appropriate diagonals. Note in particular that

$$Spt(X)^0 = X(S^0) = X(\mathbf{1}^+).$$

This construction is natural in X, so it applies to diagrams of Γ-spaces as well.

Returning to the case that we started with, if $X : I \to Sch$ is an I-indexed diagram of schemes, and if we feed the resulting pseudo-functor $Q\mathcal{P}X$ of symmetric monoidal categories defined on I^{op} to the process just described, then we get an I^{op}-indexed diagram of spectra $Spt(Q\mathcal{P}X)$. The *K-theory presheaf* KX associated to X is defined to be the functor $I^{op} \to Spt$ which is given by the assignment

$$i \mapsto \mathbf{hom}_*(S^1, Spt(Q\mathcal{P}X)_{Kan})(i).$$

We shall be more interested in special cases of this construction. In particular, if $et|_S$ is the étale site of a scheme S, then the assignment

$$U \xrightarrow{\phi} S \quad \mapsto \quad U$$

defined for each étale map ϕ gives a functor

$$F_S : et|_S \to Sch,$$

and the associated K-theory presheaf, denoted by K^{et}, is a model for the K-theory presheaf of spectra on the étale site for S. The K-theory presheaves of spectra for any of the standard geometric Grothendieck sites (such as K^{Zar} for the Zariski site, or K^{fl} for the flat site) can be constructed entirely analogously.

The notion of a presheaf of K-theory spectra is a generalization of something quite standard: the K-*theory spectrum* KA of an exact category A is defined by

$$KA = \mathbf{hom}_*(S^1, Spt(QA)_{Kan}).$$

Note in particular that, if $X : I \to Sch$ is an I-diagram of schemes as above, then the spectrum $KX(i)$ which results from evaluation at $i \in I$ is stably equivalent to the K-theory spectrum that arises from the exact category $\mathcal{P}X(i)$.

Suppose that A is an arbitrary exact category. Waldhausen [58] defines a simplicial exact category $S.A$ by specifying the category $S_n A$ of n-simplices to be the exact category whose objects are functors $M : Arr(\mathbf{n}) \to A$ such that for $i \leq j \leq k$ the sequence

$$0 \to M(i,j) \to M(i,k) \to M(j,k) \to 0$$

is exact, and such that each $M(i,i)$ is a zero object of A. Here, $Arr(\mathbf{n})$ is the category of arrows in the poset associated to the finite ordinal number $\mathbf{n}$, and the simplicial structure of $S.A$ comes from the structure of the finite ordinal number category $\mathbf{\Delta}$.

Waldhausen shows that the simplicial set of objects $s.A$ of the simplicial category $S.A$ is weakly equivalent to the space BQA which arises from the Quillen Q-construction. His proof of this assertion (see also [28, pp.167-169]) is partially based on the fact that the simplicial category $Iso(S.A)$ determines a bisimplicial set $BIso(S.A)$ whose diagonal is naturally weakly equivalent to $s.A$, as well as to BQA. The category of n-simplices $Iso(S_n A)$ of the simplicial object $Iso(S.A)$ is the groupoid of isomorphisms in $S_n A$.

$Iso(S.A)$ is a simplicial symmetric monoidal category. It therefore determines a simplicial pseudo-functor which shall be denoted by $\Gamma^o Iso(S.A)$, as well as a simplicial spectrum $n \mapsto Spt(Iso(S_n A))$. One defines a spectrum $Spt(Iso(S.A))$ to be a homotopy colimit

$$Spt(Iso(S.A)) = \varinjlim_{n \in \mathbf{\Delta}} Spt(Iso(S_n A)) \tag{5.3}$$

in the category of spectra. Alternatively, $Spt(Iso(S.A))$ may be defined to be the diagonal spectrum of this simplicial spectrum (see [9, p.337], as well as Section 4.3 above). A similar definition of the associated diagonal spectrum can be made for all simplicial or pseudo-simplicial symmetric monoidal categories.

Waldhausen's result that $s.A$ is weakly equivalent to BQA extends to the following spectrum level result [28, Prop. 5.5]:

PROPOSITION 5.4. *The spectra $Spt(QA)$ and $Spt(Iso(S.A))$ are strictly weakly equivalent.*

The corresponding result for diagrams of schemes is

COROLLARY 5.5. *Let $X : I \to Sch$ be a diagram of schemes. Then the K-theory presheaf KX is pointwise strictly equivalent to the spectrum valued functor*

$$i \mapsto \Omega Spt(Iso(S.\mathcal{P}X))_{Kan}(i).$$

It is a consequence of this result that the étale K-theory presheaf K^{et} on a scheme S can be modelled up to strict weak equivalence by the presheaf defined by

$$U \xrightarrow{\phi} S \quad \mapsto \quad \mathbf{hom}_*(S^1, Spt(Iso(S.\mathcal{P}F_S))_{Kan}(U)). \tag{5.6}$$

A final construction to be noted in this connection is based on Waldhausen's observation that an element $M : Arr(\mathbf{n}) \to A$ of the category $S_n A$ is determined up to unique isomorphism by the string of admissible monics

$$M(0,1) \rightarrowtail M(0,2) \rightarrowtail \cdots \rightarrowtail M(0,n). \tag{5.7}$$

There is an exact category $Mon_n A$ whose objects are strings of admissible monics in A

$$M_1 \rightarrowtail M_2 \rightarrowtail \cdots \rightarrowtail M_n.$$

Thus, there is an exact equivalence $M_n : S_n A \to Mon_n A$ which associates a string of the form (5.7) to an element M of $S_n A$, and this functor induces an equivalence of symmetric monoidal categories $M_n : Iso(S_n A) \to Iso(Mon_n A)$. As is noted in [28], the equivalences M_n, $n \geq 0$, can be parlayed into a pseudo-simplicial symmetric monoidal category $Iso(Mon.A)$ together with a pseudo-natural transformation $M : Iso(S.A)) \to Iso(Mon.A))$ which induces a weak equivalence of the associated nerves at each level. The resulting pseudo-simplicial structure of $Iso(Mon.A)$ has a particularly illuminating form: the face operators are given by

$$d_0(M_1 \rightarrowtail M_2 \rightarrowtail \cdots \rightarrowtail M_n) = M_2/M_1 \rightarrowtail \cdots \rightarrowtail M_n/M_1,$$

$$d_1(M_1 \rightarrowtail M_2 \rightarrowtail \cdots \rightarrowtail M_n) = M_2 \rightarrowtail \cdots \rightarrowtail M_n,$$

$$d_i(M_1 \rightarrowtail M_2 \rightarrowtail \cdots \rightarrowtail M_n) = M_1 \rightarrowtail \ldots \rightarrowtail M_{i-1} \rightarrowtail M_{i+1} \rightarrowtail \cdots \rightarrowtail M_n$$

for $0 < i < n$, and

$$d_n(M_1 \rightarrowtail M_2 \rightarrowtail \cdots \rightarrowtail M_n) = M_1 \rightarrowtail \cdots \rightarrowtail M_{n-1}.$$

Similarly, the degeneracies are defined by

$$s_i(M_1 \rightarrowtail M_2 \rightarrowtail \cdots \rightarrowtail M_n) =$$

$$\begin{cases} 0 \rightarrowtail M_1 \rightarrowtail \cdots \rightarrowtail M_n & \text{if } i = 0, \text{ and} \\ M_1 \rightarrowtail \cdots \rightarrowtail M_i \xrightarrow{1} M_i \rightarrowtail \cdots \rightarrowtail M_n & \text{for } 0 < i \leq n. \end{cases}$$

Furthermore, one can show (see also [28, Prop. 5.9])

PROPOSITION 5.8. *The simplicial equivalence*

$$M : Iso(S.A) \to Iso(Mon.A)$$

induces a strict weak equivalence

$$M : Spt(Iso(S.A)) \to Spt(Iso(Mon.A)).$$

Once again, the construction of $Iso(Mon.\mathcal{P}X(i))$ and the pseudo-natural transformation M can be made for vector bundles along a diagram of schemes $i \mapsto X(i)$, so that the ideas behind the proof of Proposition 5.8 lead to

COROLLARY 5.9. *Let* $X : I \to Sch$ *be a diagram of schemes. Then there is a pointwise strict weak equivalence*

$$M : Spt(Iso(S.\mathcal{P}X)) \to Spt(Iso(Mon.\mathcal{P}X)).$$

This last result implies that the spectrum valued functor

$$U \xrightarrow{\phi} S \quad \mapsto \quad \mathbf{hom}_*(S^1, Spt(Iso(Mon.\mathcal{P}F_S))_{Kan})(U) \tag{5.10}$$

is pointwise strictly weakly equivalent to the étale K-theory presheaf.

In much of what follows, we shall explicitly need the following technical result.

LEMMA 5.11. *Suppose that* T_* *is a simplicial spectrum such that the spectrum of m-simplices T_m is n-connected and stably fibrant, for $m \geq 0$. Then any strictly fibrant model of the diagonal spectrum dT_* is n-connected and stably fibrant.*

PROOF: The connectivity of dT_* is calculated by using the spectral sequence of Corollary 4.22.

Suppose that X is a pointed bisimplicial set, and let K be a pointed simplicial set. There is a natural map

$$\omega : d\mathbf{hom}_*(K, X_*) \to \mathbf{hom}_*(K, dX_*)$$

which is adjoint to a map ev_* of coends that is determined by the composites

$$K \wedge \mathbf{hom}_*(K, X_n) \ltimes \Delta^n \xrightarrow{ev \ltimes \Delta^n} X_n \ltimes \Delta^n.$$

It follows that there is a commutative diagram

$$
\begin{array}{ccc}
d(\Omega T_*^{i+1}) & \xrightarrow{\eta_* \omega} & \Omega d(T_*^{i+1})_{Kan} \\
\downarrow & & \downarrow \\
d(PT_*^{i+1}) & \xrightarrow{\eta_* \omega} & Pd(T_*^{i+1})_{Kan} \\
\downarrow & & \downarrow \\
d(T_*^{i+1}) & \xrightarrow{\eta} & d(T_*^{i+1})_{Kan},
\end{array}
\tag{5.12}
$$

where $\eta : d(T_*) \to d(T_*)_{Kan}$ is the canonical weak equivalence to the strictly fibrant model for $d(T_*)$, and the prefix P means "path space".

The vertical sequence on the left in the diagram (5.12) is a fibre homotopy sequence; in effect, all of the spaces T_n^{i+1} are connected by assumption, and so Theorem B.5 of [8] applies. It follows that the composite map

$$d(\Omega T_*^{i+1}) \xrightarrow{\omega} \Omega(dT_*^{i+1}) \xrightarrow{\eta_*} \Omega(dT_*^{i+1})_{Kan}$$

is a weak equivalence.

The bonding map

$$\sigma : S^1 \wedge d(T_*^i) \to d(T_*^{i+1})$$

is induced as a map of coends by the maps

$$S^1 \wedge T_n^i \ltimes \Delta^n \xrightarrow{\sigma \ltimes \Delta^n} T_n^{i+1} \ltimes \Delta^n.$$

There is therefore a commutative diagram

$$
\begin{array}{ccc}
d(T_*^i) & \xrightarrow{\hspace{3cm}\eta\hspace{3cm}} & d(T_*^i)_{Kan} \\
{\scriptstyle d(\sigma)}\downarrow \quad {\scriptstyle\sigma}\searrow & & \downarrow{\scriptstyle\sigma} \\
d(\Omega T_*^{i+1}) \xrightarrow{\omega} \Omega d(T_*^{i+1}) & \xrightarrow{\eta_*} & \Omega d(T_*^{i+1})_{Kan}
\end{array}
\tag{5.13}
$$

The left hand map $d(\sigma)$ in the diagram (5.13) is a weak equivalence, since each of the maps

$$\sigma : T_n^i \to \Omega T_n^{i+1}$$

is a weak equivalence by assumption, and we have just seen that the bottom composite $\eta_*\omega$ is a weak equivalence. The top map η is a weak equivalence by construction, and so the map

$$\sigma : (dT_*^i)_{Kan} \to \Omega(dT_*^{i+1})_{Kan}$$

is a weak equivalence, as required. ∎

COROLLARY 5.14. *Suppose that $B.$ is a pseudo-simplicial symmetric monoidal category. Then any strictly fibrant model of*

$$Spt(B.) = \varinjlim_{n} Spt(B_n)$$

is connective and stably fibrant in degrees > 0.

PROOF: Suppose that
$$Spt(B.) \to FSpt(B.)$$
is a strictly fibrant model of $Spt(B.)$, in the category of simplicial spectra. This means, in particular, that each of the induced maps
$$Spt(B_n) \to FSpt(B_n)$$
is a strict weak equivalence of spectra. Each spectrum $FSpt(B_n)$ is connective and stably fibrant in degrees > 0, where the latter assertion means that the shifted spectrum $FSpt(B_n)[1]$ is stably fibrant [8, p.99], [28]. Lemma 5.11 implies that every strictly fibrant model of the diagonal spectrum
$$d(FSpt(B.)[1]) = d(FSpt(B.))[1]$$
is 0-connected and stably fibrant. It follows that every strictly fibrant model of the spectrum $d(Spt(B.))[1]$ is 0-connected and stably fibrant, so that every strictly fibrant model of $d(Spt(B.))$ is connective and stably fibrant in degrees > 0. ∎

It is well known [58] that recursively applying the Waldhausen $S.$-construction to an exact category A gives successive deloopings of the K-theory spaces BQA. This construction can be promoted to the spectrum level (essentially in the way that Waldhausen describes) as follows.

Define a simplicial exact category $Ex.A$ by setting $Ex_n A = S_{n+1}A$ and by defining the simplicial structure map $\theta^* : Ex_n A \to Ex_m A$ to be the map $\hat{\theta}^* : S_{n+1}A \to S_{m+1}A$, where $\hat{\theta} : \mathbf{m} + \mathbf{1} \to \mathbf{n} + \mathbf{1}$ is the unique ordinal number map such that $\hat{\theta}(0) = 0$ and $\hat{\theta}(i+1) = \theta(i) + 1$ for $0 \leq i \leq n$ (see also [28, p.88]). The pseudo-natural transformation $M : S.A \to Mon.A$ induces a simplicial exact equivalence of $Ex.A$ with the nerve of the category of admissible monomorphisms in A. This nerve has an exact contracting homotopy, so it follows that the bisimplicial category $Iso(S.(Ex.A))$ gives rise to a contractible space, on taking the diagonal of the associated bisimplicial nerve.

The 0th face maps determine a simplicial exact functor
$$d_0 : Ex.A \to S.A,$$
and there is a simplicial exact functor $i : A \to Ex.A$ which is defined (for the discrete simplicial structure on A) in degree n by associating to the object $M \in A$ the functor $M : Arr(\mathbf{n}) \to A$ which is determined by identifying the string
$$M(0,1) \rightarrowtail M(0,2) \rightarrowtail \cdots \rightarrowtail M(0,n)$$
with the string of identity maps
$$M \xrightarrow{1} M \xrightarrow{1} \ldots \xrightarrow{1} M.$$

In effect, one decrees that $M(i,j) = 0$ unless $i = 0$ and $j > 0$ for a fixed choice of zero object of A.

The resulting sequence of maps of bisimplicial categories

$$Iso(S.A) \xrightarrow{i} Iso(S.Ex.A) \xrightarrow{d_0} Iso(S.S.A)$$

induces a fibre homotopy sequence of simplicial sets

$$d(BIso(S.A)) \xrightarrow{i} d(BIso(S.Ex.A)) \xrightarrow{d_0} d(BIso(S.S.A)).$$

Each sequence

$$BIso(S.A)) \xrightarrow{i} d(BIso(S.Ex_n A)) \xrightarrow{d_0} d(BIso(S.S_n A))$$

is a fibre homotopy sequence, by additivity, and the spaces $d(BIso(S.Ex_n A))$ and $d(BIso(S.S_n A))$ are connected, and so Theorem B.4 of [8] applies.

This argument can be used to prove

PROPOSITION 5.15. *The sequence*

$$Spt(Iso(S.A)) \xrightarrow{i} Spt(Iso(S.Ex.A)) \xrightarrow{d_0} Spt(Iso(S.S.A)).$$

is a fibre homotopy sequence of spectra, for each exact category A.

PROOF: It suffices to replace the given sequence by a sequence of strictly fibrant models. Then the spectra involved are connective stably fibrant spectra, by Corollary 5.14. Furthermore the sequence of spaces at level 0 can be identified up to canonical weak equivalence with the sequence

$$d(BIso(S.A)) \xrightarrow{i} d(BIso(S.Ex.A)) \xrightarrow{d_0} d(BIso(S.S.A)).$$

To see this, use Corollary 4.4 of [28]. But then we've just seen that this sequence of spaces is a fibre homotopy sequence, and the result follows. ∎

COROLLARY 5.16. *The spectrum $Spt(Iso(S.A))$ is canonically strictly weakly equivalent to $\Omega Spt(Iso(S.S.A))_{Kan}$.*

There is a multisimplicial exact category $S^n_. A$ defined recursively by

$$S^n_. A = S^{n-1}_.(S.A).$$

It determines a multisimplicial symmetric monoidal category $Iso(S^n_. A)$, with an associated spectrum which is also defined recursively by

$$Spt(Iso(S^n_. A)) = \underset{m}{\underrightarrow{\mathrm{holim}}}\, Spt(Iso(S^{n-1}_.(S_m A))).$$

The techniques in the proof of the previous result can also be used to show

PROPOSITION 5.17. *For each exact category A, the sequence*

$$Spt(Iso(S^n_\cdot A)) \xrightarrow{S^n_\cdot i} Spt(Iso(S^n_\cdot Ex.A)) \xrightarrow{S^n_\cdot d_0} Spt(Iso(S^{n+1}_\cdot A)).$$

is a strict fibre homotopy sequence of spectra, and $Spt(Iso(S^n_\cdot Ex.A))$ is contractible, so that $Spt(Iso(S^n_\cdot A))$ is canonically strictly weakly equivalent to

$$\Omega Spt(Iso(S^{n+1}_\cdot A))_{Kan}.$$

Suppose that $X : I \to Sch$ is an I-indexed diagram of schemes as before. Applying the $S.$ family of constructions to the I^{op}-indexed pseudo-functor $i \mapsto \mathcal{P}X(i)$ gives multisimplicial pseudo-functors $Iso(S^n_\cdot \mathcal{P}X)$ and $Iso(S^n_\cdot Ex.\mathcal{P}X)$, as well as multisimplicial pseudo-natural transformations of symmetric monoidal categories

$$Iso(S^n_\cdot \mathcal{P}X) \xrightarrow{S^n_\cdot i} Iso(S^n_\cdot Ex.\mathcal{P}X) \xrightarrow{S^n_\cdot d_0} Iso(S^{n+1}_\cdot \mathcal{P}X).$$

This means in particular that the sequence is really a multisimplicial pseudo-functor which is defined on the index category $I^{op} \times \mathbf{2}$. Subject to this caveat [28, Remark 4.1], the previous result leads to

PROPOSITION 5.18. *For each I-indexed diagram of schemes X, the sequence*

$$Spt(Iso(S^n_\cdot \mathcal{P}X)) \xrightarrow{S^n_\cdot i} Spt(Iso(S^n_\cdot Ex.\mathcal{P}X)) \xrightarrow{S^n_\cdot d_0} Spt(Iso(S^{n+1}_\cdot \mathcal{P}X)).$$

is a pointwise strict fibre homotopy sequence of diagrams of spectra, and the diagram $Spt(Iso(S^n_\cdot Ex.\mathcal{P}X))$ is pointwise contractible, so that $Spt(Iso(S^n_\cdot \mathcal{P}X))$ is pointwise strictly weakly equivalent to

$$\Omega Spt(Iso(S^{n+1}_\cdot \mathcal{P}X))_{Kan}.$$

In particular, on the étale site $et|_S$ of a scheme S, the presheaf of spectra $Spt(Iso(S^n_\cdot \mathcal{P}F_S))$ is a strict pointwise n-fold delooping of the K-theory presheaf of spectra K^{et}.

5.2. Products

Suppose that A is a symmetric monoidal category, and let $\Gamma^o A$ be the associated pseudo-Γ^o-functor. Observe that the assignment $(\mathbf{n}^+, \mathbf{m}^+) \mapsto \mathbf{n}^+ \wedge \mathbf{m}^+ \cong (\mathbf{nm})^+$ determines a functor $\wedge : \Gamma^o \times \Gamma^o \to \Gamma^o$. This functor naturally associates a pseudo-$\Gamma^o \times \Gamma^o$-category $\Gamma^o A^\wedge$ to the symmetric monoidal category A. The object $\Gamma^o A^\wedge(\mathbf{m}^+, \mathbf{n}^+)$ can be identified with the collection of $m \times n$ matrices with entries in A, and morphisms in the first variable amount to row operations in these matrices. Explicitly, $\Gamma^o A^\wedge(s^j, \mathbf{n}^+)$ adds (ie. forms direct sums) the jth to the $(j+1)^{st}$ row if $j > 0$ whereas $\Gamma^o A^\wedge(s^0, \mathbf{n}^+)$ deletes the first row, $\Gamma^o A^\wedge(d^i, \mathbf{n}^+)$ inserts a row consisting of copies of the identity e of A in the ith place, and the morphisms $\Gamma^o A^\wedge(\omega, \mathbf{n}^+)$ corresponding to ω in the permutation group Σ_m permute rows. Morphisms in the second variable are column operations in a completely analogous way.

Suppose that F and G are pseudo-functors $I \dashrightarrow cat$, and recall that a *pseudo-natural transformation* $(f, \omega) : F \to G$ consists of functors $f_i : F(i) \to G(i)$, $i \in I$, and natural isomorphisms $\omega : G(\alpha)f_i \to f_j F(\alpha)$ for each morphism $\alpha : i \to j$ in I, such that

(1) if $i \xrightarrow{\alpha} j \xrightarrow{\beta} k$ is a composable pair of morphism of I, then the following diagram commutes:

$$
\begin{array}{ccccc}
G(\beta)G(\alpha)f_i & \xrightarrow{\ G(\beta)\omega\ } & G(\beta)f_j F(\alpha) & \xrightarrow{\ \omega F(\alpha)\ } & f_k F(\beta)F(\alpha) \\
{\scriptstyle \theta f_i}\big\uparrow & & & & \big\uparrow{\scriptstyle f_k \theta} \\
G(\beta\alpha)f_i & & \xrightarrow{\hspace{3cm}\omega\hspace{3cm}} & & f_k F(\beta\alpha),
\end{array}
$$

(2) the diagram

$$
\begin{array}{ccc}
G(1_i)f_i & \xrightarrow{\ \ \omega\ \ } & f_i F(1_i) \\
{\scriptstyle \eta_i f_i}\searrow & & \swarrow{\scriptstyle f_i \eta_i} \\
& f_i &
\end{array}
$$

commutes.

Observe that we have written θ for the canonical morphisms

$$\theta(\beta, \alpha) : G(\beta\alpha) \to G(\beta)G(\alpha) \qquad \text{and} \qquad \theta(\beta, \alpha) : F(\beta\alpha) \to F(\beta)F(\alpha)$$

which are associated to the pseudo-functors F and G respectively.

LEMMA 5.19. *Suppose that F and G are pseudo-functors $I \times J \dashrightarrow cat$. Then a pseudo natural transformation $F \to G$ consists of functors $f : F(i,j) \to G(i,j)$, $(i,j) \in I \times J$ which are part of the data for pseudo-natural transformations $(f, \omega_L) : F(*, j) \to G(*, j)$, $j \in J$, and $(f, \omega_R) : F(i, *) \to G(i, *)$ for $i \in I$, such that the diagrams of natural isomorphisms*

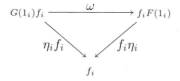

$$
\begin{array}{ccccc}
G(\alpha,1)G(1,\beta)f & \xrightarrow{\ G(\alpha,1)\omega_R\ } & G(\alpha,1)fF(1,\beta) & \xrightarrow{\ \omega_L F(1,\beta)\ } & fF(\alpha,1)F(1,\beta) \\
{\scriptstyle \kappa f}\big\downarrow & & & & \big\downarrow{\scriptstyle f\kappa} \qquad (5.20) \\
G(1,\beta)G(\alpha,1)f & \xrightarrow[\ G(1,\beta)\omega_L\ ]{} & G(1,\beta)fF(\alpha,1) & \xrightarrow[\ \omega_R F(\alpha,1)\ ]{} & fF(1,\beta)F(\alpha,1)
\end{array}
$$

commute for each morphism (α, β) of $I \times J$.

The notation κ in the statement of Lemma 5.19 is for the compositions

$$G(\alpha, 1)G(1, \beta) \xrightarrow{\theta^{-1}} G(\alpha, \beta) \xrightarrow{\theta} G(1, \beta)G(\alpha, 1)$$

and

$$F(\alpha, 1)F(1, \beta) \xrightarrow{\theta^{-1}} F(\alpha, \beta) \xrightarrow{\theta} F(1, \beta)F(\alpha, 1).$$

PROOF: The necessity of the conditions is evident. Suppose conversely that one is given a list of functors $f : F(i, j) \to G(i, j)$ and natural isomorphisms ω_L and ω_R which satisfy the conditions of the lemma. Define the natural isomorphism

$$\tilde{\omega} : G(\alpha, \beta)f \to fF(\alpha, \beta)$$

to be the composite

$$
\begin{array}{l}
G(\alpha, \beta)f \\
\quad \Big\downarrow \theta f \\
G(\alpha, 1)G(1, \beta)f \xrightarrow{\;G(\alpha, 1)\omega_R\;} G(\alpha, 1)fF(1, \beta) \xrightarrow{\;\omega_L F(1, \beta)\;} fF(\alpha, 1)F(1, \beta) \\
\hspace{8.8cm} \Big\downarrow f\theta^{-1} \\
\hspace{8.6cm} fF(\alpha, \beta).
\end{array}
$$

Then the "interchange conditions" of (5.20) guarantee (after a little diagram drawing) that the isomorphisms $\tilde{\omega}$ satisfy the defining commutativity conditions for a pseudo-natural transformation

$$(f, \tilde{\omega}) : F \to G.$$

Note, in particular that there is a commutative diagram

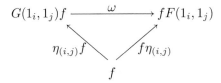

in which ω can be either $\tilde{\omega}$, ω_L, or ω_R. In particular, $\tilde{\omega} = \omega_L = \omega_R$ at all of the identity morphisms $(1_i, 1_j)$ of $I \times J$. It follows that $\tilde{\omega} = \omega_R$ for morphisms $(1, \beta)$ and $\tilde{\omega} = \omega_L$ for morphisms $(\alpha, 1)$. ∎

In the situation of Lemma 5.19, say that the arrow α *interchanges* with β. Then the *interchange condition* (ie. diagram (5.20)) can be rephrased to say that all arrows α of I interchange with all arrows β of J.

LEMMA 5.21. *Suppose that F and G are pseudo-functors $I \times J \dashrightarrow \text{cat}$, and suppose that we are given functors $f : F(i,j) \to G(i,j)$, $(i,j) \in I \times J$ which form part of the data for pseudo-natural transformations $(f, \omega_L) : F(*, j) \to G(*, j)$ and $(f, \omega_R) : F(i, *) \to G(i, *)$ for $i, j \in I$.*

(1) *If α_2 and α_1 interchange with β, then so does $\alpha_2 \alpha_1$.*

(2) *If α interchanges with β_2 and β_1, then α interchanges with $\beta_2 \beta_1$.*

PROOF: Draw the same sort of diagrams that are necessary for (but were suppressed in) the proof of Lemma 5.19.   ∎

The following result gives a different characterization of pseudo-natural transformations between pseudo-functors on categories $I \times J$ that will be useful later.

COROLLARY 5.22. *Suppose that F and G are pseudo-functors $I \times J \dashrightarrow \text{cat}$. Then a pseudo-natural transformation $F \to G$ consists of pseudo-natural transformations*

$$(f, \omega_L) : F(*, j) \to G(*, j),$$

and homotopies

$$\omega_\beta : G(1, \beta)f \to fF(1, \beta),$$

one for each arrow β of J, such that the following diagrams commute:

$$
\begin{array}{ccc}
G(1, \gamma\beta)f & \xrightarrow{\ \theta f\ } & G(1, \gamma)G(1, \beta)f \\
\Big\downarrow{\scriptstyle \omega_{\gamma\beta}} & & \Big\downarrow{\scriptstyle G(1,\gamma)\omega_\beta} \\
 & & G(1, \gamma)fF(1, \beta) \\
 & & \Big\downarrow{\scriptstyle \omega_\gamma F(1,\beta)} \\
fF(1, \gamma\beta) & \xrightarrow[\ f\theta\ ]{} & fF(1, \gamma)F(1, \beta)
\end{array}
\qquad (5.23)
$$

$$
\begin{array}{ccc}
G(1, 1)f & \xrightarrow{\ \omega_1\ } & fF(1, 1) \\
 & & \\
{\scriptstyle \eta f}\searrow & & \swarrow{\scriptstyle f\eta} \\
 & f &
\end{array}
\qquad (5.24)
$$

PROOF: For each $i \in I$, the collection of isomorphisms

$$\omega_\beta : G(i, \beta)f \xrightarrow{\ \cong\ } fF(i, \beta), \qquad \beta \text{ in } J$$

define a pseudo-natural transformation

$$(f, \omega_R) : F(i, *) \to G(i, *),$$

since the diagrams (5.23) and (5.24) commute. The interchange condition (5.20) is equivalent to the assertion that the ω_β's are homotopies. ∎

Suppose that A, B and C are symmetric monoidal categories, and denote each of their additions by $\oplus$ and their identities by 0. Part of the data for what will be called a "bilinear map" of symmetric monoidal categories consists of a functor $\otimes : A \times B \to C$ such that the canonical adjoints, namely

$$A \xrightarrow{\otimes_*} C^B \qquad \text{and} \qquad B \xrightarrow{\otimes_*} C^A,$$

are part of the data for morphisms of symmetric monoidal categories. Here, for example, C^B is the category of functors from B to C, with natural transformations as morphisms; it inherits a (pointwise) symmetric monoidal category structure from that of C. This means in particular that there are natural isomorphisms

$$(a_2 \oplus a_1) \otimes b \xrightarrow{\omega_L} (a_2 \otimes b) \oplus (a_1 \otimes b), \qquad 0 \otimes b \xrightarrow{\omega_L} 0,$$

which are natural in the variables a_i and b, and make the following diagrams commute [28, p.26,64]:

$$
\begin{array}{ccc}
(a_3 \oplus (a_2 \oplus a_1)) \otimes b & \xrightarrow{\ \alpha \otimes b\ } & ((a_3 \oplus a_2) \oplus a_1) \otimes b \\
\omega_L \downarrow & & \downarrow \omega_L \\
(a_3 \otimes b) \oplus ((a_2 \oplus a_1) \otimes b) & & ((a_3 \oplus a_2) \otimes b) \oplus (a_1 \otimes b) \\
1 \otimes \omega_L \downarrow & & \downarrow \omega_L \otimes 1 \\
(a_3 \otimes b) \oplus ((a_2 \otimes b) \oplus (a_1 \otimes b)) & \xrightarrow{\ \alpha\ } & ((a_3 \otimes b) \oplus (a_2 \otimes b)) \oplus (a_1 \otimes b)
\end{array}
$$

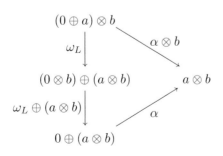

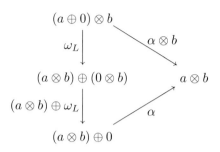

$$(a \oplus d) \otimes b \xrightarrow{\ \omega_L\ } (a \otimes b) \oplus (d \otimes b)$$

$$c \otimes b \Big\downarrow \qquad\qquad\qquad \Big\downarrow c$$

$$(d \oplus a) \otimes b \xrightarrow{\ \omega_L\ } (d \otimes b) \oplus (a \otimes b)$$

In these diagrams, α and c are the canonical isomorphisms which are part of the symmetric monoidal category structure on A.

Note that one is also insisting that there are natural isomorphisms

$$a \otimes (b_1 \oplus b_2) \xrightarrow{\ \omega_R\ } (a \otimes b_1) \oplus (a \otimes b_2), \qquad a \otimes 0 \xrightarrow{\ \omega_R\ } 0,$$

which make an analogous list of diagrams commute. The morphisms $(\otimes_*, \omega_L)$ and $(\otimes_*, \omega_R)$ of symmetric monoidal categories induce pseudo-natural transformations

$$(\otimes, \omega_L) : \Gamma^o A \times B \to \Gamma^o C$$

and

$$(\otimes, \omega_R) : A \times \Gamma^o B \to \Gamma^o C.$$

Formally now, a *bilinear map*

$$(\otimes, \omega_L, \omega_R) : A \times B \to C$$

of symmetric monoidal categories consists of a bifunctor $\otimes : A \times B \to C$, together with morphisms of symmetric monoidal categories

$$(\otimes_*, \omega_L) : A \to C^B \qquad \text{and} \qquad (\otimes_*, \omega_R) : B \to C^A,$$

such that

$$\omega_L = \omega_R : 0 \otimes 0 \to 0,$$

and the following diagrams of isomorphisms commute:

$$\begin{array}{ccc}
((a_1\otimes b_1)\oplus(a_1\otimes b_2))\oplus((a_2\otimes b_1)\oplus(a_2\otimes b_2)) & \xrightarrow{\;\alpha\;} & ((a_1\otimes b_1)\oplus(a_2\otimes b_1))\oplus((a_1\otimes b_2)\oplus(a_2\otimes b_2)) \\
\big\uparrow{\scriptstyle\omega_R\oplus\omega_R} & & \big\uparrow{\scriptstyle\omega_L\oplus\omega_L} \\
(a_1\otimes(b_1\oplus b_2))\oplus(a_2\otimes(b_1\oplus b_2)) & & ((a_1\oplus a_2)\otimes b_1)\oplus((a_1\oplus a_2)\otimes b_2) \\
\big\uparrow{\scriptstyle\omega_L} & \nearrow{\scriptstyle\omega_R} & \\
(a_1\oplus a_2)\otimes(b_1\oplus b_2) & &
\end{array}$$

$$(5.25)$$

$$
(a_1\oplus a_2)\otimes 0 \xrightarrow{\;\omega_L\;} (a_1\otimes 0)\oplus(a_2\otimes 0) \xrightarrow{\;\omega_R\oplus\omega_R\;} 0\oplus 0 \xrightarrow{\;\alpha\;} 0 \qquad (5.26)
$$
with ω_R the diagonal $(a_1\oplus a_2)\otimes 0 \to 0$.

$$
0\otimes(b_1\oplus b_2) \xrightarrow{\;\omega_R\;} (0\otimes b_1)\oplus(0\otimes b_2) \xrightarrow{\;\omega_L\oplus\omega_L\;} 0\oplus 0 \xrightarrow{\;\alpha\;} 0 \qquad (5.27)
$$
with ω_L the diagonal $0\otimes(b_1\oplus b_2) \to 0$.

In most examples, the identity element of a symmetric monoidal category is actually a zero object (ie. initial and terminal), so that diagrams (5.26) and (5.27) automatically commute and $\omega_R = \omega_L : 0\otimes 0 \to 0$. Thus, diagram (5.25) is the only non-trivial condition in practice.

PROPOSITION 5.28. *Any bilinear map* $(\otimes, \omega_L, \omega_R) : A \times B \to C$ *of symmetric monoidal categories canonically induces a pseudo-natural transformation of pseudo-*$(\Gamma^o \times \Gamma^o)$*-functors*

$$(\otimes, \omega_L, \omega_R) : \Gamma^o A \times \Gamma^o B \to \Gamma^o C^\wedge.$$

PROOF: The underlying bifunctors

$$\otimes : A^n \times B^m \to \Gamma^o C^\wedge(\mathbf{n}^+, \mathbf{m}^+)$$

are defined by

$$((a_1,\ldots,a_n),(b_1,\ldots,b_m)) \mapsto \begin{pmatrix} a_1\otimes b_1 & \cdots & a_1\otimes b_m \\ \vdots & \ddots & \vdots \\ a_n\otimes b_1 & \cdots & a_n\otimes b_m \end{pmatrix}.$$

Furthermore, the pseudo-natural transformations

$$(\otimes, \omega_L) : \Gamma^o A \times B \to \Gamma^o C$$

induce pseudo-natural transformations

$$(\otimes, \omega_L) : \Gamma^o A \times B^m \to \Gamma^o C^\wedge(*, \mathbf{m}^+).$$

One simply applies the isomorphisms ω_L columnwise. A few special cases are worth noting: ω_L is actually the identity map on all permutations and on all maps s^0, and the instance of ω_L corresponding to s^j for $j > 1$, namely

$$
\begin{pmatrix}
a_1 \otimes b_1 & \cdots & a_1 \otimes b_m \\
\vdots & & \vdots \\
(a_j \oplus a_{j+1}) \otimes b_1 & \cdots & (a_j \oplus a_{j+1}) \otimes b_m \\
\vdots & & \vdots \\
a_n \otimes b_1 & \cdots & a_n \otimes b_m
\end{pmatrix}
$$

$$
\xrightarrow{\;\omega_L\;}
\begin{pmatrix}
a_1 \otimes b_1 & \cdots & a_1 \otimes b_m \\
\vdots & & \vdots \\
(a_j \otimes b_1) \oplus (a_{j+1} \otimes b_1) & \cdots & (a_j \otimes b_m) \oplus (a_{j+1} \otimes b_m) \\
\vdots & & \vdots \\
a_n \otimes b_1 & \cdots & a_n \otimes b_m
\end{pmatrix},
$$

is the identity off the jth row. Similarly the instance of ω_L corresponding to d^i for $i > 0$ is the identity off the ith row. Analogously, the pseudo-natural transformations

$$(\otimes, \omega_R) : A \times \Gamma^o B \to \Gamma^o C$$

induce pseudo-natural transformations

$$(\otimes, \omega_R) : A^n \times \Gamma^o B \to \Gamma^o C^\wedge(\mathbf{n}^+, *),$$

such that ω_R is the identity on all permutations as well as on s^o, and is the identity off of the jth column for both s^j and d^j if $j > 0$.

   In view of Lemmas 5.19 and 5.21 the interchange conditions are reduced to considering generators of the category Γ^o, namely all permutations, the cofaces d^i, $i > 0$, and all codegeneracies s^j, $j \geq 0$. But the permutations and s^0 interchange and can be interchanged with anything. For the remaining cases, we use the above remarks about the effects of ω_L and ω_R on rows and columns to show that:

   (1) d^i interchanges with any d^j since

$$\omega_R = \omega_L : 0 \otimes 0 \to 0,$$

(2) the commutativity of diagram (5.26) implies that s^j interchanges with any d^i,

(3) diagram (5.27) implies that d^i interchanges with any s^j, and

(4) diagram (5.25) implies that s^i interchanges with any s^j. ∎

Suppose henceforth that that the following condition holds:

CONDITION 5.29. *Every symmetric monoidal category A has the property that the category A_0 of objects isomorphic to the identity object is a trivial groupoid.*

This would be true, for example, if the identity object of A is a zero object. Condition 5.29 is a simplifying assumption from several points of view — we have already noted above that all but one of the conditions in the definition of bilinear map of symmetric monoidal categories are vacuous in this case. Furthermore, A_0 is itself a symmetric monoidal category, and the inclusion $A_0 \hookrightarrow A$ is a morphism of symmetric monoidal categories which induces a pointwise monomorphism $\Gamma^o(A_0)_* \to \Gamma^o A_*$, and hence a pointwise cofibration $Spt(A_0) \to Spt(A)$ of associated spectra [8, p.101]. The category A_0 is contractible, so that the spectrum $Spt(A_0)$ is strictly contractible, and the cofibre

$$Spt_*(A) = Spt(A)/Spt(A_0)$$

is strictly weakly equivalent to $Spt(A)$. Observe finally that $Spt_* A$ can be constructed as the spectrum associated to the Γ-space $\Gamma^o(A/A_0)$ which is defined at $\mathbf{n}^+$ to be the cofibre of the map

$$B(\pi_{\Gamma^o A_0} \downarrow \mathbf{n}^+) \hookrightarrow B(\pi_{\Gamma^o A} \downarrow \mathbf{n}^+).$$

Suppose that

$$(\otimes, \omega_L, \omega_R) : A \times B \to C$$

is a bilinear map of symmetric monoidal categories, and consider the associated pseudo-natural transformation

$$(\otimes, \omega_L, \omega_R) : \Gamma^o A \times \Gamma^o B \to \Gamma^o C^\wedge$$

that we laboured to produce in Proposition 5.28. The pairing $\otimes$ restricts to pseudo-natural transformations

$$\Gamma^o A_0 \times \Gamma^o B \to \Gamma^o C_0^\wedge$$

and

$$\Gamma^o A \times \Gamma^o B_0 \to \Gamma^o C_0^\wedge,$$

and so there is an induced morphism of $\Gamma^o \times \Gamma^o$-spaces

$$\Gamma^o(A/A_0) \wedge \Gamma^o(B/B_0) \to \Gamma^o(C/C_0)^\wedge.$$

Here, $\Gamma^o(C/C_0)^\wedge$ is the bi-Γ-space defined at $(\mathbf{n}^+, \mathbf{m}^+) \in (\Gamma^o)^2$ to be the cofibre of the map

$$B(\pi_{\Gamma^o C_0^\wedge} \downarrow (\mathbf{n}^+, \mathbf{m}^+)) \to B(\pi_{\Gamma^o C^\wedge} \downarrow (\mathbf{n}^+, \mathbf{m}^+)).$$

Any bi-Γ-space X has a bispectrum $Spt^2(X)$ canonically associated to it, by an extension of the methods of [8]. This follows from the fact that, if K_i and L_i are finite pointed sets and $i = 1, 2$, then there is a commutative diagram pointed functions

$$
\begin{array}{ccccc}
K_1 \wedge L_1 \wedge X(K_2, L_2) & \xrightarrow{\ \tau \wedge 1\ } & L_1 \wedge K_1 \wedge X(K_2, L_2) & \xrightarrow{\ 1 \wedge \sigma_L\ } & L_1 \wedge X(K_1 \wedge K_2, L_2) \\
{\scriptstyle 1 \wedge \sigma_R} \downarrow & & & & \downarrow {\scriptstyle \sigma_R} \\
K_1 \wedge X(K_2, L_1 \wedge L_2) & & \xrightarrow{\hspace{3cm} \sigma_L \hspace{3cm}} & & X(K_1 \wedge K_2, L_1 \wedge L_2),
\end{array}
$$

where σ_L is the canonical map for the left hand factor, and σ_R is the canonical map on the right, as in (5.1). Then the associated bispectrum is defined on the space level by

$$Spt^2(X)^{n,m} = \underrightarrow{\mathrm{holim}}\, X(S^n, S^m), \qquad (5.30)$$

meaning that this space is the diagonal of a trisimplicial set $X(S^n, S^m)$, where S^n is the n-fold smash product $S^1 \wedge \cdots \wedge S^1$ of copies of the simplicial circle S^1.

It is not hard to see, for example, that if X and Y are Γ-spaces, then $X \wedge Y$ is a bi-Γ-space, and the corresponding bispectrum $Spt^2(X \wedge Y)$ is canonically isomorphic to $Spt(X) \wedge Spt(Y)$.

All Γ-spaces of the form $\Gamma^o(A/A_0)$ which arise from the sorts of symmetric monoidal categories that we are now discussing are *special* in the sense of [8, p.97]. This means that the collapse maps $pr_i : \mathbf{n}^+ \to \mathbf{1}^+$ (see Section 3.2) induce a weak equivalence

$$\Gamma^o(A/A_0)(\mathbf{n}^+) \xrightarrow{\ pr_1 \times \cdots \times pr_n\ } \prod_{i=1}^{n} \Gamma^o(A/A_0)(\mathbf{1}^+)$$

of pointed simplicial sets, as is readily verified. It follows that the strictly fibrant models of the spectra

$$Spt^2(\Gamma^o(A/A_0)^\wedge)^{n,*} \qquad \text{and} \qquad Spt^2(\Gamma^o(A/A_0)^\wedge)^{*,m}$$

are stably fibrant if $n, m \geq 1$. In effect, the underlying Γ-spaces

$$\Gamma^o(A/A_0)^\wedge(S^n \wedge \mathbf{m}^+) \qquad \text{and} \qquad \Gamma^o(A/A_0)^\wedge(\mathbf{n}^+ \wedge S^m)$$

are *very special* in the sense that the monoids

$$\pi_0 \Gamma^o(A/A_0)^\wedge (S^n \wedge \mathbf{1}^+) \qquad \text{and} \qquad \pi_0 \Gamma^o(A/A_0)^\wedge (\mathbf{1}^+ \wedge S^m)$$

are singleton sets. Now use Theorem 4.2 of [8], which asserts that the spectrum associated to a very special Γ-space is an Ω-spectrum.

It follows that, if one takes a stably fibrant model

$$\nu : Spt^2(\Gamma^o(A/A_0)^\wedge)_{Kan} \to QSpt^2(\Gamma^o(A/A_0)^\wedge)_{Kan}$$

of the strictly fibrant bispectrum $Spt^2(\Gamma^o(A/A_0)^\wedge)_{Kan}$, then the map ν consists of maps

$$Spt^2(\Gamma^o(A/A_0)^\wedge)^{i,j}_{Kan} \to QSpt^2(\Gamma^o(A/A_0)^\wedge)^{i,j}_{Kan}$$

which are weak equivalences of pointed simplicial sets if either $i > 0$ or $j > 0$. In particular, Corollary 3.6 implies that the associated diagonal spectrum

$$dQSpt^2(\Gamma^o(A/A_0)^\wedge)_{Kan}$$

is stably equivalent to the spectrum

$$QSpt^2(\Gamma^o(A/A_0)^\wedge)^{*,0}_{Kan},$$

which is a stably fibrant model for the spectrum

$$Spt(\Gamma^o(A/A_0)) = Spt_*(A).$$

This is a special case of a very general argument which gives:

LEMMA 5.31. *Suppose that X is a special Γ-space, and let $X^\wedge$ denote the bi-Γ-space which is defined by*

$$(\mathbf{n}^+, \mathbf{m}^+) \mapsto X(\mathbf{n}^+ \wedge \mathbf{m}^+).$$

Then the associated diagonal spectrum $dSpt^2(X^\wedge)$ is naturally stably homotopy equivalent to $Spt(X)$.

Here's the moral: any bilinear map

$$(\otimes, \omega_L, \omega_R) : A \times B \to C$$

of symmetric monoidal categories induces a map of bispectra

$$Spt_*(A) \wedge Spt_*(B) \xrightarrow{\otimes} Spt^2(\Gamma^o(C/C_0)^\wedge).$$

Further, the diagonal spectrum $d(Spt^2(\Gamma^o(C/C_0)^\wedge))$ is naturally stably equivalent to $Spt_*(C)$, and so any such bilinear map induces a morphism

$$Spt_*(A) \wedge Spt_*(B) \xrightarrow{\otimes} Spt_*(C) \tag{5.32}$$

in the stable homotopy category.

A *homotopy* of bilinear maps

$$h : (\otimes, \omega_L, \omega_R) \to (\tilde{\otimes}, \tilde{\omega}_L, \tilde{\omega}_R)$$

consists of a natural isomorphism $h : \otimes \to \tilde{\otimes}$ such that h simultaneously induces a homotopy of morphisms of symmetric monoidal categories

(1) from $(\otimes_*, \omega_L)$ to $(\tilde{\otimes}_*, \tilde{\omega}_L)$, and
(2) from $(\otimes_*, \omega_R)$ to $(\tilde{\otimes}, \tilde{\omega}_R)$.

In other words [28, p.65], there are natural isomorphisms $h : a \otimes b \to a\tilde{\otimes}b$ such that the following diagrams commute:

$$
\begin{array}{ccc}
(a_1 \oplus a_2) \otimes b & \xrightarrow{\ h\ } & (a_1 \oplus a_2)\tilde{\otimes}b \\
\omega_L \downarrow & & \downarrow \tilde{\omega}_L \\
(a_1 \otimes b) \oplus (a_2 \otimes b) & \xrightarrow{h \oplus h} & (a_1\tilde{\otimes}b) \oplus (a_2\tilde{\otimes}b)
\end{array}
$$

$$
\begin{array}{ccc}
0 \otimes b & \xrightarrow{\ h\ } & 0\tilde{\otimes}b \\
& {\omega_L}\searrow \quad \swarrow{\tilde{\omega}_L} & \\
& 0 &
\end{array}
$$

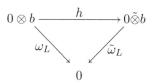

$$
\begin{array}{ccc}
a \otimes (b_1 \oplus b_2) & \xrightarrow{\ h\ } & a\tilde{\otimes}(b_1 \oplus b_2) \\
\omega_R \downarrow & & \downarrow \tilde{\omega}_R \\
(a \otimes b_1) \oplus (a \otimes b_2) & \xrightarrow{h \oplus h} & (a\tilde{\otimes}b_1) \oplus (a\tilde{\otimes}b_2)
\end{array}
$$

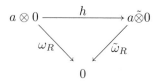

$$
\begin{array}{ccc}
a \otimes 0 & \xrightarrow{\ h\ } & a\tilde{\otimes}0 \\
& {\omega_R}\searrow \quad \swarrow{\tilde{\omega}_R} & \\
& 0 &
\end{array}
$$

Such a homotopy h induces a homotopy

$$h : (\otimes, \omega_L, \omega_R) \to (\tilde{\otimes}, \tilde{\omega}_L, \tilde{\omega}_R)$$

between the corresponding pseudo-natural transformations

$$\Gamma^o A \times \Gamma^o B \to \Gamma^o C^\wedge,$$

which is compatible with the various inclusions of categories of objects isomorphic to 0. There is therefore a homotopy between the induced bi-Γ-space maps

$$\Gamma^o(A/A_0) \wedge \Gamma^o(B/B_0) \to \Gamma^o(C/C_0)^\wedge,$$

which means that the maps

$$\otimes, \tilde{\otimes} : Spt(\Gamma^o(A/A_0)) \wedge Spt(\Gamma^o(B/B_0)) \to Spt^2(\Gamma^o(C/C_0)^\wedge)$$

of bispectra are homotopic. Thus, the existence of such a categorical homotopy h implies that the stable homotopy category morphisms

$$\otimes, \tilde{\otimes} : Spt_*(A) \wedge Spt_*(B) \to Spt_*(C)$$

coincide.

This material can be generalized in several directions. For example, an *n-fold multilinear map* of symmetric monoidal categories consists of a functor

$$\otimes : A_1 \times \cdots \times A_n \to B,$$

written

$$(a_1, \ldots, a_n) \mapsto a_1 \otimes a_2 \otimes \cdots \otimes a_n,$$

together with natural isomorphisms

$$\omega_i : a_1 \otimes \cdots \otimes \overset{i}{(b_1 \oplus b_2)} \otimes \cdots \otimes a_n \to (a_1 \otimes \cdots \otimes \overset{i}{b_1} \otimes \cdots \otimes a_n) \oplus (a_1 \otimes \cdots \otimes \overset{i}{b_2} \otimes \cdots \otimes a_n),$$

$$\omega_i : a_1 \otimes \cdots \otimes \overset{i}{0} \otimes \cdots \otimes a_n \to 0,$$

such that

(1) the isomorphisms ω_i and the functor

$$b \mapsto a_1 \otimes \cdots \otimes \overset{i}{b} \otimes \cdots \otimes a_n$$

together determine a morphism of symmetric monoidal categories $A_i \to B$, for each list of elements $a_j \in A_j$, $j \neq i$, and

(2) if $1 \le i < j \le n$, then the functor

$$A_i \times A_j \to B$$

defined by

$$(a, b) \mapsto a_1 \otimes \cdots \otimes \overset{i}{a} \otimes \cdots \otimes \overset{j}{b} \otimes \cdots \otimes a_n,$$

together with the natural isomorphisms ω_i and ω_j determine a bilinear map of symmetric monoidal categories, and this for each list of elements $a_k \in A_k$, $i, j \ne k$.

In other words, maps in the various factors interchange in pairs, but in view of Lemmas 5.19 and 5.21 the existence of such an n-fold multilinear map $(\otimes, \omega_i)$ is enough to guarantee the existence of a pseudo-natural transformation of pseudo-$(\Gamma^o)^{\times n}$-functors

$$(\otimes, \omega_i) : \Gamma^o A_1 \times \cdots \times \Gamma^o A_n \to \Gamma^o B^{\wedge^n},$$

where $\Gamma^o B^{\wedge^n}$ denotes the composition of the pseudo-functor $\Gamma^o B$ with the functor

$$\wedge^n : \Gamma^o \times \cdots \times \Gamma^o \to \Gamma^o$$

which is defined by

$$(\mathbf{m}_1^+, \ldots, \mathbf{m}_n^+) \mapsto \mathbf{m}_1^+ \wedge \cdots \wedge \mathbf{m}_n^+.$$

The categories A_i and B have subcategories of objects isomorphic to 0 which are killed by analogy with the above to produce maps of n-fold Γ^o spaces which then induce maps of n-fold spectra

$$Spt_*(A_1) \wedge \cdots \wedge Spt_*(A_n) \overset{\otimes}{\to} Spt^n(\Gamma^o(B/B_0)^{\wedge^n}). \tag{5.33}$$

Here $Spt^n(Y)$ is the n-fold spectrum which is associated to an n-fold Γ-space Y. The definition of this functor is analogous to the definition of the bispectrum associated to a bi-Γ-space which is given in (5.30).

The analogue of Lemma 5.31 in this case is

LEMMA 5.34. *Suppose that X is a special Γ-space, and let $X^{\wedge^n}$ denote the n-fold Γ-space which is defined by composition with the functor*

$$\wedge^n : \Gamma^o \times \cdots \times \Gamma^o \to \Gamma^o.$$

Then the diagonal spectrum $d(Spt^n(X^{\wedge^n}))$ is naturally stable homotopy equivalent to $Spt(X)$.

PROOF: The proof is essentially the same as that of Lemma 5.31, except that one uses Corollary 3.8. ∎

In view of Lemma 5.34, any n-fold multilinear map $(\otimes, \omega_i)$ of symmetric monoidal categories determines an n-fold pairing

$$\otimes : Spt_*(A_1) \wedge \cdots \wedge Spt_*(A_n) \to Spt_*(B)$$

in the stable category.

There is a definition of homotopy

$$h : (\otimes, \omega_i) \to (\tilde{\otimes}, \tilde{\omega}_i)$$

of n-fold multilinear maps, by analogy with what we have seen before. Homotopic n-fold multilinear maps induce the same morphism in the stable category.

The same trick which underlies the definition of n-fold multilinear maps of symmetric monoidal categories, namely the observation that one only needs to do pairwise interchanges, allows one to introduce extra parameters at will. Suppose that I is a small index category, and that A_i, $1 \le i \le n$, and B are I-indexed pseudo-functors which take values in symmetric monoidal categories. Then, in view of Corollary 5.22, we can say that an n-fold multilinear map $(\otimes, \omega_i, h_\gamma)$ of such objects consists of n-fold multilinear maps

$$(\otimes, \omega_i) : A_1(j) \times \cdots \times A_n(j) \to B(j),$$

one for each $j \in I$, together with homotopies

$$h_\gamma : \gamma_*(\otimes, \omega_i) \to (\otimes, \omega_i)\gamma_*$$

of n-fold multilinear maps, one for each arrow γ of I, such that the following diagrams commute:

$$
\begin{array}{ccc}
(\gamma\beta)_*(\otimes, \omega_i) & \xrightarrow{\theta(\otimes, \omega_i)} & \gamma_*\beta_*(\otimes, \omega_i) \\
\Big\downarrow{h_{\gamma\beta}} & & \Big\downarrow{\gamma_* h_\beta} \\
 & & \gamma_*(\otimes, \omega_i)\beta_* \\
 & & \Big\downarrow{h_\gamma \beta_*} \\
(\otimes, \omega_i)(\gamma\beta)_* & \xrightarrow[(\otimes, \omega_i)\theta]{} & (\otimes, \omega_i)\gamma_*\beta_*
\end{array}
\tag{5.35}
$$

$$
\begin{array}{ccc}
1_*(\otimes, \omega_i) & \xrightarrow{h_1} & (\otimes, \omega_i)1_* \\
& & \\
\eta(\otimes, \omega_i) \searrow & & \swarrow (\otimes, \omega_i)\eta \\
& (\otimes, \omega_i) &
\end{array}
\tag{5.36}
$$

It hasn't yet been specified how it is that the composites

$$\gamma_*(\otimes, \omega_i) \qquad \text{and} \qquad (\otimes, \omega_i)\gamma_*$$

are n-fold multilinear maps — indeed the notation is really something of an abuse. Suppose that α denotes the natural isomorphisms

$$\gamma_*(a \oplus b) \to \gamma_*(a) \oplus \gamma_*(b) \qquad \text{and} \qquad \gamma_*(0) \to 0$$

that are implicit in the definition of γ_* as a morphism of symmetric monoidal categories. Then one sees that the pairs

$$(\gamma_*\otimes, \alpha \cdot \gamma_*(\omega_i)) \qquad \text{and} \qquad (\otimes\gamma_*, \omega_i \cdot \otimes(\alpha_i))$$

are n-fold multilinear maps, provided that we agree that α_i is the isomorphism

$$(\gamma_*(a_1), \ldots, \gamma_*(b \oplus c), \ldots, \gamma_*(a_n)) \xrightarrow[\cong]{\alpha_i} (\gamma_*(a_1), \ldots, \gamma_*(b) \oplus \gamma_*(c), \ldots, \gamma_*(a_n))$$

which is the isomorphism α in the ith factor, and the identity elsewhere. Now define

$$\gamma_*(\otimes, \omega_i) = (\gamma_*\otimes, \alpha \cdot \gamma_*(\omega_i)), \qquad \text{and}$$
$$(\otimes, \omega_i)\gamma_* = (\otimes\gamma_*, \omega_i \cdot \otimes(\alpha_i)).$$

REMARK 5.37. From this point of view, all n-fold multilinear maps $(\otimes, \omega_i)$: $A_1 \times \cdots \times A_n \to B$ of pseudo-functors taking values in symmetric monoidal categories are preserved by composition with pseudo-natural transformations. Abusing notation as above, one can say that, if $(\otimes, \omega_i)$ is an n-fold multilinear map as above, and $f : B \to B'$ as well as $g_i : D_i \to A_i$ are pseudo-natural transformations in symmetric monoidal categories over the index category I, then the composite

$$f \otimes (g_1 \times \cdots \times g_n) : D_1 \times \cdots \times D_n \to B'$$

is an n-fold multilinear map.   ∎

From what we have seen before, the n-fold multilinear maps $(\otimes, \omega_i)$ give rise to pseudo-natural transformations

$$\otimes : \Gamma^o A_1(i) \times \cdots \times \Gamma^o A_n(i) \to \Gamma^o B(i)^{\wedge^n}$$

for each $i \in I$, and the homotopies h_γ determine homotopies

$$h_\gamma : \gamma_*\otimes \to \otimes\gamma_*$$

of pseudo-natural transformations, such that analogues of diagrams (5.35) and (5.36) commute. But this is enough to specify a pseudo-natural transformation

$$\otimes : \Gamma^o A_1 \times \cdots \times \Gamma^o A_n \to \Gamma^o B^{\wedge^n}$$

of $((\Gamma^o)^{\times n} \times I)$-indexed pseudofunctors.

The extra wrinkle in this case is that the Grothendieck construction

$$[\Gamma^o A_1 \times \cdots \times \Gamma^o A_n]$$

is isomorphic to the fibred product

$$[\Gamma^o A_1] \times_I \cdots \times_I [\Gamma^o A_n]$$

over the index category I. Write

$$\pi : [\Gamma^o A_1 \times \cdots \times \Gamma^o A_n] \to (\Gamma^o)^{\times n} \times I,$$

and

$$\pi : [\Gamma^o A_j] \to \Gamma^o \times I$$

for the respective canonical functors. Then projection onto the jth factor of $(\Gamma^o)^{\times n}$ induces a functor

$$pr_j : \pi \downarrow (\mathbf{m}_1^+, \ldots, \mathbf{m}_n^+, i) \to \pi \downarrow (\mathbf{m}_j^+, i),$$

and these projection functors together induce a functor

$$pr : \pi \downarrow (\mathbf{m}_1^+, \ldots, \mathbf{m}_n^+, i) \to (\pi \downarrow (\mathbf{m}_1^+, i)) \times \cdots \times (\pi \downarrow (\mathbf{m}_n^+, i)), \qquad (5.38)$$

which gives a weak equivalence of simplicial sets after taking nerves of the respective categories [28, p.141].

The functor pr is natural in $i \in I$, as well as in each of the A_j. Define an n-fold I-indexed (Γ^o) space $\Gamma^o(A_1, \ldots, A_n)_*$ on the space level to be the quotient of the space

$$B(\pi_{A_1 \times \cdots \times A_n} \downarrow (\mathbf{m}_1^+, \ldots, \mathbf{m}_n^+, i))$$

by the union of the subspaces

$$B(\pi_{A_1 \times \cdots \times (A_j)_0 \times \cdots \times A_n} \downarrow (\mathbf{m}_1^+, \ldots, \mathbf{m}_n^+, i)),$$

$1 \leq j \leq n$, where $(A_j)_0$ is the subcategory of 0-objects of the symmetric monoidal category A_j. The pairing $\otimes$ takes all products

$$A_1 \times \cdots \times (A_j)_0 \times \cdots \times A_n$$

into the zero object subcategory B_0 of B, while the transformation pr of (5.38) induces a space-level (or pointwise) weak equivalence

$$pr : \Gamma^o(A_1, \ldots, A_n)_* \xrightarrow{\simeq} \Gamma^o(A_1/(A_1)_0) \wedge \cdots \wedge \Gamma^o(A_n/(A_n)_0)$$

of I-indexed n-fold Γ-spaces.

This construction gives rise to maps

$$Spt^n(\Gamma^o(A_1, \ldots, A_n)_*) \xrightarrow{\quad \otimes \quad} Spt^n(\Gamma^o(B/B_0)^{\wedge^n})$$

$$pr \Big\vert \simeq$$

$$Spt_*(A_1) \wedge \cdots \wedge Spt_*(A_n)$$

of I-diagrams of n-fold spectra, and hence to a map

$$\otimes : Spt_*(A_1) \wedge \cdots \wedge Spt_*(A_n) \to Spt_*(B)$$

in the *pointwise* stable category of I-diagrams of spectra.

Suppose finally that $(\otimes, \omega_i, h_\alpha)$ and $(\tilde{\otimes}, \tilde{\omega}_i, \tilde{h}_\alpha)$ are two I-indexed n-fold pairings

$$A_1 \times \cdots \times A_n \to B.$$

A *homotopy* from $(\otimes, \omega_i, h_\gamma)$ to $(\tilde{\otimes}, \tilde{\omega}_i, \tilde{h}_\gamma)$ consists of homotopies

$$H_j : (\otimes, \omega_i) \xrightarrow{\simeq} (\tilde{\otimes}, \tilde{\omega}_i)$$

of n-fold pairings

$$A_1(j) \times \cdots \times A_n(j) \to B(j)$$

such that the following diagram of homotopies of n-fold pairings commutes for each $\gamma : j \to k$ in I:

$$\begin{array}{ccc} \gamma_*(\otimes, \omega_i) & \xrightarrow{\gamma_* H_j} & \gamma_*(\tilde{\otimes}, \tilde{\omega}_i) \\ h_\gamma \Big\downarrow & & \Big\downarrow \tilde{h}_\gamma \\ (\otimes, \omega_i)\gamma_* & \xrightarrow[H_k \gamma_*]{} & (\tilde{\otimes}, \tilde{\omega}_i)\gamma_* \end{array} \qquad (5.39)$$

Homotopic I-indexed n-fold multilinear maps give rise to the same map of I-diagrams of n-fold spectra in the stable homotopy category of I-diagrams of n-fold spectra.

5.3. The algebraic K-theory product

Suppose that

$$\otimes : A \times B \to C$$

is a biexact pairing of exact categories. Then $\otimes$ induces a collection of functors

$$\otimes : Iso(S_n A) \times Iso(S_m B) \to Iso(S_n S_m C), \qquad n, m \geq 0. \qquad (5.40)$$

LEMMA 5.41. *The functors appearing in (5.40) form a bisimplicial pairing of symmetric monoidal categories.*

PROOF: The claim will follow if we can show that the original tensor product

$$\otimes : A \times B \to C$$

is a pairing of symmetric monoidal categories.

Any exact functor is automatically a morphism of symmetric monoidal categories. The functors $b \mapsto a \otimes b$ and $a \mapsto a \otimes b$ are exact, by the biexactness assumption on the pairing $\otimes$, and so there are canonical isomorphisms

$$a \otimes (b_1 \oplus b_2) \xrightarrow{\omega_R} (a \otimes b_1) \oplus (a \otimes b_2), \qquad a \otimes 0 \xrightarrow{\omega_R} 0,$$

and

$$(a_1 \oplus a_2) \otimes b \xrightarrow{\omega_L} (a_1 \otimes b) \oplus (a_2 \otimes b), \qquad 0 \otimes b \xrightarrow{\omega_L} 0,$$

such that $(\otimes_*, \omega_L)$ and $(\otimes_*, \omega_R)$ are morphisms of symmetric monoidal categories. Note in particular that ω_L^{-1} is the unique homomorphism such that the following diagram commutes:

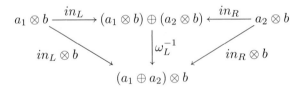

The subcategory of objects isomorphic to 0 in an exact category is a trivial groupoid. Thus, as was pointed out in the last section, we have only to verify that the following diagram of natural isomorphisms commutes:

$$
\begin{array}{ccc}
((a_1 \otimes b_1) \oplus (a_1 \otimes b_2)) \oplus ((a_2 \otimes b_1) \oplus (a_2 \otimes b_2)) & \xrightarrow{\ \alpha\ } & ((a_1 \otimes b_1) \oplus (a_2 \otimes b_1)) \oplus ((a_1 \otimes b_2) \oplus (a_2 \otimes b_2)) \\
\Big\uparrow{\scriptstyle \omega_R \oplus \omega_R} & & \Big\uparrow{\scriptstyle \omega_L \oplus \omega_L} \\
(a_1 \otimes (b_1 \oplus b_2)) \oplus (a_2 \otimes (b_1 \oplus b_2)) & \xrightarrow{\quad} & ((a_1 \oplus a_2) \otimes b_1) \oplus ((a_1 \oplus a_2) \otimes b_2) \\
\Big\uparrow{\scriptstyle \omega_L} & {\scriptstyle \omega_R} & \\
(a_1 \oplus a_2) \otimes (b_1 \oplus b_2) & &
\end{array}
$$

$$(5.42)$$

But this is done by using the canonical definition of ω_L and ω_R, and by restricting to each of the factors $a_i \otimes b_j$ in

$$((a_1 \otimes b_1) \oplus (a_1 \otimes b_2)) \oplus ((a_2 \otimes b_1) \oplus (a_2 \otimes b_2)). \qquad \blacksquare$$

The spectrum $Spt_*(Iso(S.A))$ will be defined for an exact category A by

$$Spt_*(Iso(S.A)) = \varinjlim_n Spt_*(Iso(S_n A)).$$

The difference between this gadget and the spectrum that was denoted by

$$Spt(Iso(S.A))$$

in (5.3) is that one collapses the full subcategories of zero objects to obtain

$$Spt_*(Iso(S.A))$$

(see the development following Condition 5.29). There is a "natural" strict weak equivalence

$$Spt(Iso(S.A)) \to Spt_*(Iso(S.A)).$$

To make the notation easier to deal with, write

$$Spt_*^2(D^\wedge) = Spt_*^2(\Gamma^o(D/D_0)^\wedge))$$

for any symmetric monoidal category D which satisfies Condition 5.29.

Then the pairings obtained in Lemma 5.41 induce maps of bisimplicial bispectra

$$Spt_*(Iso(S_n A)) \wedge Spt_*(Iso(S_m B)) \xrightarrow{\otimes} Spt_*^2(Iso(S_n S_m C)^\wedge).$$

By Lemma 5.31, the bispectrum $Spt_*^2(Iso(S_n S_m C))^\wedge)$ has an associated diagonal spectrum which is stably equivalent to $Spt_*(Iso(S_n S_m C))$. This equivalence respects the bisimplicial structure, and so applying the functor $\varinjlim_n \varinjlim_m$ gives a morphism of bispectra

$$\otimes : Spt_*(Iso(S.A)) \wedge Spt_*(Iso(S.B)) \to Spt_*^2(Iso(S_.^2 C)^\wedge), \qquad (5.43)$$

which then induces a morphism

$$\otimes : Spt_*(Iso(S.A)) \wedge Spt_*(Iso(S.B)) \to Spt_*(Iso(S_.^2 C))$$

in the stable homotopy category.

Note that $Spt_*(Iso(S_*^2C))$ is defined to be the homotopy colimit of the obvious bisimplicial spectrum. Similarly, $Spt_*(Iso(S_*^nC))$ is defined to be the homotopy colimit of the n-fold simplicial spectrum

$$Spt_*(Iso(S_{m_1} \ldots S_{m_n}C)).$$

The map

$$\otimes : Spt_*(Iso(S.A)) \wedge Spt_*(Iso(S.B)) \rightarrow Spt_*^2(Iso(S_*^2C)^\wedge) \qquad (5.44)$$

of bispectra which underlies the morphism (5.43) is the object of interest in what follows.

Very generally, suppose that X and Y are spectra, and that Z is a bispectrum. Suppose also that $\phi : X \wedge Y \rightarrow Z$ is a map of bispectra. X, Y and Z can be replaced up to strict weak equivalence by strictly fibrant models by forming the diagram

$$(5.45)$$

$$
\begin{array}{ccccc}
X_c \wedge Y_c & \xrightarrow{\pi_X \wedge \pi_Y} & X \wedge Y & \xrightarrow{\phi} & Z \\
\downarrow{\scriptstyle i_X \wedge i_Y} & & & & \downarrow{\scriptstyle i_Z} \\
X_{cf} \wedge Y_{cf} & \dashrightarrow[\phi]{} & & & Z_f,
\end{array}
$$

where π_X and π_Y are trivial strict fibrations, X_c and Y_c are cofibrant, i_X, i_Y and i_Z are cofibrations and strict weak equivalences, X_{cf}, Y_{cf} and Z_f are strictly fibrant, and the dotted arrow exists because $i_X \wedge i_Y$ is a cofibration and a strict weak equivalence by Lemma 3.14. The resulting map $\phi : X_{cf} \wedge Y_{cf} \rightarrow Z_f$ of bispectra induces a morphism of bispectra

$$\mathbf{hom}_*(S^1, X_{cf}) \wedge \mathbf{hom}_*(S^1, Y_{cf}) \xrightarrow{\phi_*} \mathbf{hom}_*(S^2, Z_f),$$

where $S^2 = S^1 \wedge S^1$, as always.

The 2-fold loop bispectrum

$$\mathbf{hom}_*(S^2, Spt_*^2(Iso(S_*^2C)^\wedge)_f)$$

can be identified with the K-theory spectrum KC in the stable category, by Corollary 5.16, and so the pairing (5.44) induces a smash product pairing

$$\otimes : KA \wedge KB \rightarrow KC \qquad (5.46)$$

of K-theory spectra, by the yoga of diagram (5.45).

LEMMA 5.47. *Suppose that A, B and C are pseudo-functors defined on an index category I and taking values in the category of exact categories and exact functors. Suppose that the functors*

$$\otimes : A(i) \times B(i) \to C(i)$$

comprise part of the data for a pseudo-natural biexact pairing $(\otimes, h)$. Then $(\otimes, h)$ gives rise to a bisimplicial pseudo-natural pairing

$$\otimes : Iso(S_n A(i)) \times Iso(S_m B(i)) \to Iso(S_n S_m C(i))$$

of symmetric monoidal categories.

PROOF: We have already seen in Lemma 5.41 that each of the biexact functors

$$\otimes : A(i) \times B(i) \to C(i)$$

gives rise to a bisimplicial pairing

$$\otimes : Iso(S_n A(i)) \times Iso(S_m B(i)) \to Iso(S_n S_m C(i))$$

of symmetric monoidal categories. We have to establish pseudo-naturality. Suppose that $f : i \to j$ is a morphism of the index category I, and let

$$\zeta : f_*(a \oplus b) \xrightarrow{\cong} f_*(a) \oplus f_*(b)$$

denote the canonical isomorphism arising from the exactness of the induced functor f_* in each of the categories $A(j)$, $B(j)$ and $C(j)$. Let

$$h_f : f_*(a \otimes b) \xrightarrow{\cong} f_*(a) \otimes f_*(b)$$

be the natural isomorphism arising from the pseudo-naturality of the pairing $\otimes$.

I claim that the map h_f determines a homotopy of bilinear maps of symmetric monoidal categories

$$h_f : (f_*\otimes, \zeta f_*(\omega_L), \zeta f_*(\omega_R)) \to (\otimes f_*, \omega_L \otimes (\zeta_L), \omega_R \otimes (\zeta_R)).$$

This means precisely that the following diagrams commute:

$$
\begin{array}{ccc}
f_*((a_1 \oplus a_2) \otimes b) & \xrightarrow{\quad h_f \quad} & f_*(a_1 \oplus a_2) \otimes f_*(b) \\
{\scriptstyle f_*(\omega_L)} \downarrow & & \downarrow {\scriptstyle \zeta \otimes 1} \\
f_*((a_1 \otimes b) \oplus (a_2 \otimes b)) & & (f_*(a_1) \oplus f_*(a_2)) \otimes f_*(b) \\
{\scriptstyle \zeta} \downarrow & & \downarrow {\scriptstyle \omega_L} \\
f_*(a_1 \otimes b) \oplus f_*(a_2 \otimes b) & \xrightarrow{\; h_f \oplus h_f \;} & (f_*(a_1) \otimes f_*(b)) \oplus (f_*(a_2) \otimes f_*(b))
\end{array}
$$

$$\begin{array}{ccc}
f_*(a \otimes (b_1 \oplus b_2)) & \xrightarrow{\quad h_f \quad} & f_*(a) \otimes f_*(b_1 \oplus b_2) \\
{\scriptstyle f_*(\omega_R)}\Big\downarrow & & \Big\downarrow{\scriptstyle 1 \otimes \zeta} \\
f_*((a \otimes b_1) \oplus (a \otimes b_2)) & & (f_*(a) \otimes (f_*(b_1) \oplus f_*(b_2))) \\
{\scriptstyle \zeta}\Big\downarrow & & \Big\downarrow{\scriptstyle \omega_R} \\
f_*(a \otimes b_1) \oplus f_*(a \otimes b_2) & \xrightarrow[h_f \oplus h_f]{} & (f_*(a) \otimes f_*(b_1)) \oplus (f_*(a) \otimes f_*(b_2))
\end{array}$$

But this is a consequence of the exactness of f_* and the biexactness of $\otimes$ — use the definitions of ω_L, ω_R, ζ and h_f. The pairing $\otimes$ is presumed to be a pseudo-functor, so the homotopies automatically satisfy the commutativity conditions (5.35) and (5.36). ∎

The reader is invited to formulate and prove an n-fold analogue of Lemma 5.47.

This same result guarantees that a pseudo-natural biexact pairing

$$\otimes : A(i) \times B(i) \to C(i)$$

induces a pairing

$$\otimes : Spt_*(Iso(S.A(i))) \wedge Spt_*(Iso(S.B(i))) \to Spt_*^2(Iso(S_.^2 C(i))^\wedge)$$

in the stable category of I-diagrams of bispectra.

Suppose that Y is a scheme, and recall that ordinary tensor product determines a biexact functor on vector bundles over Y

$$\otimes : \mathcal{P}Y \times \mathcal{P}Y \to \mathcal{P}Y \tag{5.48}$$

By Lemma 5.41, this functor induces a bisimplicial pairing of symmetric monoidal categories

$$\otimes : Iso(S_n \mathcal{P}Y) \times Iso(S_m \mathcal{P}Y) \to Iso(S_n S_m \mathcal{P}Y)$$

which gives rise, via the process described above, to the K-theory smash product pairing

$$\otimes : KY \wedge KY \to KY \tag{5.49}$$

on Y.

Suppose more generally that $X : I \to Sch$ is an I-diagram of schemes, and take the associated categories of vector bundles $i \mapsto \mathcal{P}X(i)$ to get an

I-indexed pseudo-functor taking values in exact categories, and hence in symmetric monoidal categories. For us, the main consequence of Lemma 5.47 is that the bilinear maps

$$(\otimes, \omega_L, \omega_R) : \mathcal{P}X(i) \times \mathcal{P}X(i) \to \mathcal{P}X(i), \qquad i \in I,$$

and the homotopies $h_{X(\gamma)}$, γ in I, together determine a bilinear map

$$(\otimes, \omega_L, \omega_R, h_{X(\gamma)}) : \mathcal{P}X \times \mathcal{P}X \to \mathcal{P}X$$

of I-indexed pseudo-functors taking values in symmetric monoidal categories. To repeat part of the proof of Lemma 5.47, this implies that there is a bisimplicial bilinear pairing of pseudo-functors

$$(\otimes, \omega_L, \omega_R, h_{X(\gamma)}) : Iso(S_n \mathcal{P}X) \times Iso(S_m \mathcal{P}X) \to Iso(S_n S_m \mathcal{P}X).$$

This pairing induces bisimplicial maps

$$
\begin{array}{ccc}
Spt^2(\Gamma^o(Iso(S_n \mathcal{P}X), Iso(S_m \mathcal{P}X))_*) & \xrightarrow{\ \otimes\ } & Spt^2_*(Iso(S_n S_m \mathcal{P}X)^\wedge) \\
pr \downarrow \simeq & & \\
Spt_*(Iso(S_n \mathcal{P}X)) \wedge Spt_*(Iso(S_m \mathcal{P}X)) & &
\end{array}
$$

of I-diagrams of bispectra, and hence determines maps of I-diagrams of bispectra

$$
\begin{array}{ccc}
Spt^2(\Gamma^o(Iso(S.\mathcal{P}X), Iso(S.\mathcal{P}X))_*) & \xrightarrow{\ \otimes\ } & Spt^2_*(Iso(S^2_{\cdot} \mathcal{P}X)^\wedge) \\
pr \downarrow \simeq & \nearrow & \\
Spt_*(Iso(S.\mathcal{P}X)) \wedge Spt_*(Iso(S.\mathcal{P}X)) & &
\end{array} \qquad (5.50)
$$

after taking homotopy colimits in both simplicial directions.

The dotted arrow in diagram (5.52) is the induced morphism in the homotopy category of I-diagrams of bispectra. It is represented by a natural morphism

$$Spt_*(Iso(S.\mathcal{P}X))_c \wedge Spt_*(Iso(S.\mathcal{P}X))_c \xrightarrow{\ \otimes\ } Spt^2_*(Iso(S^2_{\cdot} \mathcal{P}X)^\wedge)_f,$$

which is unique up to homotopy, provided that $Spt_*(Iso(S.\mathcal{P}X))_c$ is a cofibrant model for $Spt_*(Iso(S.\mathcal{P}X))$, and $Spt^2_*(Iso(S^2_{\cdot}\mathcal{P}X)^\wedge)_f$ is a stably pointwise fibrant model for $Spt_*^2(Iso(S_*^2 \mathcal{P}X)^\wedge)$. Use Lemma 3.14 to see this, together with the usual closed model category trick.

In general, if $\phi : X_c \wedge Y_c \to Z_f$ is a morphism of I-diagrams of bispectra such that X_c and Y_c are cofibrant I-diagrams of spectra, and Z_f is stably pointwise fibrant, then there are trivial cofibrations

$$j_X : X_c \to X_{cf} \quad \text{and} \quad j_Y : Y_c \to Y_{cf}$$

such that the I-diagrams X_{cf} and Y_{cf} are fibrant as well as cofibrant. Then Lemma 3.14 implies that the map $j_X \wedge j_Y$ is a trivial cofibration of I-diagrams of bispectra, and so the map ϕ has an extension

$$
\begin{array}{ccc}
X_c \wedge Y_c & \xrightarrow{\ \phi\ } & Z_f \\
{\scriptstyle j_X \wedge j_Y} \downarrow & \nearrow & \\
X_{cf} \wedge Y_{cf}. & &
\end{array}
$$

It follows that the maps in (5.50) uniquely determine a morphism

$$\mathbf{hom}_*(S^1, Spt_*(Iso(S.\mathcal{P}X))_{cf}) \wedge \mathbf{hom}_*(S^1, Spt_*(Iso(S.\mathcal{P}X))_{cf})$$

$$\otimes \downarrow \qquad\qquad\qquad (5.51)$$

$$\mathbf{hom}_*(S^2, Spt_*^2(Iso(S_*^2 \mathcal{P}X)^\wedge)_f),$$

in the pointwise strict homotopy category of I-diagrams of bispectra. This map can be identified in the pointwise stable category of I-diagrams with a smash product pairing

$$\otimes : KX \wedge KX \to KX,$$

of I-diagrams of K-theory spectra.

The construction of the natural pairing just given is really only a prototype. One can, for example, also use tensor product to pair G-theory (quasi-coherent sheaves) with K-theory to obtain natural pairings

$$\otimes : KX \wedge GX \to GX$$

for any diagram of schemes X. There is also the important special case where the diagram of schemes X is the étale site of a scheme S. In this case, one obtains the smash product pairing

$$\otimes : K^{et} \wedge K^{et} \to K^{et}$$

on the étale K-theory presheaf.

If one defines the mod ℓ étale K-theory presheaf $K/\ell = (K/\ell)^{et}$ to be the pointwise smash product $K^{et} \wedge Y_\ell$ of K^{et} with the mod ℓ Moore spectrum Y_ℓ, then the ring spectrum structure $Y_\ell \wedge Y_\ell \to Y_\ell$ (for primes $\ell > 3$) and the pairing $\otimes$ together determine a smash product pairing

$$\otimes : K/\ell \wedge K/\ell \to K/\ell.$$

The associativity, commutativity and the existence of 2-sided identity properties for the tensor product (up to canonical homotopies) can be used, in conjunction with the discussion of n-fold multilinear maps of symmetric monoidal categories and pseudo-functors of such, to show that the tensor product gives the K-theory spectra KX of schemes and diagrams of schemes X the structure of ring spectra (or diagrams of such). In particular, the mod ℓ étale K-theory presheaf is a presheaf of associative ring spectra if $\ell > 3$.

5.4. K-theory transfer
Suppose that

$$
\begin{array}{ccc}
A & \xrightarrow{\ f\ } & C \\
\pi \downarrow & & \downarrow \pi' \\
B & \xrightarrow{\ f'\ } & D,
\end{array}
\tag{5.52}
$$

is a commutative diagram of ring homomorphisms, and let N be a B-module. The *base change* map is a natural C-linear map

$$\omega : C \otimes_A N \to D \otimes_B N \tag{5.53}$$

which is defined for B-modules N by the assignment $c \otimes n \mapsto \pi'(c) \otimes n$.

The map ω is an isomorphism for $N = B$, and therefore for all finitely generated projective B-modules N, if the square (5.52) is a pushout in the category of rings.

If the ring B is a finitely generated projective A-module, then the direct image (or restriction of scalars) functor π_* preserves finitely generated projectives, and hence defines an exact functor

$$\pi_* : \mathcal{P}(B) \to \mathcal{P}(A)$$

which we shall call the *transfer*, because it induces such on the level of K-theory spectra.

If the ring B is a finitely generated projective A-module and the square (5.52) is a pushout, then D is a finitely generated projective C-module, and the base change map ω restricts to an isomorphism

$$C \otimes_A P \xrightarrow[\cong]{\ \omega\ } D \otimes_B P$$

of projective C-modules, for all finitely generated projective B-modules P. This isomorphism ω respects direct sums up to canonical isomorphism, and so the diagram (5.52) induces a homotopy-commutative diagram

$$\begin{array}{ccc} \mathcal{P}(B) & \xrightarrow{(f')^*} & \mathcal{P}(D) \\ \pi_* \downarrow & & \downarrow (\pi')_* \\ \mathcal{P}(A) & \xrightarrow{f^*} & \mathcal{P}(C) \end{array}$$

of morphisms of symmetric monoidal categories, with specific homotopy given by ω.

The base change map is horizontally and vertically pseudo-natural:

(1) any commutative diagram

$$\begin{array}{ccccc} A_1 & \xrightarrow{g} & A_2 & \xrightarrow{f} & A_3 \\ \pi_1 \downarrow & & \pi_2 \downarrow & & \downarrow \pi_3 \\ B_1 & \xrightarrow[g']{} & B_2 & \xrightarrow[f']{} & B_3 \end{array}$$

of ring homomorphisms gives rise to a commutative diagram of natural transformations

$$\begin{array}{ccccc} f^* g^* (\pi_1)_* & \xrightarrow{f^* \omega} & f^* (\pi_2)_* (g')^* & \xrightarrow{\omega(g')^*} & (\pi_3)_* (f')^* (g')^* \\ \theta(\pi_1)_* \downarrow & & & & \downarrow (\pi_3)_* \theta \\ (fg)^* (\pi_1)_* & & \xrightarrow{\hspace{3cm} \omega \hspace{3cm}} & & (\pi_3)_* (f'g')^*, \end{array}$$

(2) any commutative diagram

$$\begin{array}{ccc} A_1 & \xrightarrow{f_1} & B_1 \\ \pi_1 \downarrow & & \downarrow \pi_1' \\ A_2 & \xrightarrow{f_2} & B_2 \\ \pi_2 \downarrow & & \downarrow \pi_2' \\ A_3 & \xrightarrow[f_3]{} & B_3 \end{array}$$

of rings induces a diagram of transformations

$$f_1^*(\pi_1)_*(\pi_2)_* \xrightarrow{\omega(\pi_2)_*} (\pi_1')_*f_2^*(\pi_2)_* \xrightarrow{(\pi_1')_*\omega} (\pi_1')_*(\pi_2')_*f_3^*$$

$$f_1^*(\pi_2\pi_1)_* \xrightarrow{\hspace{4cm}\omega\hspace{4cm}} (\pi_2'\pi_1')_*f_3^*,$$

and

(3) the diagrams

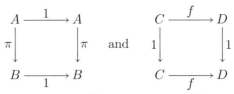

and

commute.

The instances of ω in item (3) arise from (pushout) diagrams

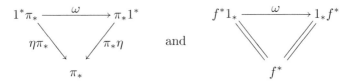

respectively, and the maps $\eta : 1^* \xrightarrow{\cong} 1$ and $\theta : g^*f^* \xrightarrow{\cong} (gf)^*$ are the standard isomorphisms. One shows that all of these properties are satisfied, either by using adjunction maps or by chasing elements through canonical maps of tensor products.

EXAMPLE 5.54. Suppose that A and B are I-diagrams in the category of commutative rings, and that $\pi : A \to B$ is a natural transformation. Suppose further that

(1) each ring homomorphism $\pi : A(i) \to B(i)$ gives $B(i)$ the structure of a finitely generated projective $A(i)$-module, and

(2) for each morphism $\alpha : i \to j$ in the index category I, the diagram

$$\begin{array}{ccc} A(i) & \xrightarrow{\alpha} & A(j) \\ \pi \downarrow & & \downarrow \pi \\ B(i) & \xrightarrow{\alpha} & B(j) \end{array}$$

is a pushout.

Then the properties of the base change map given above (specifically horizontal pseudo-naturality) imply that the transfer maps $\pi_* : \mathcal{P}(B(i)) \to \mathcal{P}(A(i))$ and the base change isomorphisms $\omega : \alpha^* \pi_* \cong \pi_* \alpha^*$ together determine a pseudo-natural transformation

$$(\pi_*, \omega) : \mathcal{P}(B) \to \mathcal{P}(A)$$

between the pseudo-functors taking values in symmetric monoidal categories which are associated to finitely generated projective modules along the diagrams A and B. It follows, by the methods of the last chapter, that transfer along π induces a natural transformation

$$\pi_* : KB \to KA$$

of the associated I-diagrams of K-theory spectra, and that, for each $i \in I$, this map restricts to the standard K-theory transfer

$$\pi_* : KB(i) \to KA(i)$$

up to stable homotopy equivalence.   ∎

EXAMPLE 5.55. The example of this phenomenon that will consume our attention later on arises from the pushout diagrams

$$
\begin{array}{ccc}
k & \xrightarrow{\ 1\ } & k \\
{\scriptstyle i}\downarrow & & \downarrow{\scriptstyle i} \\
L & \xrightarrow[\ g\ ]{\cong} & L
\end{array}
$$

that one has when L/k is a finite Galois extension, and where $g \in G = Gal(L/k)$. It follows in particular that the K-theory transfer map $i_* : K(L) \to K(k)$ can be modelled up to stable equivalence by a G-equivariant map, where the Galois group G acts as it should on $K(L)$ and $K(k)$.   ∎

EXAMPLE 5.56. Suppose that L/k is a Galois extension with Galois group $G = Gal(L/k)$ as above, and that N/k is a Galois extension with Galois group $H = Gal(N/k)$ such that L is contained in N. Denote all possible field inclusions by i, as in the diagram

$$N.$$

Let $\pi : H \to G$ be the induced epimorphism of Galois groups. Then there are iterated pushout diagrams

$$
\begin{array}{ccc}
k & \xrightarrow{\ \ 1\ \ } & k \\
{\scriptstyle i}\downarrow & & \downarrow{\scriptstyle i} \\
L & \xrightarrow{\ \pi(h)\ } & L \\
{\scriptstyle i}\downarrow & & \downarrow{\scriptstyle i} \\
N & \xrightarrow{\ \ h\ \ } & N
\end{array}
$$

corresponding to each element h of the group $H.$, and so the K-theory transfer induces H-equivariant maps $i_* : K(N) \to K(L)$ and $i_* : K(L) \to K(k)$. Furthermore, vertical pseudo-naturality for the base change isomorphism ω implies that the composite of the H-equivariant pseudo-natural transformations $i_* : \mathcal{P}(N) \to \mathcal{P}(L)$ and $i_* : \mathcal{P}(L) \to \mathcal{P}(k)$ is the pseudo-natural transformation $i_* : \mathcal{P}(N) \to \mathcal{P}(k)$, on the nose. Thus, successive transfers give a commutative diagram of H-equivariant maps of spectra

$$
\begin{array}{ccc}
K(N) & \xrightarrow{\ i_*\ } & K(L) \\
& {\scriptstyle i_*}\searrow & \downarrow{\scriptstyle i_*} \\
& & K(k)
\end{array}
\qquad\blacksquare
$$

EXAMPLE 5.57. Suppose that L/k is a Galois extension with Galois group G as above, and that there is a diagram of field extensions

$$
\begin{array}{ccc}
L & \xhookleftarrow{\ j\ } & L \cdot M \\
{\scriptstyle i}\uparrow & & \uparrow{\scriptstyle i} \\
k & \xhookleftarrow{\ j\ } & M,
\end{array}
\tag{5.58}
$$

where $k = L \cap M$. Then the compositum $L \cdot M$ is Galois over M with Galois group G in such a way that the field inclusion $j : L \to L \cdot M$ is G-equivariant. It follows that there are G-equivariant pseudo-natural transformations

$$
\mathcal{P}(L) \xrightarrow{\ j^*\ } \mathcal{P}(L \cdot M) \xrightarrow{\ i_*\ } \mathcal{P}(M)
$$

and

$$
\mathcal{P}(L) \xrightarrow{\ i_*\ } \mathcal{P}(k) \xrightarrow{\ j^*\ } \mathcal{P}(M).
$$

It is again a consequence of horizontal pseudo-naturality for the base change map that these two composites are G-equivariantly homotopic, via the base change isomorphism

$$\omega : j^* i_* \xrightarrow{\cong} i_* j^*.$$

One has merely to note that the diagram (5.58) is a pushout in the category of rings, and then make sure that the appropriate diagram of canonical isomorphisms commutes. ∎

Suppose that the ring homomorphism $\pi : A \to B$ gives B the structure of a finitely generated projective A-module, and consider the (non-commutative) diagram

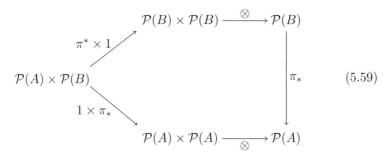

$$(5.59)$$

Observe that, if P is a projective A-module and Q is a projective B-module, then

$$\pi_* \otimes (\pi^* \times 1)(P, Q) = (B \otimes_A P) \otimes_B Q,$$

whereas

$$\otimes(1 \times \pi_*)(P, Q) = P \otimes_A Q.$$

There is a canonical A-module isomorphism

$$P \otimes_A Q \xrightarrow[\cong]{m} (B \otimes_A P) \otimes_B Q$$

given by the assignment

$$p \otimes q \mapsto (1 \otimes p) \otimes q.$$

This isomorphism respects direct sums in P and Q, so it determines a homotopy of bilinear maps

$$m : \otimes(1 \times \pi_*) \xrightarrow[\cong]{m} \pi_* \otimes (\pi^* \times 1).$$

Suppose that

$$\begin{array}{ccc} A_1 & \longrightarrow & A_2 \\ \pi_1 \downarrow & & \downarrow \pi_2 \\ B_1 & \longrightarrow & B_2 \end{array}$$

$$(5.60)$$

is a pushout diagram of ring homomorphisms such that B_1 is a finitely generated projective A_1-module. Suppose that $M \in \mathcal{P}(A_1)$ and $N \in \mathcal{P}(B_1)$. Then the following diagram of canonical isomorphisms commutes:

$$
\begin{array}{ccc}
A_2 \otimes_{A_1} ((B_1 \otimes_{A_1} M) \otimes_{B_1} N) & \xleftarrow{\quad 1 \otimes m \quad} & A_2 \otimes_{A_1} (M \otimes_{A_1} N) \\
\omega \downarrow & & \downarrow \theta \\
B_2 \otimes_{B_1} ((B_1 \otimes_{A_1} M) \otimes_{B_1} N) & & (A_2 \otimes_{A_1} M) \otimes_{A_2} (A_2 \otimes_{A_1} N) \\
\theta \downarrow & & \\
(B_2 \otimes_{B_1} (B_1 \otimes_{A1} M)) \otimes_{B_2} (B_2 \otimes_{B_1} N) & & \downarrow 1 \otimes \omega \\
\downarrow & & \\
(B_2 \otimes_{A_2} (A_2 \otimes_{A_1} M)) \otimes_{B_2} (B_2 \otimes_{B_1} N) & \xleftarrow{\quad m \quad} & (A_2 \otimes_{A_1} M) \otimes_{A_2} (B_2 \otimes_{B_1} M)
\end{array}
$$

commutes. In other words, the homotopy m is natural with respect to pushout diagrams (5.60). We have therefore proved

LEMMA 5.61. *Suppose given a natural transformation* $\pi : A \to B$ *of I-diagrams of rings, as in Example 5.54. Then the natural $A(i)$-module isomorphisms*

$$
m : (P \otimes_{A(i)} B(i)) \otimes_{B(i)} Q \xrightarrow{\cong} P \otimes_{A(i)} Q,
$$

defined for $P \in \mathcal{P}(A(i))$ and $Q \in \mathcal{P}(B(i))$ and all $i \in I$ determine a homotopy

$$
m : \pi_* \otimes (\pi^* \otimes 1) \to \otimes (1 \times \pi_*)
$$

of pseudo-natural bilinear maps of symmetric monoidal categories.

COROLLARY 5.62. *The natural transformation of functors in Lemma 5.61 induces a commutative diagram in the pointwise stable category of I-diagrams of spectra*

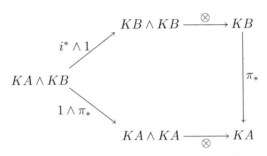

PROOF: Use Lemma 5.61 and the results of Section 5.3. ∎

Corollary 5.62 is also called the *projection formula*. The non-equivariant version of it is well known. The case of particular interest for us in what follows arises from Galois extensions of fields.

COROLLARY 5.63. *Suppose that L/k is a finite Galois extension of a field k, with Galois group G, and let i denote the inclusion map $k \subset L$. Then there is a commutative diagram*

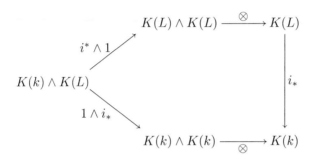

in the pointwise stable category of G-spectra.

5.5. Join transformations

Suppose that C is a category, and let $X : I \to C$ and $Y : J \to C$ be functors. Let $\tilde{X} : I \times J \to C$ be the composite functor

$$I \times J \xrightarrow{pr} I \xrightarrow{X} C,$$

and let $\tilde{Y} : I \times J \to C$ be the composite

$$I \times J \xrightarrow{pr} J \xrightarrow{Y} C.$$

A *join transformation* ζ from X to Y is defined to be a natural transformation

$$\zeta : \tilde{X} \to \tilde{Y}.$$

Observe that such a ζ consists of maps

$$X(i) = \tilde{X}(i, j) \xrightarrow{\zeta} \tilde{Y}(i, j) = Y(j)$$

such that the following diagram commutes for all morphisms $(\alpha, \beta) : (i, j) \to (i', j')$ of $I \times J$:

$$
\begin{array}{ccc}
X(i) & \xrightarrow{\zeta} & Y(j) \\
{\scriptstyle X(\alpha)}\downarrow & & \downarrow{\scriptstyle Y(\beta)} \\
X(i') & \xrightarrow{\zeta} & Y(j').
\end{array}
$$

Similarly, suppose that $X : I \rightsquigarrow cat$ and $Y : J \rightsquigarrow cat$ are pseudo-functors, and write $\tilde{X} : I \times J \rightsquigarrow cat$ for the composite

$$I \times J \xrightarrow{pr} I \xrightarrow{X} cat,$$

respectively $\tilde{Y} : I \times J \rightsquigarrow cat$ for the composite

$$I \times J \xrightarrow{pr} J \xrightarrow{Y} cat.$$

A *pseudo join transformation* is defined to be a pseudo-natural transformation

$$\zeta : \tilde{X} \to \tilde{Y}.$$

Recall from Lemma 5.19 that such a gadget must consist of pseudo natural transformations

$$(\zeta, \omega_L) : \tilde{X}(*, j) \to \tilde{Y}(*, j), \qquad j \in J,$$

and

$$(\zeta, \omega_R) : \tilde{X}(i, *) \to \tilde{Y}(i, *), \qquad i \in I,$$

which satisfy the interchange condition (5.1). In particular, the pseudo join transformation ζ consists of functors

$$\zeta : X(i) \to Y(j)$$

together with natural isomorphisms

$$\omega_L : \zeta \xrightarrow{\cong} \zeta X(\alpha), \qquad \alpha \text{ in } I,$$

and

$$\omega_R : Y(\beta)\zeta \xrightarrow{\cong} \zeta, \qquad \beta \text{ in } J,$$

such that ω_L and ω_R satisfy the axioms for pseudo natural transformations. The interchange condition in this case is the requirement that the following diagram of natural isomorphisms commutes for all α in I and β in J:

$$
\begin{array}{ccc}
Y(\beta)\zeta & \xrightarrow{\ \omega_R\ } & \zeta \\
{\scriptstyle Y(\beta)\omega_L}\downarrow & & \downarrow{\scriptstyle \omega_L} \\
Y(\beta)\zeta X(\alpha) & \xrightarrow[\ \omega_R X(\alpha)\ ]{} & \zeta X(\alpha).
\end{array}
$$

This diagram commutes trivially, so the interchange condition is no condition at all for pseudo-join transformations.

A *homotopy* $h : \zeta \to \zeta'$ of pseudo join transformations $\zeta, \zeta' : X \to Y$ consists of natural isomorphisms

$$h : \zeta \xrightarrow{\cong} \zeta'$$

such that the diagrams

$$
\begin{array}{ccc}
Y(\beta)\zeta & \xrightarrow{Y(\beta)h} & Y(\beta)\zeta' \\
{\scriptstyle \omega_R}\Big\downarrow & & \Big\downarrow{\scriptstyle \omega_R} \\
\zeta & \xrightarrow{\quad h \quad} & \zeta'
\end{array}
$$

and

$$
\begin{array}{ccc}
\zeta & \xrightarrow{\quad h \quad} & \zeta' \\
{\scriptstyle \omega_L}\Big\downarrow & & \Big\downarrow{\scriptstyle \omega_L} \\
\zeta X(\alpha) & \xrightarrow{hX(\alpha)} & \zeta' X(\alpha)
\end{array}
$$

commute.

EXAMPLE 5.64. Let $X : I \rightsquigarrow cat$ and $Y : J \rightsquigarrow cat$ be pseudo-functors as above. Suppose that Z is a category, and that

$$(\epsilon, \tilde{\omega}_L) : X \to Z$$

is a pseudo-natural transformation, where Z has the trivial I-diagram structure. Suppose also that there is a pseudo-natural transformation

$$(\zeta, \tilde{\omega}_R) : Z \to Y,$$

for the trivial J-diagram structure on Z. Then the composite transformations

$$X(i) \xrightarrow{\epsilon} Z \xrightarrow{\zeta} Y(j),$$

together with the natural isomorphisms

$$Y(\beta)\zeta\epsilon \xrightarrow{\tilde{\omega}_R \epsilon} \zeta\epsilon,$$

and

$$\zeta\epsilon \xrightarrow{\zeta\tilde{\omega}_L} \zeta\epsilon X(\alpha)$$

determine a pseudo join transformation

$$(\zeta\epsilon, \zeta\tilde{\omega}_L, \tilde{\omega}_R\epsilon) : X \to Y.$$ ∎

EXAMPLE 5.65. Suppose that L/k is a finite Galois extension of a field k, with Galois group G. Example 5.64 implies that the transfer functor

$$i_* : \mathcal{P}(L) \to \mathcal{P}(k)$$

is part of the data for a pseudo-natural G-transformation $(i_*, \tilde{\omega}_L)$ with respect to the G-structure on $\mathcal{P}(L)$, and for the trivial G-structure on $\mathcal{P}(k)$. The base change functor

$$i^* : \mathcal{P}(k) \to \mathcal{P}(L)$$

is well known to be pseudo-G-equivariant: let $\tilde{\omega}_R$ denote the corresponding structural isomorphism. It follows that the composite

$$\mathcal{P}(L) \xrightarrow{i_*} \mathcal{P}(k) \xrightarrow{i^*} \mathcal{P}(L)$$

is a pseudo join transformation, for the G-structure on $\mathcal{P}(L)$.   ∎

EXAMPLE 5.66. Suppose that L/k and the k-algebra k are as above. There is a morphism

$$\tilde{N} : \mathcal{P}(L) \to \mathcal{P}(L)$$

of symmetric monoidal categories, which is defined on finite dimensional L-vector spaces V by

$$V \mapsto \bigoplus_{g \in G} g^*V.$$

For each $r \in G$, there is a natural isomorphism $\omega_L : \tilde{N}(V) \to \tilde{N}r^*(V)$, which is defined to be the inverse of the composite

$$\bigoplus_{g \in G} g^*r^*V \cong \bigoplus_{g \in G} (gr)^*V \xrightarrow[\cong]{\sigma_r} \bigoplus_{g \in G} g^*V,$$

where σ_r is the "shuffle" defined by the commutativity of the diagram

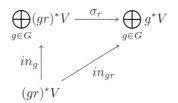

Similarly, for each $h \in G$, there is a natural isomorphism $\omega_R : h^*N(V) \rightarrow N(V)$, given by the composite

$$h^*\left(\bigoplus_{g \in G} g^* P\right) \cong \bigoplus_{g \in G} h^* g^* P \cong \bigoplus_{g \in G} (gh)^* P \xrightarrow[\cong]{s_h} \bigoplus_{g \in G} g^* P,$$

where the shuffle s_h is defined by analogy with σ_k. The unlabelled isomorphisms in both of these compositions arise from the structure of the pseudo-functor $B \mapsto \mathcal{P}(B)$ taking values in symmetric monoidal categories. The transformation $\tilde{N}$ and the natural isomorphisms ω_L and ω_R together form a pseudo join transformation

$$(\tilde{N}, \omega_L, \omega_R) : \mathcal{P}(L) \rightarrow \mathcal{P}(L)$$

of G-pseudo functors. $\blacksquare$

PROPOSITION 5.67. *There is a homotopy of pseudo join transformations*

$$H : (i^* i_*, i^* \tilde{\omega}_L, \tilde{\omega}_R i_*) \xrightarrow{\cong} (\tilde{N}, \omega_L, \omega_R).$$

PROOF: The map

$$L \otimes_k V \xrightarrow{H} \bigoplus_{g \in G} g_* V$$

defined by $\beta \otimes v \mapsto (g(\beta)v)$ is an L-linear vector space isomorphism for all L-vector spaces V. The summand $g_* V$ is canonically isomorphic to $(g^{-1})^* V$. It's easier (and sufficient) to work with direct images within the context of this proof.

Take $h \in G$. The instance of $\tilde{\omega}_L$ corresponding to h is the k-linear base change map $V \rightarrow L \otimes_h V$ which is defined by $v \mapsto 1 \otimes v$, whereas the instance of the map ω_L corresponding to h is the composite

$$\bigoplus_{g \in G} g_* V \xrightarrow{s_h} \bigoplus_{g \in G} (h^{-1}g)_* V = \bigoplus_{g \in G} g_* h_*^{-1} V \cong \bigoplus_{g \in G} g_* h^* V,$$

where s_h shuffles factors.

The instance of $\tilde{\omega}_R i_*$ corresponding to h is the L-linear isomorphism

$$h^*(L \otimes_k V) = L \otimes_h (L \otimes_k V) \rightarrow L \otimes_k V$$

defined by

$$\alpha \otimes (\beta \otimes v) \mapsto \alpha h(\beta) \otimes v.$$

The instance of ω_R corresponding to h is the composite

$$h^*\left(\bigoplus_{g \in G} g_* V\right) \cong \bigoplus_{g \in G} h^* g_* V \cong \bigoplus_{g \in G} h_*^{-1} g_* V = \bigoplus_{g \in G} (gh^{-1})_* V \xrightarrow{\sigma_h} \bigoplus_{g \in G} g_* V,$$

where σ_h shuffles factors again.

These are explicit maps. One shows that the required diagrams commute by chasing elements. ∎

The K-*theory norm* is defined to be the pseudo join transformation

$$(i^*i_*, i^*\tilde{\omega}_L, \tilde{\omega}_R i_*) : \mathcal{P}(L) \to \mathcal{P}(L), \tag{5.68}$$

or equivalently (in view of Proposition 5.67), the transformation

$$(\tilde{N}, \omega_L, \omega_R).$$

Recall that the G-action on the exact category $\mathcal{P}(L)$ determines a pseudofunctor

$$\Gamma^o \mathcal{P}(L) : \Gamma^o \times G \rightsquigarrow cat,$$

with

$$\Gamma^o \mathcal{P}(L)(\mathbf{m}^+, *) = \mathcal{P}(L)^{\times m},$$

and with G-action given by applying $1 \otimes g^*$ factorwise, for each $g \in G$. Let n be the order of the Galois group G. Then the K-theory norm

$$\tilde{N} : \mathcal{P}(L) \to \mathcal{P}(L)$$

can be reinterpreted in this context as the composite

$$\Gamma^o \mathcal{P}(L)(\mathbf{1}^+) \xrightarrow{\Delta_G} \prod_{g \in G} \Gamma^o \mathcal{P}(L)(\mathbf{1}^+) \xleftarrow[\cong]{pr} \Gamma^o \mathcal{P}(L)(\mathbf{n}^+) \xrightarrow{\mu_n} \Gamma^o \mathcal{P}(L)(\mathbf{1}^+). \tag{5.69}$$

Explicitly, Δ_G is defined by the commmutative diagram

$$
\begin{array}{ccc}
\Gamma^o \mathcal{P}(L)(\mathbf{1}^+) & \xrightarrow{\Delta_G} & \prod\limits_{g \in G} \Gamma^o \mathcal{P}(L)(\mathbf{1}^+) \\
& {}_{g^*}\searrow & \downarrow {}^{pr_g} \\
& & \Gamma^o \mathcal{P}(L)(\mathbf{1}^+),
\end{array}
$$

where pr_g is projection onto the factor corresponding to g. The isomoprhism pr is defined by the commutativity of the diagram

$$
\begin{array}{ccc}
\Gamma^o \mathcal{P}(L)(\mathbf{n}^+) & \xrightarrow{pr} & \prod\limits_{g \in G} \Gamma^o \mathcal{P}(L)(\mathbf{1}^+) \\
& {}_{\delta_g}\searrow & \downarrow {}^{pr_g} \\
& & \Gamma^o \mathcal{P}(L)(\mathbf{1}^+),
\end{array}
$$

where δ_g is induced by the map

$$\delta_g : \mathbf{n}^+ = \{*\} \cup G \to \mathbf{1}^+$$

of the same name in the category Γ^o which is defined by

$$\delta_g(h) = \begin{cases} 1 & \text{if } g = h, \\ 0 & \text{if } g \neq h. \end{cases}$$

The map μ_n is induced by the map $\mu_n : \mathbf{n}^+ \to \mathbf{1}^+$ of Γ^o which sends all non-zero elements of $\mathbf{n}^+$ to 1; in other words, μ_n models the direct sum functor. These maps are analogous to various maps seen in Sections 3.2 and 3.3, and it should be no surprise that each of them is pseudo $(G \times G)$-equivariant, for appropriate pseudo actions of the group $G \times G$ on the objects of (5.69). In particular, there is a functor

$$G \times G \to \Gamma^o \times G$$

which is defined by sending the unique object of the groupoid $G \times G$ to the object $(\mathbf{n}^+, *)$, and sends the arrow (g, h) to the morphism $((h\cdot)(\cdot g^{-1}), h)$, where $(h\cdot)$ is left multiplication by h on $\mathbf{n}^+ = G \cup *$, and $(\cdot g^{-1})$ is right multiplication by g^{-1}. This functor induces a pseudo $(G \times G)$-action on $\mathcal{P}(L)(\mathbf{n}^+)$.

More generally, suppose that A is a symmetric monoidal category equipped with a pseudo G-action, where G is a finite group. Then A determines a pseudo-functor

$$\Gamma^o A : \Gamma^o \times G \rightsquigarrow cat,$$

and a pseudo join transformation

$$\Gamma^o A(\mathbf{1}^+) \xrightarrow{\Delta_G} \prod_{g \in G} \Gamma^o A(\mathbf{1}^+) \xleftarrow[\cong]{pr} \Gamma^o A(\mathbf{n}^+) \xrightarrow{\mu_n} \Gamma^o A(\mathbf{1}^+) \qquad (5.70)$$

is defined in the category of symmetric monoidal categories, where n is the order of G. This is seen most effectively by using the composite pseudo-functor

$$\Gamma^o A^\wedge : \Gamma^o \times \Gamma^o \times G \xrightarrow{\wedge \times 1} \Gamma^o \times G \xrightarrow{\Gamma^o A} cat$$

to show that there are induced pseudo-transformations

$$\Gamma^o A^\wedge(*, \mathbf{1}^+) \xrightarrow{\Delta_G} \prod_{g \in G} \Gamma^o A^\wedge(*, \mathbf{1}^+) \xleftarrow[\cong]{pr} \Gamma^o A^\wedge(*, \mathbf{n}^+) \xrightarrow{\mu_n} \Gamma^o A^\wedge(*, \mathbf{1}^+)$$

of pseudo-functors defined on the category $G \times G \times \Gamma^o$. The collections of pointed functions $in_g : \mathbf{1}^+ \to \mathbf{n}^+$ defined by $in_g(1) = g$, $g \in G$ and $\delta_h : \mathbf{n}^+ \to \mathbf{1}^+$, $h \in G$, induce $(G \times G)$-equivariant maps

$$\bigvee_{g \in G} Spt(\Gamma^o A(\mathbf{1}^+)) \to Spt(\Gamma^o A(\mathbf{n}^+)) \to \prod_{g \in G} Spt(\Gamma^o A(\mathbf{1}^+))$$

of associated spectra, with composite the canonical stable equivalence c. We have therefore proved

LEMMA 5.71. *Suppose that A is a symmetric monoidal category with a pseudo G-action, where G is a finite group of order n. Then the pseudo join transformation (5.70) induces a map $Spt(A) \to Spt(A)$ in the homotopy category of $(G \times G)$-spectra which coincides with the abstract norm for the G-spectrum $Spt(A)$.*

The following is an immediate consequence:

THEOREM 5.72. *Suppose that L/k is a finite Galois extension with Galois group G. Then the K-theory norm $\tilde{N} : \mathcal{P}(L) \to \mathcal{P}(L)$ induces a map $K(L) \to K(L)$ of $(G \times G)$-spectra, which coincides in the homotopy category of $(G \times G)$-spectra with the abstract norm for the G-spectrum $K(L)$.*

Chapter 6. Generalized étale cohomology

A generalized étale cohomology theory is a graded group $\mathbb{H}^*(T, F)$, which is associated to a presheaf of spectra F on an étale site for a scheme T. Such a theory arises from the homotopy category of presheaves of spectra on the underlying site for T: if F consists of presheaves of Kan complexes, then $\mathbb{H}^*(T, F)$ is a graded group consisting of morphisms in the associated stable category in the sense that

$$\mathbb{H}^{-n}(T, F) = [\Gamma^* S, \Omega^n F],$$

where $\Gamma^* S$ is the constant presheaf associated to the ordinary sphere spectrum S. Basic examples include étale K-theory, which can be defined by letting F be the K-theory presheaf of spectra that was constructed in Chapter 5, and ordinary étale cohomology. This chapter is a treatment of some of the basic principles of these theories; the material included here is a foundation for the practical applications which appear in Chapter 7.

The chapter consists of five sections. The first of these contains a formal definition of $\mathbb{H}^*(T, F)$ in terms of stable homotopy groups of global sections for a globally fibrant model of F, and a construction of the étale cohomological descent spectral sequence

$$E_2^{p,q} = H_{et}^p(T, \tilde{\pi}_q F) \Rightarrow \mathbb{H}^{p-q}(T, F),$$

in the case where the stable homotopy group sheaves $\tilde{\pi}_q F$ have a uniform bound on étale cohomological dimension and are bounded below. The existence of this spectral sequence is well known — the construction given here makes explicit use of the Postnikov resolutions $P_n F$ that were introduced in Chapter 4. It is a key point that the theory $\mathbb{H}^*(T, F_n F)$, which is associated to the homotopy fibre $F_n F$ of the section $F \to P_n F$, is bounded above in a way that depends linearly on cohomological dimension. The first section also contains a vanishing result (which is independent of any spectral sequence construction), that says that the groups $\mathbb{H}^*(T, F)$ are bounded below if the presheaves $\pi_* F$ of stable homotopy groups for F are bounded above. The moral is that the section $F \to P_n F$ induces isomorphisms

$$\mathbb{H}^i(T, F) \cong \mathbb{H}^i(T, P_n F)$$

in a finite range which grows linearly with n under the assumptions on the presheaves $\pi_q F$ which give rise to the descent spectral sequence. In other words, in this case, F may be replaced by a presheaf of spectra having only finitely many non-trivial presheaves of stable homotopy groups for the purposes of computing the groups $\mathbb{H}^*(T, F)$ in a specific finite range. This finite approximation technique is central to many practical applications.

We shall pay close attention to the case where the scheme T is the Zariski spectrum of some field. Suppose that k is a field with absolute Galois group

G, and let F be a presheaf of spectra on the site $et|_k$ of finite étale covers of the corresponding scheme $Sp(k)$. Let $G - \mathbf{Sets}_{df}$ denote the category of finite G-sets equipped with a continuous G-action. A well-known site isomorphism

$$et|_k \cong G - \mathbf{Sets}_{df} \tag{6.1}$$

identifies the category of sheaves on the étale site $et|_k$ with the classifying topos B_G for the profinite group G. The presheaf of spectra F on $et|_k$ determines a presheaf of spectra F on the site $G - \mathbf{Sets}_{df}$, and therefore gives rise to a generalized Galois cohomology theory $\mathbb{H}^*(G, F)$ which is isomorphic to the generalized étale cohomology theory $\mathbb{H}^*(k, F)$. The point is, however, that $\mathbb{H}^*(G, F)$ can be defined for any presheaf of spectra F on the site $G - \mathbf{Sets}_{df}$ which arises from *any profinite group* G. We are therefore entitled to, and shall make use of, theories which are associated to any Galois extension.

Generalized Galois cohomology theories are the subject of Sections 2-4 of this chapter. The second section contains generalities on the site $G-\mathbf{Sets}_{df}$ and the classifying topos B_G for "arbitrary" profinite groups $G = \{G_i\}_{i \in I}$, including exactness properties and a demonstration of the well known equivalence of B_G with the category of discrete G-modules.

All cohomological results in these sections are derived from the homotopy theories of presheaves and sheaves of simplicial sets and of presheaves of spectra on the Grothendieck site $G - \mathbf{Sets}_{df}$, which are themselves special cases of results for arbitrary Grothendieck sites given in [22], [23] and [24]. The simplicial sheaf case is originally due to Joyal [29]. Goerss has shown [18] that the category of simplicial discrete G-modules has a naturally defined closed model structure. In view of the site isomorphism (6.1), Goerss' result can be seen to be a consequence of Joyal's theorem, and the results of [24] give it a natural stable homotopy theoretic generalization.

The Galois cohomology groups $H^*(G, A)$ for G with coefficients in an abelian discrete G-module A can either be calculated as derived functors of the global sections functor for the corresponding abelian sheaf on $G - \mathbf{Sets}_{df}$ or, classically (see [49]), as cohomology groups of the complex $\hom_{cts}(EG, A)$ of continuous G-equivariant A-valued cochains. The fact that these two methods of calculation coincide can be translated into the assertion that a canonically defined map

$$\varinjlim_{i \in I} H^*(G_i, A(G_i)) \to H^*(G, A) \tag{6.2}$$

is an isomorphism, where the thing on the right is defined to be the derived functor cohomology theory. The groups $H^*(G_i, A(G_i))$ are isomorphic to the cohomology groups of the cochain complex $\hom(EG_i^{op} \times_{G_i^{op}} G_i, A)$ of presheaf homomorphisms arising from the Borel construction for the canonical contravariant action of G_i on the sheaf represented by the G-set G_i. This Borel construction, or rather its associated simplicial sheaf, can be identified up to isomorphism with the Čech resolution associated to the covering $G_i \to *$ in the classifying topos B_G. The filtered colimit on the left in (6.2) is therefore a type of Čech cohomology theory, and the assertion that the map of (6.2) is an isomorphism is a variant, or generalization, of the assertion that ordinary Čech and étale cohomology theories coincide.

There is a corresponding Čech invariant

$$\check{H}^*(G, B) = \varinjlim_{i \in I} H^*(G_i, B(G_i))$$

and a canonical map

$$\check{H}^*(G, B) \to \mathbb{H}^*(G, B) \tag{6.3}$$

analogous to (6.2) which is defined for arbitrary abelian presheaves B on the site $G - \mathbf{Sets}_{df}$. This map is shown in the third section of this chapter to be an isomorphism when B is additive in a suitable sense. Čech cohomology with coefficients in an abelian presheaf B is, in turn, a special case of a generalized Čech cohomology theory $\check{H}^*(G, F)$ which is associated to any presheaf of spectra on $G - \mathbf{Sets}_{df}$, and the map (6.3) extends to a comparison map

$$\check{H}^*(G, F) \to \mathbb{H}^*(G, F). \tag{6.4}$$

This map (6.4) is shown, in Section 4, to be an isomorphism if F is an additive presheaf of stably fibrant spectra whose presheaves of stable homotopy groups are bounded above. The proof of this result depends on first showing that (6.4) is an isomorphism if F has only finitely many non-trivial presheaves of stable homotopy groups. This weaker statement is the basis of all subsequent applications; it is proved by an inductive argument that starts with Eilenberg-Mac Lane objects, and the proof in that case is the ordinary cohomological argument from the third section.

This last stream of ideas can be quite subtle. It's not clear that the generalized Čech construction takes local stable equivalences of presheaves of spectra to isomorphisms of cohomology theories. We don't even know if the groups $\check{H}^*(G, F)$ vanish in the case when F is locally contractible. As a consequence, the Postnikov tower tricks that are used in the first section for generalized étale cohomology don't work at all in this context, and so there's no analogue of the finite approximation technique for generalized Čech cohomology theories.

The final section of this chapter contains a description of a naive set theoretic technique for replacing big geometric étale sites by small sites for the purposes of computing ordinary and generalized étale cohomology. This is convenient for applications in the last chapter (and elsewhere), where it is natural to want to work with sheaf cohomology on étale sites for a scheme T which are bigger than the big site $(Sch|_T)_{et}$, and yet avoid the standard set-theoretic paradoxes. The technique applies, in particular, to the big site $(Sch|_T)_{et}$, and perhaps one should have been using it all along in place of faith in God and Grothendieck's higher universes. The section closes with an application of these principles and the finite approximation technique to show a continuity property for generalized étale cohomology theories. This is a generalization of the continuity property for ordinary étale cohomology theory.

The reader will recall (from Section 2.3) that there are generally three different sorts of stable equivalences that will be discussed here. One of them is the ordinary notion of stable homotopy equivalence in the category of spectra. A map $f : Z \to W$ of presheaves of spectra on an étale site for T is a *pointwise stable equivalence* if each of the induced maps of sections $f(U) : Z(U) \to W(U)$ is an ordinary stable equivalence of n-fold spectra. The map f will be called a *stalkwise stable equivalence* if each of the induced maps $f_x : Z_x \to W_x$ of stalks is a stable equivalence. In other words, a stalkwise stable equivalence is a local stable equivalence of presheaves of spectra, but specialized to presheaves on an étale site for the field k. Note that every pointwise stable equivalence is a stalkwise stable equivalence, but the converse is definitely false. We will similarly refer to *strict weak equivalences* in the ordinary category of spectra, as well as to *pointwise strict weak equivalences* and *stalkwise strict weak equivalences* in categories of presheaves of spectra. The results of Chapter 3 imply that each of these notions of weak equivalence has a closed model structure associated to it; the closed model theory for pointwise weak equivalences, in particular, arises naturally from the chaotic topology.

Each such theory also has an associated notion of global fibration. When I say that an object is globally fibrant, or that a map is a global fibration, it is usually with respect to some topology that is clear from the context. The choice of adjectives will be more precise otherwise.

A similar array of definitions applies to categories of presheaves of n-fold spectra. All of the results of Chapter 3 have consequences for presheaves of spectra, which are either direct or by analogy. The reader can supply reformulations and proofs in the presheaf context, and their analogues in the last section will be referred to without comment. The ability to just do this here is the point of the insistence on naturality that appears throughout the material presented up to now.

6.1. The descent spectral sequence

Suppose that ℓ is a prime number. Suppose that T is a separated Noetherian scheme, and that there is a uniform bound M on the Galois cohomological dimension with respect to ℓ-torsion sheaves for all or its residue fields. In this case [55, p.464], T, all its finite étale patches, and all its stalks have a common bound on étale cohomological dimension with respect to ℓ-torsion sheaves, namely M. We shall say that such schemes T *have a global bound in étale cohomological dimension with respect to ℓ-torsion sheaves*, and talk about a number M if there is a need for explicitness.

The principal example of schemes of this type will be the Zariski spectra $Sp(k)$ arising from fields of characteristic not equal to ℓ, and having finite Galois cohomological dimension with respect to ℓ-torsion modules.

Such schemes T have a convergent descent spectral sequence for generalized étale cohomology with coefficients in a presheaf of spectra F whose sheaves of stable homotopy groups are ℓ-torsion, and which is stalkwise bounded below in the sense that all its sheaves of stable homotopy groups vanish below some integer. This spectral sequence is well known, from several points of view (see [23], [24], [55]); one of the methods of constructing it will be reviewed here.

The context for the construction is the observation that the stable homotopy group $\pi_n GF(T)$ of the global sections spectrum $GF(T)$ of any globally fibrant model $i : F \to GF$ of the presheaf F coincide with groups of morphisms

$$[\Gamma^* S[n], F] \xrightarrow[\cong]{i_*} [\Gamma^* S[n], GF]$$

in the stable homotopy category which are associated to the stable stalkwise closed model structure on presheaves of spectra on the big site $(Sch|_T)_{et}$. Here, S is the sphere spectrum

$$S^1, \quad S^1 \wedge S^1, \quad \ldots,$$

and $\Gamma^* S$ is the constant presheaf of spectra associated to S.

The stable homotopy groups $\pi_* GF(T)$ also coincide up to isomorphism with the homotopy groups $\pi_* \mathbb{H}(T; F)$ that Thomason constructs in [55] from the Godement resolution $\mathbb{H}(T; F)$, in the case where F consists of presheaves of Kan complexes. Define the *generalized étale cohomology groups* $\mathbb{H}^*(T, F)$ of T with coefficients in F by

$$\mathbb{H}^{-n}(T; F) = \pi_n GF(T).$$

The change of sign in the indexing is there to accomodate the isomorphism

$$\mathbb{H}^n(T, H(A)) \cong H_{et}^n(T, A),$$

that one finds when the coefficient spectrum is the Eilenberg-Mac Lane presheaf of spectra $H(A)$ which is associated to a sheaf of abelian groups A.

To construct the descent spectral sequence, we may suppose without loss of generality that F consists of presheaves of Kan complexes: use the pointwise weak equivalence $\eta : F \to F_{Kan}$ of Lemma 2.41, for example. Suppose also that F is stalkwise connective in the sense that $\tilde{\pi}_j F = 0$ for $j < 0$. Form the Postnikov tower

$$\cdots \to P_2 F \to P_1 F \to P_0 F.$$

for F as in Section 4.7 (see Proposition 4.65). The canonical restriction map $F \to P_n F$ induces an isomorphism $\pi_i F \cong \pi_i P_n F$ in presheaves of stable homotopy groups for $i \leq n$, and $\pi_i P_n F = 0$ if $i > n$. Furthermore, the pointwise stable homotopy fibre of the map $P_n F \to P_{n-1} F$ may be identified with a presheaf of spectra $K(\pi_n F, n)$, up to pointwise stable homotopy. Finally, since

F is stalkwise connective, P_0F is a $K(\tilde{\pi}_0F, 0)$ up to stable stalkwise equivalence (see Lemma 6.10 below).

Now construct a tower

$$\cdots \to GP_2F \to GP_1F \to GP_0F \tag{6.5}$$

of global fibrations between globally fibrant objects: start by taking a globally fibrant model

$$P_0F \xrightarrow{i} GP_0F$$

for P_0F, and then factorize the composition

$$P_1F \to P_0F \xrightarrow{i} GP_0F$$

as a stalkwise stably trivial cofibration $i_1 : P_1F \to GP_1F$, followed by a global fibration $p : GP_1F \to GP_0F$. Note that GP_1F is automatically globally fibrant. Performing exactly analogous factorizations for the composites

$$P_{n+1}F \to P_nF \xrightarrow{i} GP_nF$$

finishes the construction of (6.5) inductively.

The fibre of $p : GP_nF \to GP_{n-1}F$ is a globally fibrant model $GK(\tilde{\pi}_nF, n)$ for the Eilenberg-Mac Lane object $K(\tilde{\pi}_nF, n)$, where $\tilde{\pi}_nF$ denotes the sheaf associated to the presheaf π_nF. For any object $U \to T$ in the big étale site $(Sch|_T)_{et}$, the homotopy groups of the spectrum of sections $GK(\tilde{\pi}_nF, n)(U)$ are given by

$$\pi_j GK(\tilde{\pi}_nF, n)(U) = \begin{cases} H_{et}^{n-j}(U, \tilde{\pi}_nF) & \text{if } j \leq n, \text{ and} \\ 0 & \text{otherwise.} \end{cases}$$

In particular, if $U \to T$ is finite and étale, and M is the global bound on cohomological dimension that we have assumed for T, then $GK(\tilde{\pi}_nF, n)(U)$ is $n - M - 1$ connected.

A standard argument shows that the inverse limit

$$\varprojlim_n GP_nF$$

is a globally fibrant presheaf of spectra. Furthermore, since the fibres of the maps $P_{m+1}F \to P_mF$ are pointwise m-connected, the previous paragraph implies that the induced map

$$\pi_j \varprojlim_n GP_nF(U) \to \pi_j GP_nF(U)$$

in stable homotopy groups of sections is an isomorphism if $j \leq n - M$, for all finite étale T-schemes $U \to T$. It follows that the map

$$F \to \varprojlim_n GP_n F$$

is a weak equivalence of presheaves of spectra, after restriction to the finite étale site $et|_T$. In particular,

$$\varprojlim_n GP_n F$$

is a globally fibrant model for F after restriction to $et|_T$, so that the global sections spectrum

$$\varprojlim_n GP_n F(T)$$

has the stable homotopy type of the global sections spectrum $GF(T)$ for any globally fibrant model GF of F on the big site $(Sch|_T)_{et}$.

Applying the methods of Bousfield and Kan [9] (using their indexing conventions in particular) to the tower of fibrations

$$\ldots GP_2 F(T) \to GP_1 F(T) \to GP_0 F(T)$$

of spectra therefore yields a spectral sequence with

$$\mathcal{E}_1^{p,q} = H_{et}^{2p-q}(T; \tilde{\pi}_p F) \Rightarrow \pi_{q-p} GF(T). \tag{6.6}$$

and having differentials

$$d_r : \mathcal{E}_r^{p,q} \to \mathcal{E}_r^{p+r,q+r-1}.$$

Finally, applying Thomason's reindexing trick (see p.542 of [55])

$$E_{s-1+r}^{p,q} = \mathcal{E}_r^{p+(s-1)(q-p),q+(s-1)(q-p)}$$

with $s = 2$ yields a spectral sequence with

$$E_2^{p,q} = H_{et}^p(T; \tilde{\pi}_q F) \Rightarrow \pi_{q-p} GF(T), \tag{6.7}$$

and with differentials

$$d_r : E_r^{p,q} \to E^{p+r,q+r-1}.$$

The spectral sequence (6.7) will be referred to as the *descent spectral sequence* for F over T in all that follows. It converges strongly under the stated assumptions on F and T. Note, however, that whatever this convergence statement means, it tends to conceal the far more powerful fact (implicitly shown above) that there is an isomorphism

$$\pi_j GF(T) \cong \pi_j GP_n F(T) \tag{6.8}$$

if $j \leq n - M$, where M is the cohomological dimension of T. More generally, one has

LEMMA 6.9. *Suppose that the scheme T has a global bound, namely M, in étale cohomological dimension with respect to ℓ-torsion sheaves, and suppose that F is a presheaf of spectra on $(Sch|_T)_{et}$ whose sheaves of stable homotopy groups are ℓ-torsion. Suppose that F is stalkwise n-connected, meaning that $\tilde{\pi}_j F = 0$ if $j \leq n$, and let GF be a globally fibrant model for F. Then the global sections spectrum $GF(T)$ is $(n - M)$-connected.*

PROOF: In this case, the canonical map $P_n F \to *$ is a local stable equivalence, so that the map $GP_n F \to *$ is a pointwise stable equivalence. It follows that $\pi_i GP_n F(T) = 0$ for all i. Now invoke the isomorphism (6.8). ∎

There is also a vanishing result for the stable homotopy groups $\pi_j GK(T)$ for presheaves of spectra K which are stalkwise bounded above in the sense that $\tilde{\pi}_j K = 0$ for j above some integer. This is a special case of a result which holds over arbitrary Grothendieck sites, the proof of which starts with the following observation:

LEMMA 6.10. *Suppose that X is a sheaf (of sets) on an arbitrary Grothendieck site $\mathcal{C}$, and form the simplicial presheaf $K(X, 0)$. Then $K(X, 0)$ is a globally fibrant simplicial presheaf.*

PROOF: X is a sheaf, so the presheaf level isomorphism

$$\hom(Y, K(X, 0)) \cong \hom(\pi_0 Y, X)$$

induces an isomorphism

$$\hom(Y, K(X, 0)) \cong \hom(\tilde{\pi}_0 Y, X),$$

where $\tilde{\pi}_0 Y$ denotes the sheaf associated to the presheaf $\pi_0 Y$. But any trivial cofibration $i : U \to V$ of simplicial presheaves induces an isomorphism $i_* : \tilde{\pi}_0 U \to \tilde{\pi}_0 V$, by definition, so that $K(X, 0)$ has the required lifting property. ∎

PROPOSITION 6.11 (UNSTABLE). *Suppose that Y is a presheaf of Kan complexes on an arbitrary Grothendieck site $\mathcal{C}$ such that the canonical map $res : Y \to P_n Y$ is a local weak equivalence, and let GY be a globally fibrant model for Y. Then*

$$\pi_j GY(U) = 0$$

for $j > n$, for any $U \in \mathcal{C}$, and at any choice of base point in $GY(U)$.

PROOF: Restriction along the forgetful functor $Q : \mathcal{C} \downarrow U \to \mathcal{C}$ preserves local weak equivalences and global fibrations. It is therefore enough to assume that $\mathcal{C}$ has a terminal object t, and then show that $\pi_j GY(t) = 0$ for $j > n$ and for any choice of base point in $Y(t)$.

We can also assume that Y is globally fibrant, since any globally fibrant model $i : Y \to GY$ determines a commutative diagram

$$
\begin{array}{ccc}
Y & \xrightarrow{\text{res}} & P_n Y \\
{\scriptstyle i} \downarrow {\scriptstyle \simeq} & & \downarrow {\scriptstyle P_n i} \\
GY & \xrightarrow{\text{res}} & P_n GY,
\end{array}
$$

and P_n preserves local weak equivalences, so that res $: GY \to P_n GY$ is a local weak equivalence.

The fibre sequence

$$ K(\pi_n Y, n) \to P_n Y \to P_{n-1} Y $$

determined by any choice of base point in $Y(t)$ induces a fibre sequence

$$ GK(\pi_n Y, n)(t) \to GP_n Y(t) \to GP_{n-1} Y(t), $$

and

$$
\pi_j GK(\pi_n Y, n)(t) = \begin{cases} H^{n-j}(\mathcal{C}, \tilde{\pi}_n Y) & \text{if } 0 \le j \le n, \text{ and} \\ 0 & \text{if } j > n. \end{cases}
$$

Thus, $\pi_j GP_n Y(t) = 0$ for $j > n$ provided we know that $\pi_j GP_{n-1} Y(t) = 0$ for $j > n - 1$. The induction starts in degree 0, which is given by Lemma 6.10. Finally, use the fact that the map res $: Y(t) \to GP_n Y(t)$ is a weak equivalence of simplicial sets. ∎

The assertion that res $: Y \to P_n Y$ is a local weak equivalence means precisely that the sheaves $\tilde{\pi}_j(Y|_U, x)$ are 0 for all $j > n$ and for all local choices of base point $x \in Y(U)$, $U \in \mathcal{C}$.

PROPOSITION 6.12 (STABLE). *Suppose that F is a presheaf of spectra on an arbitrary Grothendieck site $\mathcal{C}$ which consists of presheaves of Kan complexes, and suppose that $\tilde{\pi}_j F = 0$ for $j > n$. Then*

$$ \pi_j GF(U) = 0 $$

if $j > n$, for any $U \in \mathcal{C}$.

PROOF: By shifting appropriately, we can assume that $n = 0$. We can also assume that F is globally fibrant. Then the simplicial presheaf F^0 at level 0 is globally fibrant, and $\tilde{\pi}_j F = 0$ for $j > 0$ implies that $\tilde{\pi}_j F^0 = 0$ for $j > 0$. Proposition 6.11 implies that $\pi_j F^0(U) = 0$ for $j > 0$, and $F(U)$ is a stably fibrant spectrum, so that $\pi_j F(U) = 0$ for $j > 0$. ∎

COROLLARY 6.13. *Suppose that F is a presheaf of spectra on an arbitrary Grothendieck site C which consists of presheaves of Kan complexes, and suppose that F_nF is the pointwise homotopy fibre of the restriction map res : $F \to P_nF$. Then the map $GF_nF \to GF$ of globally fibrant models coming from the inclusion $i : F_nF \to F$ induces isomorphisms*

$$\pi_j GF_nF(U) \cong \pi_j GF(U)$$

for all $j \geq n+1$ and for all $U \in C$.

COROLLARY 6.14. *Suppose that T has global bound M in étale cohomological dimension with respect to ℓ-torsion sheaves, and that F is a presheaf of spectra on the big site $(Sch|_T)_{et}$ whose sheaves of stable homotopy groups are ℓ-torsion. Suppose further that F consists of presheaves of Kan complexes. Suppose finally that n and m are integers such that $m < n - M$. Then the maps*

$$P_nF_mF \leftarrow F_mF \to F$$

induce isomorphisms

$$\pi_j GP_nF_mF(T) \xleftarrow{\cong} \pi_j GF_mF(T) \xrightarrow{\cong} \pi_j GF(T)$$

if $m < j \leq n - N$.

Corollary 6.14 means that ℓ-torsion generalized étale cohomology theories on decent schemes T can be approximated by theories arising from presheaves of spectra having only finitely many non-trivial presheaves of stable homotopy groups. The main reason to be interested in the latter is that they satisfy Galois cohomological descent over fields, subject to a suitable additivity condition.

6.2. The classifying topos

Let $G = \{G_i\}_{i \in I}$ be a profinite group such that all transition homomorphisms $G_i \to G_j$ are surjective, where (implicitly) I is a left filtered index category. Write also

$$G = \varprojlim_{i \in I} G_i$$

for the inverse limit. One can show, by using a cofinality argument and a basic result of Serre [49, p.I-4], that the canonical homomorphisms

$$p : G = \varprojlim_{i \in I} G_i \to G_i$$

are also surjective.

A *discrete G-set* is a set X equipped with a G action $G \times X \to X$ which factors through some G_i-action in the sense that there is a commutative diagram

A *map* of discrete G sets is simply a G-equivariant map. I shall write $G - \mathbf{Sets}_d$ for the resulting category.

I shall also write $G_i - \mathbf{Sets}$ for the category of sets carrying G_i actions and G_i-equivariant maps between them. There is a functor

$$\gamma_i : G_i - \mathbf{Sets} \to G - \mathbf{Sets}_d,$$

which is defined by associating to a G_i-set $G_i \times X \to X$ the composite G-action

$$G \times X \xrightarrow{p \times 1} G_i \times X \to X.$$

LEMMA 6.15. *The category $G - \mathbf{Sets}_d$ has all finite limits and colimits.*

PROOF: Limits and colimits of ordinary G-sets are formed as in the set category. In particular, each of the functors γ_k preserves all limits and colimits. Thus, it suffices to show that each member of a suitable list of finite diagrams of discrete G-sets factors through some γ_k.

More explicitly, let $\{0, 1\}$ denote the discrete category on two objects, namely 0 and 1, and let Arr_2 be the category with objects 0 and 1, and having non-identity arrows $0 \rightrightarrows 1$. The lemma is proved by showing that all diagrams

$$\{0, 1\} \to G - \mathbf{Sets}_d$$

or

$$Arr_2 \to G - \mathbf{Sets}_d$$

factor through some γ_k.

A diagram $D : \{0, 1\} \to G - \mathbf{Sets}_d$ simply consists of two objects, say X and Y. We can assume that X is in the image of γ_i, so that the G-action $G \times X \to X$ factors as a composite

$$G \times X \xrightarrow{p \times 1} G_i \times X \to X.$$

Similarly, we can assume that the G-action on Y has the form

$$G \times Y \xrightarrow{p \times 1} G_j \times Y \to Y.$$

The groups G_i and G_j have a common refinement G_k in the pro-group G, so the diagram D factors through γ_k.

Any map $f : X \to Y$ in $G - \mathbf{Sets}_d$ is in the image of some γ_k. In effect, we can assume that X is in the image of γ_i and Y is in the image of γ_j as above, and further find a common refinement G_k of G_i and G_j in the pro-group G. Then there is a diagram

$$
\begin{array}{ccc}
G \times X & \xrightarrow{\ 1 \times f\ } & G \times Y \\
{\scriptstyle p \times 1}\big\downarrow & & \big\downarrow \\
G_k \times X & \xrightarrow{\ 1 \times f\ } & G_k \times Y \\
\big\downarrow & & \big\downarrow \\
G_i \times X & & G_j \times Y \\
\big\downarrow & & \big\downarrow \\
X & \xrightarrow[\ f\ ]{} & Y,
\end{array}
$$

which commutes because the indicated map $p \times 1$ is surjective. In particular, the map f is in the image of the functor γ_k.

A functor $Arr_2 \to G - \mathbf{Sets}_d$ consists of a pair of maps

$$ X \underset{g}{\overset{f}{\rightrightarrows}} Y. $$

By the previous paragraph, we can assume that f is G_i-equivariant and that g is G_j-equivariant, for some i and j respectively. But, once again, G_i and G_j have a common refinement G_k, so that f and g are G_k-equivariant. ∎

Write $G - \mathbf{Sets}_{df}$ for the full subcategory of finite discrete G-sets in $G - \mathbf{Sets}_d$. The category $G - \mathbf{Sets}_{df}$ has a pretopology specified by covering families $U_i \to X$ which are surjective in the sense that the resulting functions $\sqcup U_i \to X$ are surjections. The associated Grothendieck topos is called the *classifying topos* for the profinite group G, and is denoted by B_G.

An object of B_G, or a sheaf of sets on the site $G - \mathbf{Sets}_{df}$ is a contravariant functor

$$ F : G - \mathbf{Sets}_{df}^{op} \to \mathbf{Sets} $$

which satisfies the usual patching criterion for covering families $U_i \to X$, in that the induced diagram

$$ F(X) \to \prod_i F(U_i) \rightrightarrows \prod_{i,j} F(U_i \times_X U_j) $$

should be an equalizer. Any sheaf F takes disjoint unions to products, so that F is completely determined by its restriction to the full subcategory of objects of the form G_i/H in $G - \mathbf{Sets}_{df}$. Furthermore, the canonical surjection $G_i \to G_i/H$ is covering, and there is a bijection

$$G_i \times H \cong G_i \times_{G_i/H} G_i$$

specified by $(g, h) \mapsto (g, gh)$, so that $F(G_i/H)$ can be identified with the set $F(G_i)^H$ of H-fixed points in $F(G_i)$.

Define a set-valued functor L on the presheaf category on $G - \mathbf{Sets}_{df}$ by specifying that

$$LF = \varinjlim_i F(G_i).$$

Right multiplication by elements of G_i induces a left G_i-action on $F(G_i)$, and so there is an induced left G-action on LF. Recall that $p : G \to G_i$ denotes the canonical surjective homomorphism, and write $\tilde{H} = p^{-1}(H) \subset G$. Observe that the canonical map

$$F(G_i) \to \varinjlim_i F(G_i) = LF$$

induces a map

$$\phi : F(G_i/H) \to (LF)^{\tilde{H}}. \tag{6.16}$$

LEMMA 6.17. *The function ϕ is a bijection for any sheaf F on $G - \mathbf{Sets}_{df}$. Furthermore, ϕ is natural with respect to G-equivariant maps $\theta : G_j/K \to G_i/H$.*

PROOF: The G-equivariant isomorphism

$$\varinjlim_j F(G_j) \cong \varinjlim_{j \to i} F(G_j)$$

induces an isomorphism on $\tilde{H}$-fixed points. Write H_{ji} for the preimage of H under the structure map $G_j \to G_i$. The canonical map

$$F(G_j) \to \varinjlim_{j \to i} F(G_j)$$

is G-equivariant for the G-action on $F(G_j)$, and induces a bijection

$$\varinjlim_{j \to i} F(G_j)^{\tilde{H}} \cong (\varinjlim_{j \to i} F(G_j))^{\tilde{H}}.$$

But there are coherent isomorphisms

$$F(G_j)^{\tilde{H}} \cong F(G_j)^{H_{ij}} \cong F(G_i)^H \cong F(G_i/H),$$

so that ϕ is an isomorphism, as claimed.

One proves the naturality statement by showing that any G-equivariant map $\theta : G_j/K \to G_i/H$ induces a commutative diagram

$$
\begin{array}{ccc}
F(G_i/H) & \xrightarrow{\ \cong\ } & F(G_i)^{\tilde{H}} \\
\theta^* \downarrow & & \downarrow \theta^* \\
F(G_j/K) & \xrightarrow{\ \cong\ } & F(G_j)^{\tilde{K}},
\end{array}
$$

where the indicated isomorphisms are canonical. This is a case check. ∎

Any presheaf F has canonically associated to it an "additive" presheaf AF, which is defined by

$$
AF(X_1 \sqcup \cdots \sqcup X_n) = F(X_1) \times \cdots \times F(X_n),
$$

where each summand X_i has a transitive G-action. Furthermore, inclusion of summands induces a natural map

$$
F(X_1 \sqcup \cdots \sqcup X_n) \to F(X_1) \times \cdots \times F(X_n),
$$

giving a map $\nu : F \to AF$ which is natural in presheaves F. This map is an isomorphism if F is a sheaf.

The G-set LF represents a sheaf RLF on $G - \mathbf{Sets}_{fd}$, which is defined by $RLF(X) = \hom_G(X, LF)$. Note that there are isomorphisms

$$
\hom_G(G_i/H, LF) \cong \hom_G(G/\tilde{H}, LF) \cong LF^{\tilde{H}}
$$

which are natural with respect to G-equivariant maps $G_j/K \to G_i/H$. It follows that the maps ϕ induce a natural map $\phi_* : AF \to RLF$. I also write

$$
\phi : F \to RLF \tag{6.18}
$$

for the composite $\phi_* \nu$. It follows from Lemma 6.17 that this map $\phi : F \to RLF$ is a natural isomorphism if F is a sheaf.

Write H_i for the kernel of the homomorphism $p : G \to G_i$. The canonical map $F(G_i) \to LF$ factors through a composite

$$
F(G_i) \to LF^{H_i} \hookrightarrow LF, \tag{6.19}
$$

and this composite is natural in structure maps $G_j \to G_i$. The G-set LF is defined to be the filtered colimit $\varinjlim_i F(G_i)$, so that the factorizations (6.19) induce an isomorphism

$$
LF \cong \varinjlim_i LF^{H_i}.
$$

In other words, the G-set LF is a discrete G-module in the sense of Serre: a *discrete G-module* is a G-set M such that the canonical inclusion

$$\varinjlim_i M^{H_i} \hookrightarrow M$$

is a bijection. Write $G - \mathbf{Mod}_d$ for the category of discrete G-modules and all G-equivariant maps between them.

We have the following well-known result:

PROPOSITION 6.20. *The functors R and L induce an equivalence of categories between the classifying topos B_G for G and the category $G - \mathbf{Mod}_d$ of discrete G-modules.*

PROOF: The natural isomorphism $F \cong RLF$ for sheaves F is the map ϕ in (6.18), while the existence of a natural isomorphism $M \cong LRM$ is essentially part of the definition of discrete G-modules M. ∎

EXAMPLE 6.21. The quotient G_i/H represents a sheaf $\hom_G(\ , G_i/H)$ on $G - \mathbf{Sets}_{df}$. Suppose that F is a discrete G-module. Then there is an isomorphism of G-modules $G_i/H \cong G/\tilde{H}$, and so

$$RF(G_i/H) = \hom_G(G_i/H, F) \cong \hom_G(G/\tilde{H}, F) \cong F^{\tilde{H}}.$$

On the other hand, there are isomorphisms

$$\begin{aligned} RF(G_i/H) &\cong \hom(\hom_G(\ , G_i/H), RF) \\ &\cong \hom(L\hom_G(\ , G_i/H), LRF) \\ &\cong \hom(L\hom_G(\ , G_i/H), F), \end{aligned}$$

by the Yoneda lemma, and since L and R together form an equivalence of categories. These isomorphisms are natural in discrete G-modules F, so that there is an isomorphism

$$L\hom_G(\ , G_i/H) \cong G_i/H$$

in the category of discrete G-modules. ∎

COROLLARY 6.22. *Suppose that F is a presheaf on the site $G - \mathbf{Sets}_{df}$. Then the natural map $\phi : F \to RLF$ coincides up to isomorphism with the associated sheaf map $\eta : F \to \tilde{F}$.*

PROOF: The method of proof is to show that $\phi : F \to RLF$ satisfies the universal property for maps $f : F \to G$ to sheaves G.

There is a commutative diagram

$$
\begin{array}{ccc}
F & \xrightarrow{\ \phi\ } & RLF \\
{\scriptstyle f}\downarrow & & \downarrow{\scriptstyle RLf} \\
G & \xrightarrow[\ \phi\ ]{\cong} & RLG,
\end{array}
$$

so that f extends to a map of sheaves $\phi^{-1}RLf : RLF \to G$.

If there is a map of sheaves $g : RLF \to RLG$ making the diagram

$$
\begin{array}{ccc}
F & \xrightarrow{\ \phi\ } & RLF \\
{\scriptstyle f}\downarrow & & \downarrow{\scriptstyle g} \\
G & \xrightarrow[\ \phi\ ]{\cong} & RLG
\end{array}
$$

commute, then $Lg = LRLf$ since the map $L\phi$ is an isomorphism. But then $RLg = RLRLf$, and the fact that RL is naturally isomorphic to the identity functor on $G - \mathbf{Mod}_d$, together imply that $g = RLf$. ∎

COROLLARY 6.23. *A presheaf F on $G - \mathbf{Sets}_{df}$ is a sheaf if and only if*

(1) *F takes finite disjoint unions to finite products.*

(2) *Each canonical map $G_i \to G_i/H$ induces a bijection*

$$
F(G_i/H) \cong F(G_i)^H.
$$

PROOF: The necessity of these conditions was demonstrated above, and they are exactly the properties that were used to show that the map $\phi : F \to RLF$ is an isomorphism for sheaves F. ∎

The terminal object in the category $G - \mathbf{Sets}_{df}$ is the one point set $*$, equipped with the only G-action that it can carry. It follows that there is an isomorphism

$$
\Gamma_* F = \varprojlim_{X \in G-\mathbf{Sets}_{df}} F(X) \cong F(*),
$$

for any presheaf F. The set $\Gamma_* F$ is usually called the set of *global sections* of F. If F happens to be a sheaf, then there are isomorphisms

$$
F(*) \cong F(G_i)^{G_i} \cong F(G_i)^G
$$

for all of the groups G_i, so that there are isomorphisms

$$
LF^G \cong \varinjlim_i F(G_i)^G \cong F(*).
$$

This proves

COROLLARY 6.24. *The set $\Gamma_* F$ of global sections of a sheaf F coincides up to natural isomorphism with the set LF^G of G-invariants of the associated discrete G-module LF.*

REMARK 6.25. Denote the forgetful functor $G - \mathbf{Mod}_d \to \mathbf{Sets}$ by u^*, and write $u_* X$ for the constant discrete G-module on a set X. Then $X \mapsto u_* X$ defines a functor $u_* : \mathbf{Sets} \to G - \mathbf{Sets}_d$ which is right adjoint to the forgetful functor u^*. Furthermore, u^* preserves and reflects exactness, so that

(1) the pair of functors (u^*, u_*) defines a morphism $u : \mathbf{Sets} \to G - \mathbf{Mod}_d$ of toposes in the sense of SGA4 (vol. I, p. 323), and

(2) the topos $G - \mathbf{Mod}_d$ has enough points: the requisite collection of points consists of the topos morphism u alone.   ∎

We may now say that a map $f : X \to Y$ of simplicial presheaves on $G - \mathbf{Sets}_{df}$ is a stalkwise weak equivalence if the associated map $Lf : LX \to LY$ is a weak equivalence of simplicial sets. A cofibration of simplicial presheaves on this site is a pointwise cofibration, and a global fibration is a map which has the right lifting property with respect to all maps which are simultaneously cofibrations and stalkwise weak equivalences. One of the basic results of [23] (see also Section 2.3) asserts in this case that, with these definitions, the category of simplicial presheaves on $G - \mathbf{Sets}_{df}$ has the structure of a closed model category. Recall that there is also a closed model structure on the category of presheaves of spectra on $G - \mathbf{Sets}_{df}$ which gives a corresponding stable category. In all that follows, when we say that a simplicial presheaf or a presheaf of spectra is in the G-*world*, we shall mean that it is defined on the site $G - \mathbf{Sets}_{df}$.

REMARK 6.26. We have been using the notation H_i to denote the kernel of the canonical homomorphism $p : G \to G_i$. Recall that the comma category $G - \mathbf{Sets}_{df} \downarrow G_i$ has for objects all maps $X \to G_i$ in $G - \mathbf{Sets}_{df}$, with commutative triangles for morphisms. The category $G - \mathbf{Sets}_{df} \downarrow G_i$ inherits a Grothendieck topology from $G - \mathbf{Sets}_{df}$, so that restriction along the forgetful functor

$$Q : G - \mathbf{Sets}_{df} \downarrow G_i \to G - \mathbf{Sets}_{df}$$

which is defined by sending $X \to G_i$ to X, preserves sheaves. The restriction functor $F \mapsto FQ$ is exact, and has a left adjoint which preserves monomorphisms, by formal nonsense.

Any object $\phi : X \to G_i$ of $G - \mathbf{Sets}_{df} \downarrow G_i$ is a surjective G-equivariant function, and so X has the form

$$X = \bigsqcup_{g \in G_i} \phi^{-1}(g).$$

The subset $\phi^{-1}(e)$ corresponding to the identity element $e \in G_i$ has an H_i-action. Furthermore, if $\sigma : G_i \to G$ is a fixed section of the homomorphism

$p : G \to G_i$ which is normalized in the sense that $\sigma(e) = e$, then multiplication by the various elements $\sigma(g)$ defines a collection of bijections $\sigma(g)_* : \phi^{-1}(e) \to \phi^{-1}(g)$, which together define a bijection

$$\bigsqcup_{g \in G_i} \phi^{-1}(e) \cong \bigsqcup_{g \in G_i} \phi^{-1}(g).$$

The G-action induced on the set on the left by this isomorphism gives this set the structure of the G-set $G \otimes_{H_i} \phi^{-1}(e)$ which is induced from the H_i-set $\phi^{-1}(e)$. In this way we see that there is an isomorphism

$$H_i - \mathbf{Sets}_{df} \cong G - \mathbf{Sets}_{df} \downarrow G_i$$

of Grothendieck sites, which is defined for an H_i-set Y by the functor $Y \mapsto G \otimes_{H_i} Y$, and for a G-equivariant map $\phi : X \to G_i$ by the functor $\phi \mapsto \phi^{-1}(e)$.

It follows in particular that if F is a globally fibrant presheaf of spectra in the G-world, then the spectrum $F(G_i)$ coincides with the global sections spectrum of the globally fibrant presheaf of spectra obtained by restriction along the composite functor

$$H_i - \mathbf{Sets}_{df} \cong G - \mathbf{Sets}_{df} \downarrow G_i \xrightarrow{Q} G - \mathbf{Sets}_{df}.$$

The map of spectra $F(*) \to F(G_i)$ is therefore a restriction map for the generalized Galois cohomology theory determined by F.   ∎

6.3. Ordinary Galois cohomology

The covering map $G_i \to *$ in the category $G - \mathbf{Sets}_{df}$ gives rise to a Čech resolution for the terminal object, which is a simplicial object in $G - \mathbf{Sets}_{df}$ that is best interpreted as the nerve of the trivial groupoid on the set G_i, with appropriate G-action (ie. diagonal at all levels). This groupoid is equivariantly isomorphic to the translation category for the action of the opposite group G_i^{op} on G_i by right multiplication. The Čech resolution for the covering $G_i \to *$ may therefore be identified up to G-equivariant isomorphism with the Borel construction

$$EG_i^{op} \tilde{\times}_{G_i^{op}} G_i$$

in the category $G - \mathbf{Sets}_{df}$. It represents a simplicial object in the classifying topos B_G of the same name, which can also be viewed as the simplicial sheaf associated to the simplicial presheaf $EG_i^{op} \times_{G_i^{op}} G_i$. The latter is formed in the category of simplicial presheaves in a predictable way, from the action of G_i^{op} on the presheaf (or the sheaf) represented by the G-set G_i: the presheaf of n-simplices of $EG_i^{op} \times_{G_i^{op}} G_i$ is a presheaf-theoretic disjoint union of the form

$$(EG_i^{op} \times_{G_i^{op}} G_i)_n = \bigsqcup_{* \xleftarrow{g_1} * \cdots * \xleftarrow{g_n} *} G_i,$$

where the g_j are elements of G_i. Note that each canonical homomorphism $G_j \to G_i$ induces a map of simplicial sheaves

$$EG_j^{op} \tilde{\times}_{G_j^{op}} G_j \to EG_i^{op} \tilde{\times}_{G_i^{op}} G_i,$$

which is induced by a corresponding map of simplicial presheaves.

Suppose that A is an abelian sheaf on $G - \mathbf{Sets}_{df}$. The cochain complex

$$\hom(EG_i^{op} \tilde{\times}_{G_i^{op}} G_i, A)$$

has n-chains

$$\prod_{\underset{g_1 \quad g_n}{* \leftarrow * \cdots * \leftarrow *}} A(G_i), \tag{6.27}$$

with coboundary induced by the face maps of the simplicial object

$$EG_i^{op} \tilde{\times}_{G_i^{op}} G_i.$$

The homomorphisms $G_j \to G_i$ functorially induces a maps

$$\hom(EG_i^{op} \tilde{\times}_{G_i^{op}} G_i, A) \to \hom(EG_j^{op} \tilde{\times}_{G_j^{op}} G_j, A)$$

of cochain complexes, and the *Galois* or *Čech* cohomology groups $\check{H}^n(G, A)$ are defined by

$$\check{H}^n(G, A) = \varinjlim_i H^n \; \hom(EG_i^{op} \times_{G_i^{op}} G_i, A),$$

for $n \geq 0$. Observe that there are isomorphisms

$$H^n \; \hom(EG_i^{op} \tilde{\times}_{G_i^{op}} G_i, A) \cong H^n(G_i, A(G_i))$$
$$\cong H^n(G_i, LA^{H_i}),$$

where H_i is the kernel of the canonical map $G \to G_i$, as before, so that $\check{H}^*(G, A)$ can be canonically identified with the traditional Galois cohomology of G with coefficients in LA.

A completely analogous definition of $\check{H}^*(G, B)$ is possible when the coefficient object B is an additive abelian presheaf: the additivity is used to identify the n-cochains of the complex $\hom(EG_i^{op} \tilde{\times}_{G_i^{op}} G_i, B)$, as in (6.27).

LEMMA 6.28. *Suppose that B is an additive abelian presheaf on $G - \mathbf{Sets}_{df}$ such that the associated sheaf $\tilde{B} \cong 0$. Then $\check{H}^*(G, B) \cong 0$.*

Proof: Suppose that

$$z \in \prod_{\substack{g_1 \\ * \leftarrow * \cdots * \leftarrow *}}^{g_n} B(G_i) \cong B(\coprod_{\substack{g_1 \\ * \leftarrow * \cdots * \leftarrow *}}^{g_n} G_i)$$

is a cocyle. There is a covering

$$X \to \coprod_{\substack{g_1 \\ * \leftarrow * \cdots * \leftarrow *}}^{g_n} G_i = \coprod_{(BG_i^{op})_n} G_i$$

in the underlying site $G - \mathbf{Sets}_{df}$, such that $z \mapsto 0$ in $B(X)$. Up to refinement, we can suppose that the covering $X \to \coprod_{(BG_i^{op})_n} G_i$ has the form

$$X = \coprod_{(BG_i^{op})_n} G_j \xrightarrow{\coprod p} \coprod_{(BG_i^{op})_n} G_i$$

Composing this covering with the map

$$\coprod_{(BG_j^{op})_n} G_j \to \coprod_{(BG_i^{op})_n} G_j$$

which is induced in summands by $p : G_j \to G_i$ gives the n-simplex map

$$\coprod_{(BG_j^{op})_n} G_j \to \coprod_{(BG_i^{op})_n} G_i$$

relating the respective Borel constructions, which is induced by p. It follows that z represents the class 0 in $\check{H}^n(G, B)$.   ∎

Suppose that A is an abelian sheaf on $G - \mathbf{Sets}_{df}$, and let $A \to I^*$ be an injective resolution of A in the abelian sheaf category. Write H^i for the ith cohomology presheaf of the cochain complex I^*. Then $H^0 \cong A$ and H^i is an additive abelian presheaf such that $\tilde{H}^i \cong 0$ for $i > 0$.

Write also $H^*(G, A)$ for the cohomology of the classifying topos B_G with coefficients in the sheaf A; these cohomology groups coincide, of course, with the higher derived functors of the global sections functor. There is a canonical comparison homomorphism

$$\Omega : \check{H}^*(G, A) \to H^*(G, A)$$

relating the Galois (or Čech) cohomology of G with coefficients in A to the sheaf cohomology. This comparison is most efficiently described by observing that the injective resolution $A \to I^*$ induces an isomorphism in hypercohomology

$$\check{H}^*(G, A) \to \check{H}^*(G, I^*), \tag{6.29}$$

by Lemma 6.28. Each map $EG_i^{op} \tilde{\times}_{G_i^{op}} G_i \to *$ is a hypercover of the terminal object $*$, and so the induced maps

$$\hom(*, I^*) \to \hom(EG_i^{op} \tilde{\times}_{G_i^{op}} G_i, I^*)$$

of bicomplexes induce quasi-isomorphisms on the total complex level. In particular, the canonical map

$$\check{H}^*(G, I^*) \leftarrow H^* I(*) = H^*(G, A) \tag{6.30}$$

is an isomorphism. The composite of the inverse of the map (6.30) with the map (6.29) is the comparison map Ω. We have also showed

PROPOSITION 6.31. *Suppose that A is a sheaf of abelian groups on $G-\mathbf{Sets}_{df}$. Then the comparison homomorphism*

$$\Omega : \check{H}^*(G, A) \to H^*(G, A)$$

is an isomorphism.

From a different point of view, the Verdier hypercovering theorem (see [22]) asserts that the group $H^n(G, A)$ coincides up to isomorphism with the filtered colimit

$$\varinjlim_{U \to *} H^n \hom(U, A),$$

where the indexing category is simplicial homotopy classes of maps between hypercovers of the terminal object $*$. Each simplicial presheaf $EG_i^{op} \times_{G_i^{op}} G_i$ is such a hypercover of the terminal object, and so there is a canonical map

$$\check{H}^n(G, A) \to \varinjlim_{U \to *} H^n \hom(U, A) \tag{6.32}$$

which compares the two colimits. This comparison map is isomorphic to the map Ω, by the same trick of replacing the sheaf A by the injective resolution I^*.

The following is another consequence of Lemma 6.28

COROLLARY 6.33. *Suppose that B is an additive abelian presheaf on $G - \mathbf{Sets}_{df}$. Then the canonical map $\eta : B \to \tilde{B}$ from B to its associated sheaf induces an isomorphism*

$$\eta_* : \check{H}^*(G, B) \xrightarrow{\cong} \check{H}^*(G, \tilde{B}).$$

PROOF: The kernel and cokernel of $\eta : B \to \tilde{B}$ are additive abelian presheaves with trivial associated sheaf, and any short exact sequence of additive abelian sheaves induces a long exact sequence in Čech cohomology. ∎

Suppose that k is a field with separable closure k_{sep} and absolute Galois group $G = Gal(k_{sep}/k)$. It is well known (see [42, p.54], for example) that the functor defined by

$$U \mapsto \hom_k(Sp(k_{sep}), U)$$

defines an isomorphism of sites

$$F : et|_k \xrightarrow{\cong} G - \mathbf{Sets}_{df}$$

which relates the finite étale site for k to the site associated to the profinite group G. The existence of the site isomorphism is really just Galois theory. It follows, for example, that any abelian sheaf A on the étale site $et|_k$ uniquely determines an abelian sheaf on $G-\mathbf{Sets}_{df}$ (which will be given the same name); this phenomenon and Proposition 6.31 together give rise to the well known natural isomorphism

$$H_{et}^*(k, A) \cong \check{H}^*(G, A)$$

between the étale and Galois cohomology theories for k for cohomology. This site isomorphism further induces isomorphisms of generalized cohomology theories

$$\mathbb{H}^*(k, F) \cong \mathbb{H}^*(G, F)$$

(suitably defined) for any presheaf of spectra on the étale site $et|_k$.

REMARK 6.34. It is important to remember that $\check{H}^*(G, A)$ is a type of Čech cohomology with coefficients in the abelian sheaf A. It is certainly possible to define a generalized Čech invariant $\check{H}^*(G, F)$ and a canonical comparison map

$$\check{H}^*(G, F) \to \mathbb{H}^*(G, F)$$

for any presheaf of spectra F in the G-world, in such a way that the definition and the canonical map specialize to the ordinary cohomological objects and the isomorphism we know in the case where F is an Eilenberg-Mac Lane object $K(A, n)$. It is not known, however, if this comparison map is an isomorphism for arbitrary presheaves of spectra F. This problem, and a working partial solution are the subject of the next section. ∎

Suppose that N/k is a (not necessarily finite) Galois extension, with Galois group $H = Gal(N/k)$. There is a surjective homomorphism $p : G \to H$ of pro-groups which is defined by the collection of identity homomorphisms

$$G_L \xrightarrow{1} G_L$$

corresponding to all Galois extensions L/k with $L \subset N$. This can be seen either by using ordinary Galois theory, or by invoking Proposition 1 on p. I-2 of [49].

The homomorphism p induces an inclusion functor

$$p_{df} : H - \mathbf{Sets}_{df} \to G - \mathbf{Sets}_{df},$$

given by restriction of scalars. The functor p_{df} induces a direct image functor

$$p_* : Preshv(G - \mathbf{Sets}_{df}) \to Preshv(H - \mathbf{Sets}_{df})$$

on the presheaf level, which is defined by precomposition with p_{df}. Observe that $p_* F$ is a sheaf if F is a sheaf, since p_{df} takes covering families in discrete H-sets to covering families in G-sets.

The direct image functor p_* has a left adjoint

$$p^p : Preshv(H - \mathbf{Sets}_{df}) \to Preshv(G - \mathbf{Sets}_{df})$$

given by Kan extension. More explicitly, if F is a presheaf on $H - \mathbf{Sets}_{df}$, and V is a finite discrete G-set, then

$$p^p(F)(V) = \varinjlim_{V \to p_{df}(U)} F(U),$$

where the colimit is indexed over objects $V \to p_{df}(U)$ of the comma category $V \downarrow p_{df}$. The functor p_{df} is exact in the sense that it preserves finite limits (see the proof of Lemma 6.15); it follows that the category $V \downarrow p_{df}$ is filtered.

The functor p^p is therefore exact, and hence preserves monomorphisms and stalkwise weak equivalences of simplicial presheaves on $H - \mathbf{Sets}_{df}$, so that by a standard argument we have

LEMMA 6.35. *The direct image functor*

$$p_* : Preshv(G - \mathbf{Sets}_{df}) \to Preshv(H - \mathbf{Sets}_{df}),$$

preserves global fibrations of simplicial presheaves.

Note as well that we have verified the conditions for the functor p_{df} to induce a site morphism

$$p : G - \mathbf{Sets}_{df} \to H - \mathbf{Sets}_{df},$$

so that the Leray spectral sequence machinery of [27] is applicable. It is possible, for example, to extract the standard results about Galois cohomological dimension of fields from this observation.

6.4. Generalized Čech cohomology

Suppose that $G = \{G_i\}_{i \in I}$ is a profinite group such that all transition homomorphisms are surjective, as before.

Recall that each finite group G_i represents a sheaf on the category $G -$ **Sets**$_{df}$ of finite discrete G-modules, and that this sheaf has a contravariant G_i-action which is defined by right translations. This Borel construction $EG_i^{op} \times_{G_i^{op}} G_i$ for this action is a simplicial presheaf in the G-world, such that the corresponding map

$$EG_i^{op} \times_{G_i^{op}} G_i \to *$$

is a hypercover of the terminal simplicial presheaf.

Suppose that F is a presheaf of spectra in the G-world, and recall that right translations by elements of G_i induces a covariant action of the group G_i on the spectrum $F(G_i)$. The homotopy inverse limit $\underleftarrow{\operatorname{holim}}_{G_i} F(G_i)$ for this covariant G_i-action is the total complex of the cosimplicial spectrum whose spectrum of n-cosimplices is given by

$$\prod_{* \overset{g_1}{\leftarrow} * \cdots * \overset{g_n}{\leftarrow} *} F(G_i). \tag{6.36}$$

In general, if U and X are simplicial presheaves, we are entitled to construct (but be careful with) a cosimplicial space $\hom(U, X)$ whose n-cosimplices are given by

$$\hom(U, X)^n = \hom(U_n, X),$$

where U_n is the presheaf of n-simplices of U, and *hom* means homomorphisms of presheaves. This will be a fibrant cosimplicial space if each of the maps

$$i^* : \hom(U_n, X) \to \hom(DU_n, X)$$

induced by the inclusion $i : DU_n \to U_n$ of the degenerate part of U_n is a Kan fibration. This is so, for example, if X is a globally fibrant simplicial presheaf, and in that case the Bousfield-Kan total complex Tot $\hom(U, X)$ can be identified up to isomorphism with the function complex $\mathbf{hom}(U, X)$ whose set of n-simplices consists of the maps of simplicial presheaves of the form $U \times \Delta^n \to X$.

LEMMA 6.37. *Suppose that F is a presheaf of spectra in the G-world which consists of presheaves of Kan complexes. Then there is a canonical isomorphism of spectra of the form*

$$\mathbf{hom}_*((EG_i^{op} \times_{G_i^{op}} G_i)_+, F) \cong \underleftarrow{\operatorname{holim}}_{G_i} F(G_i).$$

PROOF: The pointed function complex

$$\mathbf{hom}_*((EG_i^{op} \times_{G_i^{op}} G_i)_+, F^n)$$

coincides with the unpointed complex

$$\mathbf{hom}(EG_i^{op} \times_{G_i^{op}} G_i, F^n);$$

the Borel construction $EG_i^{op} \times_{G_i^{op}} G_i$ is made pointed in the usual way by attaching a base point, to get

$$(EG_i^{op} \times_{G_i^{op}} G_i)_+ = (EG_i^{op} \times_{G_i^{op}} G_i) \sqcup \{*\}.$$

The canonical map of spectra

$$\mathbf{hom}(\bigsqcup_{\substack{g_1 \quad g_n \\ * \leftarrow * \cdots * \leftarrow *}} G_i, F) \to \prod_{\substack{g_1 \quad g_n \\ * \leftarrow * \cdots * \leftarrow *}} F(G_i).$$

is an isomorphism, since the disjoint unions in the definition of $EG_i^{op} \times_{G_i^{op}} G_i$ are formed in the presheaf category. This map respects the cosimplicial structure, and so induces an isomorphism of cosimplicial spectra. Now apply the Tot functor. ∎

REMARK 6.38. It follows in particular that the cosimplicial spaces

$$\mathbf{hom}(EG_i^{op} \times_{G_i^{op}} G_i, F^n)$$

are fibrant in the sense of Bousfield and Kan if each F^n is a presheaf of Kan complexes. ∎

PROPOSITION 6.39. *Suppose that F is a globally fibrant presheaf of spectra in the G-world. Then the canonical map*

$$F(*) \to \varprojlim_{G_i} F(G_i)$$

is a stable equivalence.

PROOF: The canonical map $EG_i^{op} \times_{G_i^{op}} G_i \to *$ of simplicial presheaves is a weak equivalence, and so induces a stable equivalence

$$\mathbf{hom}_*(\Gamma^* S^0, F) \to \mathbf{hom}_*((EG_i^{op} \times_{G_i^{op}} G_i)_+, F),$$

since F is globally fibrant. Here, $\Gamma^* S^0$ is the constant pointed simplicial presheaf associated to the 0-sphere $S^0 = \partial \Delta^1$, and there is an isomorphism

$$\mathbf{hom}_*(\Gamma^* S^0, F) \cong F(*).$$ ∎

One often paraphrases Proposition 6.39 by saying that globally fibrant presheaves of spectra in the G-world (also anywhere else) have the *finite descent property*.

Suppose that F is a presheaf of stably fibrant spectra in the G-world, and let $i : F \to GF$ be a globally fibrant model for F. The spectrum

$$\mathbf{hom}_*((EG_i^{op} \times_{G_i^{op}} G_i)_+, F)$$

is stably fibrant, and so its stable homotopy groups coincide up to isomorphism with the homotopy groups of the Kan complexes

$$\mathbf{hom}_*((EG_i^{op} \times_{G_i^{op}} G_i)_+, F^n).$$

The jth homotopy group

$$\pi_j \mathbf{hom}_*((EG_i^{op} \times_{G_i^{op}} G_i)_+, F^n) \tag{6.40}$$

is isomorphic to the group

$$\pi(EG_i^{op} \times_{G_i^{op}} G_i, \Omega^j F^n) \tag{6.41}$$

of simplicial homotopy classes of maps of simplicial presheaves from the Borel construction $EG_i^{op} \times_{G_i^{op}} G_i$ to the iterated loop space object $\Omega^j F^n$. Here (and as usual), simplicial homotopy classes are formed by collapsing the set of all simplicial presheaf maps by the smallest equivalence relation containing the simplicial homotopy relation. The identification of (6.40) with (6.41) arises from the identification of the space

$$\mathbf{hom}_*((EG_i^{op} \times_{G_i^{op}} G_i)_+, F^n)$$

with a homotopy inverse limit that is implicit in Lemma 6.37, and the fact that homotopy inverse limits preserve path loop fibrations in a suitable sense.

Suppose that X is a simplicial presheaf in the G-world, and let

$$\pi(EG_i^{op} \times_{G_i^{op}} G_i, X)$$

denote the set of simplicial homotopy classes of maps from $EG_i^{op} \times_{G_i^{op}} G_i$ to X in the sense just described. There is a canonical map

$$\pi(EG_i^{op} \times_{G_i^{op}} G_i, X) \xrightarrow{c_i} [*, X]$$

which is defined by associating to a map

$$f : EG_i^{op} \times_{G_i^{op}} G_i \to X$$

the composite

$$* \xleftarrow[\simeq]{can} EG_i^{op} \times_{G_i^{op}} G_i \xrightarrow{f} X$$

in the homotopy category. The maps c_i, taken over all objects i of the index category I, together induce a map

$$\varinjlim_{i} \pi(EG_i^{op} \times_{G_i^{op}} G_i, X) \xrightarrow{c_X} [*, X]. \qquad (6.42)$$

This comparison map (6.42) is an isomorphism if X is globally fibrant, since X satisfies finite descent in that case — this is the unstable fact which underlies Proposition 6.39.

Returning to spectra, with F and globally fibrant model GF as above, one finds a canonical map

$$c_F : \varinjlim_{i} \pi_j \mathbf{hom}_*((EG_i^{op} \times_{G_i^{op}} G_i)_+, F) \to \pi_j GF(*) \qquad (6.43)$$

which is induced by the maps

$$\mathbf{hom}_*((EG_i^{op} \times_{G_i^{op}} G_i)_+, F) \xrightarrow{i_*} \mathbf{hom}_*((EG_i^{op} \times_{G_i^{op}} G_i)_+, GF)$$

and the homotopy group isomorphisms

$$\pi_j \mathbf{hom}_*((EG_i^{op} \times_{G_i^{op}} G_i)_+, GF) \cong \pi_j GF(*).$$

The *generalized Čech cohomology groups* $\check{H}^*(G, F)$ with coefficients in the presheaf of spectra F are defined by

$$\check{H}^{-n}(G, F) = \varinjlim_{i} \pi_n \mathbf{hom}_*((EG_i^{op} \times_{G_i^{op}} G_i)_+, F).$$

The *generalized Galois cohomology groups* $\mathbb{H}^*(G, F)$ for the classifying topos B_G with coefficients in the presheaf of spectra F are defined by

$$\mathbb{H}^{-n}(G, F) = \pi_n GF(*),$$

where $F \to GF$ is a globally fibrant model for F. The map c_F of (6.43) may therefore be interpreted as a comparison

$$c_F : \check{H}^*(G, F) \to \mathbb{H}^*(G, F)$$

which relates these two theories.

PROPOSITION 6.44. *Suppose that A is an additive presheaf of abelian groups, and that F is a presheaf of stably fibrant spectra in the G-world. Suppose that F is a $K(A, n)$ in the sense that there is a presheaf isomorphism*

$$\pi_n F \cong A,$$

and all other presheaves of stable homotopy groups of F are 0. Let $i : F \to GF$ be a globally fibrant model for F. Then the canonical map

$$c_F : \varinjlim_{i} \pi_j \mathbf{hom}_*((EG_i^{op} \times_{G_i^{op}} G_i)_+, F) \to \pi_j GF(*) \qquad (6.45)$$

is an isomorphism, for all $j \in \mathbb{Z}$.

PROOF: The spectra

$$\mathbf{hom}_*((EG_i^{op} \times_{G_i^{op}} G_i)_+, F) \quad \text{and} \quad \mathbf{hom}_*((EG_i^{op} \times_{G_i^{op}} G_i)_+, GF)$$

are stably fibrant spectra, and the latter spectrum is stably equivalent to the global sections spectrum $GF(*)$, via the map of function complexes induced by the hypercover

$$EG_i^{op} \times_{G_i^{op}} G_i \to *.$$

It follows that the maps c_F in stable homotopy groups can be identified up to isomorphism with maps

$$i_* : \varinjlim_{i \in I} \pi(EG_i^{op} \times_{G_i^{op}} G_i, \Omega^s F^m) \to \varinjlim_{i \in I} \pi(EG_i^{op} \times_{G_i^{op}} G_i, \Omega^s GF^m).$$

The level map $i : \Omega^s F^m \to \Omega^s GF^m$ is a globally fibrant model for the simplicial presheaf $\Omega^s F^m$, and there is a commutative diagram

$$
\begin{array}{ccc}
\varinjlim_{i \in I} \pi(EG_i^{op} \times_{G_i^{op}} G_i, \Omega^s F^m) & \xrightarrow{\ c\ } & [*, \Omega^s F^m] \\[2mm]
\Big\downarrow{\scriptstyle i_*} & & \Big\downarrow{\scriptstyle i_*}{\scriptstyle \cong} \\[2mm]
\varinjlim_{i \in I} \pi(EG_i^{op} \times_{G_i^{op}} G_i, \Omega^s GF^m) & \xrightarrow[\ c\ ]{\cong} & [*, \Omega^s GF^m],
\end{array}
$$

where the horizontal maps are the canonical maps of (6.42).

It follows that our original maps (6.45) may be identified up to isomorphism with maps

$$\varinjlim_{i} \pi(EG_i^{op} \times_{G_i^{op}} G_i, \Omega^s F^m) \xrightarrow{\ c\ } [*, \Omega^s F^m], \tag{6.46}$$

taking values in morphisms in the homotopy category associated to stalkwise weak equivalences of simplicial presheaves.

The presheaf of Kan complexes $\Omega^s F^m$ is either pointwise contractible, or pointwise weakly equivalent within the category of pointwise fibrant presheaves to some

$$K(A, p) = \overline{W}^p K(A, 0)$$

(Corollary 4.67). The functors on both sides of the map (6.46) take pointwise weak equivalences of pointwise fibrant presheaves to isomorphisms, so the proof reduces to showing that the map

$$\varinjlim_{i} \pi(EG_i^{op} \times_{G_i^{op}} G_i, K(A, p)) \xrightarrow{\ c\ } [*, K(A, p)], \tag{6.47}$$

is an isomorphism for all $p \geq 0$, provided that A is an additive abelian presheaf.

We can suppose that A is an abelian sheaf, by Corollary 6.33. The map (6.47) can therefore be identified up to isomorphism (by taking adjoints in the simplicial abelian presheaf category, and fiddling with normalized chain complexes [22, p.207] with the canonical isomorphism (6.32).   ∎

A presheaf F of spectra in the G-world (or anywhere else) is said to be *additive* if the natural map

$$F(U \sqcup V) \to F(U) \times F(V)$$

is a stable equivalence, for all finite discrete G-sets U and V. Observe that, if F is additive, then so are all of its Postnikov sections $P_n F$, all the dual objects $F_n F$, and hence all of the objects $P_n F_m F$; these are consequences of the resulting additivity of the presheaves of stable homotopy groups of F. The K-theory presheaves of spectra, where defined, are also additive. Another major source of such objects is the following result:

LEMMA 6.48. *All globally fibrant presheaves of spectra are additive.*

PROOF: There is a correponding condition for simplicial presheaves: a simplicial presheaf X is additive if the simplicial set map

$$X(U \sqcup V) \to X(U) \times X(V)$$

is a weak equivalence for all G-sets U and V. It is enough to show that globally fibrant simplicial presheaves are additive.

Suppose that X is a globally fibrant simplicial presheaf. Then the adjunction map $X \to \tilde{X}$ is a stalkwise weak equivalence, and the simplicial sheaf $\tilde{X}$ has a globally fibrant model $i : \tilde{X} \to G\tilde{X}$ constructed internally in the category of simplicial sheaves, by a theorem of Joyal ([29], [23, p.69]. In particular, $G\tilde{X}$ is a globally fibrant model of X which happens to be a simplicial sheaf. The simplicial presheaf $G\tilde{X}$ is additive, and so X is additive, since the composite map

$$X \to \tilde{X} \to G\tilde{X}$$

is a weak equivalence of globally fibrant simplicial presheaves, and is therefore a weak equivalence in each section.   ∎

LEMMA 6.49. *Suppose that F is an additive presheaf of stably fibrant spectra in the G-world, and that F has only finitely many non-trivial presheaves of stable homotopy groups. Then the comparison map*

$$c_F : \check{H}^n(G, F) \to \mathbb{H}^n(G, F).$$

is an isomorphism.

PROOF: Suppose that $\pi_n F$ is the non-trivial homotopy group presheaf of top dimension. Then $P_{n-1}F$ has one less non-trivial presheaf of stable homotopy groups than does F, and the pointwise strict homotopy fibre $F_{n-1}F$ of the restriction map $res : F \to P_{n-1}F$ is a presheaf of stably fibrant spectra of the form $K(\pi_n F, n)$, where $\pi_n F$ is an additive abelian presheaf. There is a comparison map of pointwise fibre sequences

$$
\begin{array}{ccccc}
F_{n-1}F & \longrightarrow & F & \xrightarrow{res} & P_{n-1}F \\
\downarrow & & \downarrow{\scriptstyle i} & & \downarrow{\scriptstyle i} \\
GF_{n-1}F & \longrightarrow & GF & \xrightarrow[res_*]{} & GP_{n-1}F.
\end{array}
$$

This diagram is constructed by, first, finding a globally fibrant model

$$i : P_{n-1}F \to GP_{n-1}F,$$

and then by factoring the composite

$$F \xrightarrow{res} P_{n-1}F \xrightarrow{i} GP_{n-1}F$$

as a stalkwise trivial cofibration $i : F \to GF$, followed by a global fibration $res_* : GF \to GP_{n-1}F$.

A global fibration $Y \to X$ of simplicial presheaves in the G-world induces a Kan fibration $Y(G_i) \to X(G_i)$ for all $i \in I$. Applying homotopy inverse limit functors $\varprojlim_{G_i}$ for all $i \in I$ therfore gives comparisons of fibre sequences

$$
\begin{array}{ccc}
\mathbf{hom}_*((EG_i^{op} \times_{G_i^{op}} G_i)_+, F_{n-1}F) & \longrightarrow & \mathbf{hom}_*((EG_i^{op} \times_{G_i^{op}} G_i)_+, GF_{n-1}F) \\
\downarrow & & \downarrow \\
\mathbf{hom}_*((EG_i^{op} \times_{G_i^{op}} G_i)_+, F) & \xrightarrow{\ i\ } & \mathbf{hom}_*((EG_i^{op} \times_{G_i^{op}} G_i)_+, GF) \\
\downarrow{\scriptstyle res} & & \downarrow{\scriptstyle res_*} \\
\mathbf{hom}_*((EG_i^{op} \times_{G_i^{op}} G_i)_+, P_{n-1}F) & \xrightarrow[i]{} & \mathbf{hom}_*((EG_i^{op} \times_{G_i^{op}} G_i)_+, GP_{n-1}F).
\end{array}
$$

Taking a filtered colimit of the resulting comparisons of long exact sequences of stable homotopy groups over all objects $i \in I$ gives a comparison of long exact sequences in generalized Čech cohomology. This comparison, together with Proposition 6.44 and the inductive hypothesis that the map

$$\check{H}^*(G, P_{n-1}F) \to \check{H}^*(G, GP_{n-1}F) \cong \mathbb{H}^*(G, P_{n-1}F)$$

is an isomorphism, implies that the map

$$c: \check{H}^*(G, F) \to \mathbb{H}^*(G, F)$$

is an isomorphism. ∎

The remainder of this section will not be used in the proofs that appear in Chapter 7.

To generalize Lemma 6.49, we shall need a technical lemma concerning the Bousfield-Kan spectral sequence [9, X.6] of a fibrant cosimplicial space X. Recall from [9] that

$$NX^s = X^s \cap ker\ s^0 \cap \cdots \cap ker\ s^{s-1},$$

on the space level, and that

$$\pi_i NX^s = \pi_i X^s \cap ker\ s^0 \cap \cdots \cap ker\ s^{s-1} \subset \pi_i X^s$$

in the cosimplicial abelian group $\pi_i X$. One also needs to know that Tot X is the inverse limit of a tower of fibrations

$$\text{Tot}_0\ X \leftarrow \text{Tot}_1\ X \leftarrow \ldots,$$

where Tot$_s$ X is given by the function space

$$\text{Tot}_s\ X = \mathbf{hom}_*(sk_s\tilde{\Delta}_+, X),$$

$\tilde{\Delta}$ is the cosimplicial space made up of the simplices Δ^n, $n \geq 0$, and $sk_s\tilde{\Delta}$ is obtained from $\tilde{\Delta}$ by applying the s-skeleton functor sk_s in each cosimplicial degree.

LEMMA 6.50.

(1) Suppose that X is a fibrant pointed cosimplicial space such that $\pi_t X^q = 0$ for all q and all $t \geq m$. Then the Bousfield-Kan spectral sequence

$$E_1^{s,t} = \pi_t NX^s \Rightarrow \pi_{t-s} \text{ Tot } X, \qquad t \geq s,$$

converges strongly. Furthermore, π_t Tot $X = 0$ if $t \geq m$.

(2) Suppose that X_i, $i \in I$ is a filtered system of fibrant pointed cosimplicial spaces such that $\pi_t X_i^q = 0$ for all i and q, and for all $t \geq m$. Then the canonical map

$$\varinjlim_{i \in I} \text{Tot } X_i \to \text{Tot } \varinjlim_{i \in I} X_i$$

is a weak equivalence of pointed simplicial sets.

PROOF: Suppose that X is a fibrant cosimplicial space as in the first statement of the lemma, and write

$$F_s = \mathbf{hom}_*(S^s, NX^s).$$

Recall that F_s is the fibre of the canonical fibration

$$\mathrm{Tot}_s \ X \to \mathrm{Tot}_{s-1} \ X$$

which is induced by the inclusion $sk_{s-1}\tilde{\Delta} \subset sk_s\tilde{\Delta}$. Consider the picture

$$
\begin{array}{ccccccc}
\pi_t \, \mathrm{Tot}_0 \ X & \longleftarrow & \pi_t \, \mathrm{Tot}_1 \ X & \longleftarrow & \cdots & \longleftarrow & \pi_t \, \mathrm{Tot}_s \ X \\
\| & & \uparrow & & & & \uparrow \\
\pi_t F_0 & & \pi_t F_1 & & & & \pi_t F_s \\
\downarrow & & \downarrow & & & & \downarrow \\
\pi_t X^0 & & \pi_{t+1} X^1 & & & & \pi_{t+s} X^s.
\end{array}
$$

The group $\pi_{t+s} N X^{s+1}$ is trivial if $t + s \geq m$, by assumption, and so the canonical fibration induces an isomorphism

$$\pi_t \, \mathrm{Tot}_{s+1} \ X \xrightarrow{\cong} \pi_t \, \mathrm{Tot}_s \ X$$

if $s \geq m - t$. It follows that the canonical map $\mathrm{Tot} \ X \to \mathrm{Tot}_s \ X$ induces an isomorphism

$$\pi_t \, \mathrm{Tot} \ X \xrightarrow{\cong} \pi_t \, \mathrm{Tot}_s \ X$$

if $s \geq m - t$. In particular

$$\pi_t \, \mathrm{Tot} \ X \cong \pi_t X^0 \cong 0$$

if $t \geq m$.

To prove part (2), write

$$X = \varinjlim_{i \in I} X_i,$$

and observe that X is a fibrant pointed cosimplicial space which satisfies the hypotheses of statement (1). Let t be arbitrary, and pick $s \geq m - t$. Then there is a commutative diagram

$$
\begin{array}{ccc}
\varinjlim_{i \in I} \pi_t \, \mathrm{Tot} \ X_i & \longrightarrow & \pi_t \, \mathrm{Tot} \ X \\
{\scriptstyle \cong} \downarrow & & \downarrow {\scriptstyle \cong} \\
\varinjlim_{i \in I} \pi_t \, \mathrm{Tot}_s \ X_i & \longrightarrow & \pi_t \, \mathrm{Tot}_s \ X
\end{array}
\qquad (6.51)
$$

in which the horizontal maps are canonical. The complex

$$\mathrm{Tot}_s\ X = \mathbf{hom}_*(sk_s\tilde{\Delta}_+, X)$$

can be naturally identified up to isomorphism with the function complex

$$\mathbf{hom}_*(\tilde{\Delta}^{[s]}, X^{[s]})$$

of morphisms of cosimplicial spaces truncated up to level s, so that the functor Tot_s preserves filtered colimits. The bottom horizontal map in (6.51) is therefore an isomorphism. ∎

COROLLARY 6.52.

(1) *Suppose that F is a preheaf of stably fibrant spectra in the G-world, and suppose that the stable homotopy group presheaves $\pi_i F$ are 0 if $i \geq m$. Then the generalized Čech cohomology groups $\check{H}^i(G, F)$ vanish if $i \leq -m$.*

(2) *Suppose that F_j, $j \in J$ is a filtered system of presheaves of stably fibrant spectra in the G-world, such that all presheaves $\pi_r F_j$ of stable homotopy groups have the property that $\pi_r F_j = 0$ if $r \geq m$. Let F denote the filtered colimit $\varinjlim_{j \in J} F_j$. Then the canonical map*

$$\varinjlim_{j \in J} \check{H}^r(G, F_j) \to \check{H}^r(G, F)$$

is an isomorphism for all $r \in \mathbb{Z}$.

THEOREM 6.53. *Suppose that F is an additive presheaf of stably fibrant spectra in the G-world, whose presheaves of stable homotopy groups have the property that $\pi_j F = 0$ for $j > m$. Then the canonical map*

$$\check{H}^*(G, F) \xrightarrow{c_F} \mathbb{H}^*(G, F)$$

is an isomorphism in all degrees.

PROOF: Write $F_0 = F$, and $F_i = P_{m-i}F$ for $i \geq 1$. I claim that the maps in the inductive system

$$F_0 \xrightarrow{\mathrm{res}} F_1 \xrightarrow{\mathrm{res}} F_2 \xrightarrow{\mathrm{res}} \dots$$

arising from the restriction maps may be replaced up to pointwise weak equivalence by maps which are strict fibrations of spectra in every section.

In effect, one inductively constructs diagrams

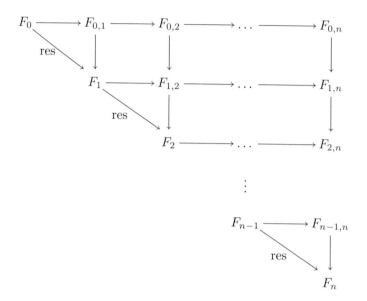

in which all horizontal maps are pointwise strict weak equivalences and all vertical maps are pointwise strict fibrations. To get the next stage from this diagram, choose a factorization

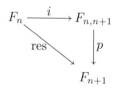

of the restriction map $F_n \to F_{n+1}$, such that i is a trivial pointwise strict cofibration and p is a pointwise strict fibration. Now find a similar factorization

$$
\begin{array}{ccc}
F_{n-1,n} & \longrightarrow & F_{n-1,n+1} \\
\downarrow & & \downarrow \\
F_n & \xrightarrow{\ i\ } & F_{n,n+1}
\end{array}
$$

of the composite

$$
F_{n-1,n} \to F_n \xrightarrow{\ i\ } F_{n,n+1},
$$

and so on, to construct the requisite maps and presheaves of spectra $F_{i,n+1}$. Now let

$$\hat{F}_n = \varinjlim_i F_{n,i}.$$

Then there is a commutative diagram

$$
\begin{array}{ccccccc}
F_0 & \xrightarrow{\mathrm{res}} & F_1 & \xrightarrow{\mathrm{res}} & F_2 & \longrightarrow & \cdots \\
\downarrow & & \downarrow & & \downarrow & & \\
\hat{F}_0 & \xrightarrow[\mathrm{res}_*]{} & \hat{F}_1 & \xrightarrow[\mathrm{res}_*]{} & \hat{F}_2 & \longrightarrow & \cdots
\end{array}
$$

in which all of the vertical maps are pointwise strict weak equivalences, and all of the maps res_* are strict fibrations in each section. This completes the proof of the claim. Note as well that the spectra $\hat{F}_i$ are presheaves of stably fibrant spectra.

The fibre of the map $\mathrm{res}_* : \hat{F}_0 \to \hat{F}_i$ is a model for the pointwise strict homotopy fibre $F_{m-i}F$ of the restriction map

$$\mathrm{res} : F \to P_i F,$$

so it will go by the same name. Consider the resulting sequence of maps

$$F_{m-1}F \to F_{m-2}F \to F_{m-3}F \to \cdots.$$

The inclusion map $F_{m-i}F \hookrightarrow \hat{F}_0$ induces an isomorphism in presheaves π_j of stable homotopy groups if $j \geq m - i + 1$, so the induced map

$$\varinjlim_i F_{m-i}F \to \hat{F}_0$$

is a pointwise stable equivalence of presheaves of stably fibrant spectra. Construct a diagram

$$
\begin{array}{ccccc}
F_{m-1}F & \longrightarrow & F_{m-2}F & \longrightarrow & \cdots \\
\downarrow{\scriptstyle i} & & \downarrow{\scriptstyle i} & & \\
GF_{m-1}F & \longrightarrow & GF_{m-2}F & \longrightarrow & \cdots
\end{array}
$$

in which each vertical map $i : F_{m-i}F \to GF_{m-i}F$ is a globally fibrant model for $F_{m-i}F$ and a trivial stalkwise cofibration. Observe that the induced map

$$i_* : \varinjlim_i F_{m-i}F \to \varinjlim_i GF_{m-i}F$$

is a stalkwise stable equivalence and a cofibration of presheaves of spectra (this last point follows from the definition of cofibration), so that any globally fibrant model $j : \hat{F}_0 \to G\hat{F}_0$ of $\hat{F}_0$ gives rise to a commutative diagram

$$
\begin{array}{ccc}
\varinjlim\limits_{i} F_{m-i}F & \longrightarrow & \hat{F}_0 \\
\Big\downarrow{i_*} & & \Big\downarrow{j} \\
\varinjlim\limits_{i} GF_{m-i}F & \dashrightarrow & G\hat{F}_0
\end{array}
$$

in which all of the maps are stalkwise stable equivalences.

We know from Proposition 6.12 that the group homomorphism

$$\pi_j GF_{m-i}F(*) \to \pi_j G\hat{F}_0(*)$$

is an isomorphism if $j \geq m - i + 1$. It follows that the canonical map

$$\varinjlim_{i} \pi_j GF_{m-i}F(*) \to \pi_j G\hat{F}_0(*)$$

is an isomorphism for all j, so that the dotted arrow in the above diagram induces a stable equivalence in global sections. Each of the maps

$$\check{H}^*(G, F_{m-i}F) \xrightarrow{c} \pi_* GF_{m-i}F(*)$$

is an isomorphism in all degrees, by Lemma 6.49, and so the induced map

$$\varinjlim_{i} \check{H}^*(G, F_{m-i}F) \xrightarrow{c_*} \varinjlim_{i} \pi_* GF_{m-i}F(*)$$

is also an isomorphism. Finally, the canonical map

$$\varinjlim_{i} \check{H}^*(G, F_{m-i}F) \to \check{H}^*(G, \hat{F}_0)$$

is an isomorphism, by Corollary 6.52, and the diagram

$$
\begin{array}{ccc}
\varinjlim\limits_{i} \check{H}^*(G, F_{m-i}F) & \xrightarrow{\cong} & \check{H}^*(G, \hat{F}_0) \\
\Big\downarrow{c_*}{\cong} & & \Big\downarrow{} \\
\varinjlim\limits_{i} \pi_* GF_{m-i}F(*) & \xrightarrow{\cong} & \pi_* G\hat{F}_0(*)
\end{array}
$$

commutes, whence the theorem. ∎

COROLLARY 6.54. *Suppose that F is an additive presheaf of spectra in the G-world, which consists of presheaves of Kan complexes, and suppose that the homotopy group presheaves $\pi_* F^n$ have the property that*

$$\pi_j F^n = 0 \qquad \text{for } j > n + m.$$

Then the canonical map

$$c_F : \check{H}^*(G, F) \to \mathbb{H}^*(G, F)$$

is an isomorphism in all degrees.

PROOF: The canonical stabilization map $\nu : F \to QF$ is a pointwise stable weak equivalence, and hence a stalkwise stable equivalence, and there is a commutative diagram

$$
\begin{array}{ccc}
\check{H}^*(G, F) & \xrightarrow{\ \nu_*\ } & \check{H}^*(G, QF) \\
{\scriptstyle c_F}\downarrow & & \downarrow{\scriptstyle c_{QF}} \\
\mathbb{H}^*(G, F) & \xrightarrow[\nu_*]{\ \cong\ } & \mathbb{H}^*(G, QF).
\end{array}
$$

The map c_{QF} is an isomorphism, by Theorem 6.53, and the map

$$\nu_* : \check{H}^*(G, F) \to \check{H}^*(G, QF)$$

is an isomorphism by Lemma 6.50.   ∎

6.5. Continuity

Suppose that S is a scheme. As a category, the big étale site $(Sch|_S)_{et}$ consists of all S-schemes $U \to S$ which are locally of finite type over S. The collection of objects of this category do not form a set, because it includes the schemes

$$\bigsqcup_W S,$$

corresponding to all sets W. Everybody knows this, but it's a common practice to insist nevertheless that the category $(Sch|_S)_{et}$ is acceptable input for the standard sheaf-theoretic machines. Indeed, if one chooses to believe in Grothendieck's heirarchy of universes, there's no problem whatsoever. We shall begin this section by presenting a slightly more naive workaround, which only depends on cardinal arithmetic. The method will then be generalized to give working models for sites which are a little bigger than the "big site" $(Sch|_S)_{et}$.

These results will be applied at the end to give a continuity lemma for generalized étale cohomology theories.

Choose some uncountable cardinal κ. We shall say that *the cardinality of a scheme U is less than κ*, and write $card(U) < \kappa$ if the cardinality of the underlying set of points of U is smaller than κ, and if $card(A) < \kappa$ for all affine patches $V = Sp(A)$ of U.

Remark 6.55. Consider an affine scheme $Sp(A)$ such that $card(Sp(A)) < \kappa$. The constraints implied by this relation on the cardinality of A and on the cardinality of its set of prime ideals are both necessary if one wants to be sure to avoid set theoretic traps.

Suppose, for example, that

$$B = \prod_X k$$

where k is a field and X is a set such that $card(X) = \alpha < \kappa$. Then the correspondence between prime ideals of B and ultrafilters in the power set of X, in conjunction with a theorem of Tarski, together imply that the cardinality of the set of prime ideals of B is 2^{2^α} (see [5, p.108], and [21]). Thus, there will be trouble with the statement that $card(Sp(B)) < \kappa$ unless κ is something like a strong limit cardinal in the sense of [5]; one is perilously close to the generalized continuum hypothesis and various axioms of infinity at this point.

On the other hand, it's common practice not to care much about the scheme $Sp(B)$. The object of general interest is rather the disjoint union

$$Y = \bigsqcup_X Sp(k)$$

in the scheme category. The scheme Y is manifestly étale over $Sp(k)$, and, by the cardinality assumption on X, $card(Y) < \kappa$ if $card(k) < \kappa$. It is an elementary consequence of the quasi-compactness of affine schemes that Y is affine if and only if X is a finite set.   ∎

Lemma 6.56. Suppose that a scheme U has an open cover V_i, $i \in I$, where $card(V_i) < \kappa$ for all $i \in I$ and $card(I) < \kappa$. Then $card(U) < \kappa$.

Proof: Suppose that A is a ring such that $card(A) < \kappa$. Then $card(A_f) < \kappa$ for all $f \in A$. It follows that every open affine subset $V = Sp(A)$ of U has a covering $W_j = Sp(B_j), j \in J$ consisting of open affine subschemes with $card(W_j) < \kappa$. Furthermore, we can assume that J is a finite set since all such V are quasi-compact. Observe also that the cardinality of the underlying set of points of V is bounded by κ, since the same is true for U. Finally there is an inclusion

$$A \to \prod_{j \in J} B_j,$$

so that $card(A) < \kappa$.   ∎

Lemma 6.57. Suppose that U is locally of finite type over S, where $card(S) < \kappa$, and that the cardinality of the underlying set of points of U is less than κ. Then $card(U) < \kappa$.

PROOF: If B is finitely generated as an A-algebra and $card(A) < \kappa$, then $card(B) < \kappa$. The assumption about $\phi : U \to S$ means that for every point $x \in U$ there is an affine open subset $Sp(B) = V \subset U$ with $x \in V$, as well as an affine open subset $Sp(A) = W \subset S$ with $\phi(x) \in W$, such that $\phi(V) \subset W$ and the resulting restricted morphism $\phi : V \to W$ is of finite type. It follows that B is a finitely generated A-algebra, so that $card(B) < \kappa$. Use Lemma 6.56: the underlying set of points of U has cardinality bounded by κ, so that U has an affine open cover $Sp(B_i)$, $i \in I$ such that $card(B_i) < \kappa$ for all i, and $card(I) < \kappa$. ∎

COROLLARY 6.58. *Suppose that* $\phi : U \to S$ *is étale and of finite type over* S, *and that* $card(S) < \kappa$. *Then* $card(U) < \kappa$.

PROOF: S has a covering by open affines V such that each $\phi^{-1}(V)$ has a finite cover by open affines, each of which is of finite type over V. It follows that the cardinality of the set of points of U is bounded above by κ. Now use Lemma 6.57. ∎

LEMMA 6.59. *The collection of isomorphism classes of schemes* U *such that* $card(U) < \kappa$ *forms a set.*

PROOF: Suppose that B is a ring such that $card(B) < \kappa$. Then B is isomorphic to a ring $\mathbb{Z}[X]/J$, where $\mathbb{Z}[X]$ is a polynomial ring over the integers on a set X of generators such that $card(X) < \kappa$, and J is an ideal of $\mathbb{Z}[X]$. Then $card(\mathbb{Z}[X]) < \kappa$, so that the cardinality of the collection of ideals of $\mathbb{Z}[X]$ is bounded above by 2^κ. It follows that the collection of isomorphism classes of all affine schemes having cardinality less than κ forms a set.

Every scheme U is a colimit of its affine subschemes in the scheme category, so that isomorphism classes of schemes U are bounded above by isomorphism classes of diagrams of affine schemes. In particular, since $card(U) < \kappa$, one can restrict to isomorphism classes of functors $F : I \to Sch$ such that each $F(i)$ is an affine scheme with $card(F(i)) < \kappa$, $card(I) < 2^\kappa$, and such that the index category I has at most one arrow between any two objects. Each such F is isomorphic to a functor $G : I \to Sch$ such that $G(i) = Sp(\mathbb{Z}[X]/J_i)$, where $card(X) < \kappa$.
    Write
$$Mor = \prod_{J,K} \hom(\mathbb{Z}[X]/J, \mathbb{Z}[X]/K).$$

Then the collection of functors of the form G is bounded above by the set of functions $I \times I \to Mor$. ∎

    Suppose that $card(S) < \kappa$. Insofar as the étale site $et|_S$ consists of schemes which are étale and of finite type over S, Corollary 6.58 and Lemma 6.59 together imply that $et|_S$ is skeletally small in the sense that there is a set of isomorphism classes of objects of this category. We are therefore entitled (as has always been known) to pretend that $et|_S$ is a small category.

Again, suppose that $card(S) < \kappa$, and write $(et|_S)^\kappa$ for the category of all étale S-schemes $U \to S$ such that $card(U) < \kappa$. The category $(et|_S)^\kappa$ and the étale covering families which reside therein certainly satisfy the axioms for a pretopology, so that $(et|_S)^\kappa$ is a bona fide étale site. Furthermore, Lemma 6.59 implies that $(et|_S)^\kappa$ is equivalent as a category to some small category, which again is a site with a topology inherited from $(et|_S)^\kappa$ through the equivalence. Thus, the category of presheaves (respectively sheaves) on $(et|_S)^\kappa$ is equivalent to the category of presheaves (respectively sheaves) on the skeleton, and the associated sheaf functor for presheaves on $(et|_S)^\kappa$ produces sheaves which are actually set-valued functors.

The inclusion of categories

$$i : et|_S \subset (et|_S)^\kappa$$

is part of the data for a morphism of Grothendieck sites

$$i : (et|_S)^\kappa \to et|_S.$$

In particular, the restriction functor

$$i_* : Preshv(et|_S)^\kappa \to Preshv(et|_S)$$

preserves sheaves, while the left Kan extension functor

$$i^p : Preshv(et|_S) \to Preshv(et|_S)^\kappa$$

is exact on presheaves. The direct image functor i_* is exact on sheaves, since the sites $(et|_S)^\kappa$ and $et|_S$ have the same stalks. It follows that both i^p and i_* preserve stalkwise weak equivalences of simplicial presheaves.

Recall that the functor i^p is defined for a presheaf F on $(et|_S)^\kappa$ is defined by

$$i^p F(V \xrightarrow{\psi} S) = \varinjlim F(U \xrightarrow{\phi} S),$$

where the colimit is taken over the category $T(\psi)$ of all commutative triangles

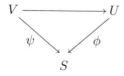

with $\phi \in et|_S$, and that this index category is filtered because $et|_S$ has all finite limits. The category $T(\psi)$ has an initial object, namely ψ itself, if ψ is an object of $et|_S$. It follows that the canonical maps

$$G(\psi) \xrightarrow{\eta} i_* i^p G(\psi) \qquad \text{and} \qquad i^p i_* F(\phi) \xrightarrow{\epsilon} F(\phi)$$

are isomorphisms at all $\psi \in et|_S$ and all $\phi \in (et|_S)^\kappa$. In particular, since every $U \in (et|_S)^\kappa$ can be covered by elements of $et|_S$, the maps η and ϵ induce equivalences of the respective sheaf categories. It also follows that η and ϵ induce stalkwise weak equivalences

$$X \xrightarrow{\eta} i_* i^p X \qquad \text{and} \qquad i^p i_* Y \xrightarrow{\epsilon} Y$$

for all simplicial presheaves X on $et|_S$ and Y on $(et|_S)^\kappa$, and so i_* and i^p induce an equivalence of the associated homotopy categories.

If A is a presheaf of abelian groups on $(et|_S)^\kappa$, then the restriction functor induces an isomorphism of abelian groups

$$[*, K(A, n)]_\kappa \xrightarrow[\cong]{i_*} [*, K(i_* A, n)],$$

where the square brackets (with decorations) denote morphisms in the associated homotopy categories. Insofar as $[*, K(A, n)]_\kappa$ is the nth cohomology group $H^n(S, A)$, this means that all of the sites $(et|_S)^\kappa$ give the same cohomology theory if $card(S) < \kappa$, namely the étale cohomology of S.

More generally, if F is a presheaf of spectra on $(et|_S)^\kappa$, and $\theta : F \to GF$ is a stalkwise weak equivalence with GF globally fibrant, then the direct image

$$i_*(\theta) : i_*(F) \to i_*(GF)$$

is a stalkwise weak equivalence, and $i_*(GF)$ is globally fibrant. Thus, the direct image functor preserves globally fibrant models of presheaves of spectra on $(et|_S)^\kappa$.

Suppose that $card(S) < \kappa$, and let $(Sch|_S)^\kappa_{et}$ denote the subcategory of the big site $(Sch|_S)_{et}$ which consists of schemes $\phi : U \to S$ which are locally of finite type over S and satisfy $card(U) < \kappa$. In fact $(Sch|_S)^\kappa_{et}$ is as good a model as any for "the" big site. If $U \to S$ is an object of $(Sch|_S)^\kappa_{et}$ then restriction $Z \mapsto Z|_U$ of simplicial sheaves along the composite functor

$$(et|_U)^\kappa \subset (Sch|_U)^\kappa_{et} \to (Sch|_S)^\kappa_{et}$$

is exact and has a left adjoint which preserves pointwise weak equivalences, trivial local fibrations, and monomorphisms, so that it preserves stalkwise trivial cofibrations. It follows that the restriction functor $Z \mapsto Z|_U$ preserves global fibrations and stalkwise weak equivalences, and therefore preserves globally fibrant models for presheaves of spectra on $(Sch|_S)^\kappa_{et}$ (see also [22, pp.219-220]).

Suppose that ζ is another cardinal such that $\kappa < \zeta$, and let S and κ be as before. By analogy with what we have seen above for the "small" étale sites the inclusion functor

$$i : (Sch|_S)^\kappa_{et} \subset (Sch|_S)^\zeta_{et}$$

defines a morphism of Grothendieck sites

$$i : (Sch|_S)^\zeta_{et} \to (Sch|_S)^\kappa_{et},$$

which induces an equivalence of the associated sheaf categories and homotopy categories of simplicial presheaves. The point is that every object of $(Sch|_S)^\zeta_{et}$ has a covering by objects of $(Sch|_S)^\kappa_{et}$, so that the base change functor i_* preserves stalkwise weak equivalences, and the canonical maps

$$\epsilon : i^p i_* F \to F \qquad \text{and} \qquad \eta : G \to i_* i^p G$$

are isomorphisms for all presheaves F and G, respectively, after restriction to the smaller category. It follows that cohomology and generalized cohomology theories defined by the site $(Sch|_S)^\kappa_{et}$ are invariant of the choice of cardinal κ, so long as $card(S) < \kappa$ for the base scheme S.

Finally, we shall denote the étale site of all S-schemes $\phi : U \to S$ such that $card(U) < \kappa$ by $(\kappa - Sch|_S)_{et}$. This category contains copies of $(Sch|_U)^\kappa_{et}$ for all objects $\phi : U \to S$. In particular, the inclusion

$$i : (Sch|_S)^\kappa_{et} \to (\kappa - Sch|_S)_{et}$$

determines a morphism of Grothendieck sites

$$i : (\kappa - Sch|_S)_{et} \to (Sch|_S)^\kappa_{et}$$

The restriction functor i_* for this morphism is exact on sheaves, while its left Kan extension i^p is exact on presheaves. These functors therefore induce an adjoint pair of functors on the homotopy category level for the associated simplicial presheaf categories. In particular, the site $(\kappa - Sch|_S)_{et}$ gives rise to the same cohomology and generalized cohomology theories as do the big site $(Sch|_S)^{et}$ and the ordinary étale site $et|_S$.

We say that $(\kappa - Sch|_S)_{et}$ is the *big κ-site for S*. It is bigger than the big site $(Sch|_S)_{et}$, but still skeletally small, by Lemma 6.59.

THEOREM 6.60. *Suppose that B is a ring, and $i \mapsto A_i$ is a left filtered system of Noetherian B-algebras, indexed on a small category I, such that the collection of all rings A_i has a uniform bound on ℓ-torsion étale cohomological dimension. Let*

$$C = \varinjlim_{i \in I} A_i,$$

and suppose that all schemes $Sp(B)$, $Sp(A_i)$ and $Sp(C)$ are bounded above by some uncountable cardinal κ. Suppose finally that F is a globally fibrant presheaf of spectra on the site $(\kappa - Sch|_B)_{et}$ whose sheaves of stable homotopy groups are ℓ-torsion. Then the canonical map

$$\varinjlim_{i \in I} \pi_* F(Sp(A_i)) \to \pi_* F(Sp(C))$$

is an isomorphism.

PROOF: The standard continuity property of étale cohomology [42, p.88] implies that the theorem holds when F is a globally fibrant model $GK(A,n)$ of any presheaf of Eilenberg-Mac Lane spectra. Corollary 6.14 implies that it is enough to prove the theorem in the case when F has only finitely many non-trivial sheaves of stable homotopy groups. In this last case, suppose that $\tilde{\pi}_n F$ is the non-trivial sheaf of stable homotopy groups of top dimension, and form the fibre sequence of globally fibrant objects

$$K(\tilde{\pi}_n F, n) \to F \to GP_{n-1}F.$$

The presheaf of spectra $GP_{n-1}F$ has fewer non-trivial sheaves of stable homotopy groups than does F, so a comparison of long exact sequences finishes the proof. ∎

Chapter 7. Bott periodic K-theory

New proofs of Thomason's descent theorem for the Bott periodic K-theory of fields (Theorem 7.27) and its corollaries are given in Section 4 of this chapter. These proofs follow the general outline given by Thomason in [55], but differ quite significantly in technical execution as they make fundamental use of the homotopy theory of presheaves of spectra, the theory of smash products of such, and the Gabber rigidity theorem. None of these techniques were available at the time that Thomason's paper [55] was written.

Several of the ideas of the proof are important in their own right, and have been highlighted in separate sections.

There is a principle underlying the spectral sequence calculations in the original description of the hypertransfer, which I have isolated and called the Tate theorem (Theorem 7.2, Corollary 7.8). Roughly speaking, it asserts that if F is a globally fibrant presheaf of spectra in the Ω-world for some profinite group Ω, and if the presheaves of stable homotopy groups for F are bounded below and have a suitable uniform upper bound in cohomological dimension, then all hypernorm maps for F are stable equivalences. From another point of view, the theorem asserts that Tate's homology spectral sequence

$$E_2^{p,-q} = H_p(G, H_{et}^q(L, A)) \Rightarrow H_{et}^{q-p}(k, A),$$

for a finite Galois extension L/k with Galois group G, has an analogue for generalized Galois cohomology theories.

The Tate theorem is the magic fact from Galois cohomology theory that figures into the proof of the existence of inductors for the Bott element in cases of low Galois cohomological dimension. The main result (Theorem 7.16) of Section 3 asserts that if a field k contains a primitive ℓ^{th} root of unity, then the Bott element $\beta \in \pi_2 K/\ell(k)$ is in the image of the map

$$(i_h)_* : \pi_2 \underset{g \in G}{\mathrm{holim}} K/\ell(L) \to \pi_2 K/\ell(k)$$

which is induced by the hypertransfer for finite Galois extensions L/k with Galois group $G = L/k$. This is subject to very restrictive conditions on the cohomological dimension of k with respect to ℓ-torsion sheaves, which are satisfied if k has cohomological dimension 1 (Corollary 7.18), or if k is a number field and L is a finite subextension of the extension $k(\mu_{\ell^\infty})/k$ given by adjoining all ℓ-primary roots of unity to k. The proof of Theorem 7.16 also uses some of the techniques appearing in the verification of the Lichtenbaum-Quillen conjecture in low degrees that appears in Section 2. Afficionados of the corresponding part of Thomason's original argument will notice that the proof given here for Theorem 7.16 is "unified", and involves no explicit spectral sequence calculations.

The main part of the argument for Thomason's descent theorem for Bott periodic K-theory (Theorem 7.27, or in practice Theorem 7.28) is given in Section 4. This proof is the raison d'être for the material developed in this monograph, and it is all involved, either explicitly or implicitly. On a further technical note, the element chase that appears in the proof of Theorem 7.21 obviates the need for any homotopy coherence statements about choices of inductors for the Bott element, so that the existence statement in Theorem 7.16 suffices. One simlarly avoids coherence problems in the construction of the Bott periodic K-theory presheaf of spectra by using results of Bousfield and Snaith that together assert that this presheaf can be constructed by smashing the mod ℓ K-theory presheaf K/ℓ with the KU-localization S_K of the sphere spectrum. All other homotopy coherence problems in the proof of Theorem 7.21 (particularly with regard to existence of cup product structures for mod ℓ K-theory presheaves of spectra) are solved by appealing to the results of Chapter 5.

More explicitly, Theorem 7.28 asserts that if k is a field of finite transcendance degree over a field k' such that k' contains a primitive ℓ^{th} root of unity and either $cd_\ell(k') \leq 1$ or $cd_\ell(k'(\mu_{\ell^\infty})) \leq 1$, then any globally fibrant model

$$j : K/\ell \wedge S_K \to G(K/\ell \wedge S_K)$$

for the Bott periodic K-theory presheaf of spectra on the étale site for k, induces a map of spectra

$$j : K/\ell \wedge S_K(k) \to G(K/\ell \wedge S_K)(k)$$

in global sections which is a stable equivalence. This is subject also to the caveat that ℓ is a prime which is distinct from the characteristic of k, and that $\ell > 3$. The restriction that $\ell > 3$ survives throughout the chapter; the Moore spectrum Y_ℓ fails to be a homotopy associative ring spectrum if $\ell = 2, 3$, and, in the interests of maintaining clarity of exposition, I don't want to get involved in the classical stable homotopy theoretic workarounds for this problem. On the other hand, the restriction that k' contains a primitive ℓ^{th} root of unity can be removed with a transfer argument (Corollary 7.29), and this result is easily extended to prime powers (Corollary 7.30). These corollaries are presented in Section 5.

Bootstrapping Corollary 7.30 to a result for more general schemes is more interesting. Theorem 7.31 asserts that if X is a regular separated Noetherian scheme with $1/\ell \in \Gamma(X, \mathcal{O}_X)$, and whose residue fields satisfy the conditions of Theorem 7.28, then any globally fibrant model

$$j : K/\ell^\nu \wedge S_K \to G(K/\ell^\nu \wedge S_K)$$

for the Bott periodic mod ℓ^ν K-theory presheaf of spectra on the étale site for X induces a stable equivalence

$$j : K/\ell^\nu \wedge S_K(X) \to G(K/\ell^\nu \wedge S_K)(X)$$

in global sections. Two proofs of this result are given. The first, which is Thomason's original argument modulo some fussing about separated étale sites, appears in Section 5.

A second, much slicker argument is given in Section 6 in the context of a general description and proof of the Nisnevich descent theorem (Corollary 7.69) for the K-theory of separated regular Noetherian schemes. This result asserts in particular that if

$$j : K/\ell^\nu \wedge S_K \to G(K/\ell^\nu \wedge S_K)$$

is a globally fibrant model for the Bott periodic K-theory presheaf of spectra on the Nisnevich site $Nis|_X$ for such a scheme X, then j induces a stable equivalence in global sections. The Nisnevich topology on a scheme X is a Grothendieck topology on the category underlying the étale site $et|_X$ which is coarser than the étale topology, but finer than the Zariski topology. The local behaviour of this topology, for the Bott periodic K-theory presheaf, can be characterized by the spectra $K/\ell^\nu \wedge S_K(\mathcal{O}_y^h)$ which arise by evaluation at all henselizations $\mathcal{O}_y^h$ of local rings $\mathcal{O}_y$ of points y on schemes U which are separated, étale and of finite type over X. The Gabber rigidity theorem, in this case, asserts that the residue map $\mathcal{O}_y^h \to k(y)$ induces a stable equivalence in mod ℓ^ν Bott periodic K-theory — Gabber's result can also be used to prove a corresponding rigidity statement for the globally fibrant model (Theorem 7.72). One then proves Theorem 7.31 with this technology by observing that any globally fibrant model for $K/\ell^\nu \wedge S_K$ on the étale site restricts to a map

$$j : K/\ell^\nu \wedge S_K \to G(K/\ell^\nu \wedge S_K)$$

on the Nisnevich site $Nis|_X$, where $G(K/\ell^\nu \wedge S_K)$ is globally fibrant for the Nisnevich topology (by the general fact, which is used repeatedly here, that direct image functors preserve global fibrations), and then this map is a stalkwise equivalence for the Nisnevich topology by rigidity and the fact that it induces a stable equivalence at all fields $k(y)$ by Corollary 7.30. This means that the map j is a globally fibrant model for the Nisnevich topology on X, and therefore induces a stable equivalence on global sections by Nisnevich descent.

The demonstration of the Nisnevich descent theorem that is given in this chapter is complete, modulo the lack of a proof for the Kato-Saito theorem that asserts the existence of a bound on cohomological dimension for the Nisnevich topology on a Noetherian scheme. The apparent brevity of this proof is achieved by eschewing the Godement resolution in favour of a statement which involves globally fibrant models. If you must still have your Godement resolution, it is related to globally fibrant models in Corollary 7.67.

The last section of this chapter contains a brief discussion of the Lichtenbaum-Quillen conjecture. The conjecture is formulated in terms of the vanishing of global sections of the presheaves of homotopy groups $\pi_j F$ of the pointwise

homotopy fibre F of a globally fibrant model $j : K/\ell^\nu \to GK/\ell^\nu$ for the mod ℓ^ν
K-theory presheaf on the étale site. Nisnevich descent techniques are used to
show that the conjecture for regular separated Noetherian schemes follows from
the statement for residue fields (Corollary 7.76), and hence from a statement
for fields containing a primitive root of unity and having a finite Tate-Tsen
filtration. In other words, this explicitly demonstrates the principle that if you
can prove Conjecture 7.73 or some similar statement, then you've got it all.
Furthermore, if one can show that the pointwise homotopy fibre "dies above
degree $n - 1$" at all residue fields $k(y)$ in the sense that $\pi_i F(k(y)) = 0$ for
$i \geq n$, then $\pi_i F(X) = 0$ for $i \geq n$ in global sections. The choice of number n is
$d - 2$, where $cd_\ell(k(y)) \leq d$ for all residue fields $k(y)$. This particular bound is
motivated by the admittedly slim evidence of the calculations of Section 2. It
therefore appears that the comparison map

$$j_* : \pi_i K/\ell^\nu(X) \to \pi_i GK/\ell^\nu(X)$$

should be an isomorphism if $i \geq d - 1$ if $cd_\ell(k(y)) \leq d$ for all residue fields
$k(y)$. This lower bound varies from that predicted by folklore, which is roughly
twice the dimension of X.

　　　Conjecture 7.73 is also reformulated in terms of a statement for Galois
groups of cohomological dimension 1 (Conjecture 7.74), by a method that mir-
rors the inductive argument that leads to the proof of the descent theorem for
Bott periodic K-theory.

7.1. The Tate theorem

Suppose that Z is a presheaf of Ω-spectra on the site $G - \mathbf{Sets}_{df}$ of finite
discrete G-sets for a profinite group $G = \{G_i\}$, as in Section 6.2. Suppose that
Z is bounded below in the sense that $\pi_j Z = 0$ for $j < N$, where N is some fixed
integer. Suppose that the associated stable homotopy group sheaves $\tilde{\pi}_* Z$ for
Z satisfy $cd(G, \tilde{\pi}_* Z) \leq M$ for some positive integer M: this means (following
Tate's definition [49, p.I-82] that

$$H^j(\tilde{H}, \tilde{\pi}_r Z) = 0$$

for all $j > M$ and all r and all closed subgroups $\tilde{H}$ of G given by pullback
diagrams

　　　Suppose that n is the order of the finite group G_i, and recall that G_i is
naturally a member of the site $G - \mathbf{Sets}_{df}$. Recall from Section 3.2 that the

norm map $N : Z(G_i) \to Z(G_i)$ is defined in the stable category of pointwise $G_i \times G_i$-spectra to be the composite

$$Z(G_i) \xrightarrow{\Delta_{G_i}} \prod_{g \in G_i} Z(G_i) \xleftarrow[\simeq]{c} \bigvee_{g \in G_i} Z(G_i) \xrightarrow{\nabla} Z(G_i). \tag{7.1}$$

As in Section 3.2, and because it is a join transformation of G_i-spectra, the norm map N induces a map

$$N_h : \underset{g \in G_i}{\mathrm{holim}} \, Z(G_i) \to \underset{g \in G_i}{\mathrm{holim}} \, Z(G_i),$$

in the ordinary stable category (of undecorated spectra) which is called the *hypernorm*. The main technical result of this section is the following:

THEOREM 7.2. *Suppose that the profinite group $G = \{G_i\}$ the presheaf of spectra Z on the site $G - \mathbf{Sets}_{df}$ are as above. Suppose further that Z is globally fibrant. Then the hypernorm*

$$N_h : \underset{g \in G_i}{\mathrm{holim}} \, Z(G_i) \to \underset{g \in G_i}{\mathrm{holim}} \, Z(G_i)$$

is a stable equivalence of spectra.

As we have seen before (Section 3.2), the norm map (7.1) consists of maps of $G_i \times G_i$-spectra, where $G_i \times G_i$ acts on the copy of $Z(G_i)$ through the projection $pr_L : G_i \times G_i \to G_i$ onto the left, and acts on the copy of $Z(G_i)$ at the right end of (7.1) through the projection $pr_R : G_i \times G_i \to G_i$ on the right.

In general, any diagram $X : I \times J \to \mathbf{Spt}$ of Ω-spectra gives rise in a natural way to a spectrum

$$\underset{i \in I}{\mathrm{holim}} \, \underset{j \in J}{\mathrm{holim}} \, X(i, j),$$

and the functor

$$X \mapsto \underset{i \in I}{\mathrm{holim}} \, \underset{j \in J}{\mathrm{holim}} \, X(i, j) \tag{7.3}$$

takes pointwise stable weak equivalences to stable equivalences — see Section 4.3, as well as [9, XI.5]). Furthermore, the cited material of [9] and Lemma 4.1 together imply that the functor (7.3) takes pointwise stable fibre sequences to stable fibre sequences of spectra.

Now apply the functor

$$\underset{g \in G_i}{\mathrm{holim}} \, \underset{g \in G_i}{\mathrm{holim}}$$

to all of the $G_i \times G_i$-spectra appearing in (7.1). Specifically, take the homotopy inverse limit with respect to G_i-action corresponding to the right hand factor in $G_i \times G_i$, and then apply the homotopy colimit functor to the resulting G_i-spectrum.

Note in particular, that for the composite functor

$$G_i \times G_i \xrightarrow{\ pr_L\ } G_i \xrightarrow{\ Z(G_i)\ } \mathbf{Spt}$$

corresponding to the copy of $Z(G_i)$ on the left of (7.1), there is an isomorphism

$$\varinjlim_{g \in G_i} \varprojlim_{g \in G_i} Z(G_i) pr_L \cong \varinjlim_{g \in G_i} \mathbf{hom}_*((BG_i)_+, Z(G_i)),$$

and so the map $t : BG_i \to *$ induces a canonical map

$$t^* : \varinjlim_{g \in G_i} Z(G_i) \to \varinjlim_{g \in G_i} \varprojlim_{g \in G_i} Z(G_i) pr_L.$$

Similarly, there is an isomorphism

$$\varinjlim_{g \in G_i} \varprojlim_{g \in G_i} Z(G_i) pr_R \cong \left(\varprojlim_{g \in G_i} Z(G_i) \right) \wedge BG_{i+},$$

so that the canonical map $t : BG_i \to *$ induces a map

$$t_* : \varinjlim_{g \in G_i} \varprojlim_{g \in G_i} Z(G_i) pr_R \to \varprojlim_{g \in G_i} Z(G_i).$$

The hypernorm N_h is the composite

$$
\begin{array}{ccc}
\varinjlim\limits_{g \in G_i} Z(G_i) & \xrightarrow{\ t^*\ } & \varinjlim\limits_{g \in G_i} \varprojlim\limits_{g \in G_i} Z(G_i) pr_L \\[2em]
 & & \Big\downarrow N_* \\[2em]
 & & \varinjlim\limits_{g \in G_i} \varprojlim\limits_{g \in G_i} Z(G_i) pr_R \xrightarrow[\ t_*\ ]{} \varprojlim\limits_{g \in G_i} Z(G_i)
\end{array}
$$

$$(7.4)$$

in the stable homotopy category. Recall that there is a canonical map

$$in_0 : Z(G_i) \to \varinjlim_{g \in G_i} Z(G_i)$$

which corresponds to "inclusion" of the spectrum in simplicial degree 0. Similarly, there is a map

$$\pi_0 : \varprojlim_{g \in G_i} Z(G_i) \to Z(G_i)$$

which picks off the spectrum in cosimplicial degree 0: it's really an instance of the canonical map Tot $\to$ Tot$_0$. The description of the hypernorm given in (7.4) implies that the composite

$$Z(G_i) \xrightarrow{in_0} \underset{g \in G_i}{\mathrm{holim}} \ Z(G_i) \xrightarrow{N_h} \underset{g \in G_i}{\mathrm{holim}} \ Z(G_i) \xrightarrow{\pi_0} Z(G_i)$$

$$(7.5)$$

coincides with the norm map N up to isomorphism.

PROOF OF THEOREM 7.2: Suppose that A is an abelian sheaf on $G - \mathbf{Sets}_{df}$ such that $cd(G, A) = 0$. Then all subgroups H of G_i have the property that

$$H^p(H, A(G_i)) = 0 \qquad \text{for } p > 0, \tag{7.6}$$

and so the Tate cohomology groups satisfy

$$\hat{H}^*(H, A(G_i)) = 0$$

for every subgroup H of every G_i: this is the substance of the Tate lemma [49, p.I-83], [50, p.145]. In particular,

$$H_p(G_i, A(G_i)) = H^p(G_i, A(G_i)) = 0 \qquad \text{if } p > 0,$$

and the standard norm homomorphism

$$N = \sum_{g \in G_i} g_* : A(G_i) \to A(G_i)$$

induces an isomorphism

$$H_0(G_i, A(G_i)) \xrightarrow[\cong]{N_*} H^0(G_i, A(G_i)).$$

Suppose that the presheaf of spectra Z is stalkwise stably equivalent to a presheaf of spectra $GK(A, n)$, where A is an abelian sheaf with $cd(A, G) = 0$. Then the presheaf of spectra Z is also a globally fibrant model for $K(A, n)$, by Corollary 3.6. Furthermore, the cohomological triviality of A implies that the spectrum $Z(G_i)$ has one non-vanishing stable homotopy group, namely

$$\pi_n Z(G_i) \cong A(G_i).$$

This isomorphism is G_i-equivariant, since it comes from the presheaf level. The norm map

$$N : Z(G_i) \to Z(G_i)$$

induces the standard abelian sheaf norm

$$N = \sum_{g \in G_i} g_* : A(G_i) \to A(G_i)$$

in the nth stable homotopy group π_n.

The spectral sequences for

$$\underrightarrow{\operatorname{holim}}_{g \in G_i} Z(G_i) \quad \text{and} \quad \underleftarrow{\operatorname{holim}}_{g \in G_i} Z(G_i)$$

both collapse, and the non-trivial stable homotopy groups of these spectra are given, respectively, by

$$\pi_n \underrightarrow{\operatorname{holim}}_{g \in G_i} Z(G_i) \cong A(G_i)_{G_i}$$

and

$$\pi_n \underleftarrow{\operatorname{holim}}_{g \in G_i} Z(G_i) \cong A(G_i)^{G_i},$$

The map

$$in_0 : Z(G_i) \to \underrightarrow{\operatorname{holim}}_{g \in G} Z(G_i)$$

induces the canonical map $A(G_i) \to A(G_i)_{G_i}$ in π_n, whereas the map

$$\pi_0 : \underleftarrow{\operatorname{holim}}_{g \in G_i} Z(G_i) \to Z(G_i)$$

induces the inclusion $A(G_i)^{G_i} \hookrightarrow A(G_i)$ in that degree. The composite (7.5) is the norm map N in the stable homotopy category, so that the composite

$$A(G_i) \to A(G_i)_{G_i} \xrightarrow{(N_h)_*} A(G_i)^{G_i} \hookrightarrow A(G_i)$$

is the standard norm. It follows that $(N_h)_*$ coincides with the isomorphism N_* induced by the standard norm, and so the hypernorm

$$N_h : \underrightarrow{\operatorname{holim}}_{g \in G_i} Z(G_i) \to \underleftarrow{\operatorname{holim}}_{g \in G_i} Z(G_i)$$

is a stable equivalence in this case.

Suppose, more generally, that Z has the form $GK(B, n)$, where B is an abelian sheaf having $cd(G, B) \leq r$. There is a short exact sequence of abelian sheaves

$$0 \to B \to I \to C \to 0,$$

where I is injective, and so C has $cd(G, C) \leq r - 1$. The hypernorm induces a comparison of fibre sequences

$$
\begin{array}{ccccc}
\underrightarrow{\operatorname{holim}}_{g \in G_i} GK(B,n)(G_i) & \longrightarrow & \underrightarrow{\operatorname{holim}}_{g \in G_i} GK(I,n)(G_i) & \longrightarrow & \underrightarrow{\operatorname{holim}}_{g \in G_i} GK(C,n)(G_i) \\
\downarrow{N_h} & & \downarrow{N_h} & & \downarrow{N_h} \\
\underleftarrow{\operatorname{holim}}_{g \in G_i} GK(B,n)(G_i) & \longrightarrow & \underleftarrow{\operatorname{holim}}_{g \in G_i} GK(I,n)(G_i) & \longrightarrow & \underleftarrow{\operatorname{holim}}_{g \in G_i} GK(C,n)(G_i).
\end{array}
$$

The sheaf I is injective, so the middle map N_h is a stable equivalence, and an inductive argument implies that N_h is a weak equivalence for the sheaf B.

Suppose that D is an abelian presheaf on $G - \mathbf{Sets}_{df}$ whose associated sheaf has bounded cohomological dimension in sense that $cd(G, \tilde{B}) < \infty$. Then the associated sheaf map $\eta : D \to \tilde{D}$ induces a pointwise stable equivalence

$$\eta_* : GK(D, n) \to GK(\tilde{D}, n),$$

and there is a commutative diagram in the stable category

$$
\begin{array}{ccc}
\underset{\underset{g \in G_i}{\longrightarrow}}{\mathrm{holim}}\, GK(D,n)(G_i) & \xrightarrow{\ N_h\ } & \underset{\underset{g \in G_i}{\longleftarrow}}{\mathrm{holim}}\, GK(D,n)(G_i) \\
\eta_* \downarrow & & \downarrow \eta_* \\
\underset{\underset{g \in G_i}{\longrightarrow}}{\mathrm{holim}}\, GK(\tilde{D},n)(G_i) & \xrightarrow{\ N_h\ } & \underset{\underset{g \in G_i}{\longleftarrow}}{\mathrm{holim}}\, GK(\tilde{D},n)(G_i).
\end{array}
$$

The copy of N_h which corresponds to the sheaf $\tilde{D}$ is a stable equivalence, by what we have just seen, and the vertical maps are stable equivalences, so the map

$$N_h : \underset{\underset{g \in G_i}{\longrightarrow}}{\mathrm{holim}}\, GK(D,n)(G_i) \to \underset{\underset{g \in G_i}{\longleftarrow}}{\mathrm{holim}}\, GK(D,n)(G_i)$$

is a stable equivalence as well.

Suppose that Z is a globally fibrant presheaf of spectra on the site $G - \mathbf{Sets}_{df}$, as in the statement of the theorem. An inductive argument applied to the fibre sequences

$$GK(\pi_n Z, n) \to GP_n Z \to GP_{n-1} Z,$$

which arise from the Postnikov tower construction for Z, now implies that the map

$$\underset{\underset{g \in G_i}{\longrightarrow}}{\mathrm{holim}}\, GP_n Z(G_i) \xrightarrow{\ N_h\ } \underset{\underset{g \in G_i}{\longleftarrow}}{\mathrm{holim}}\, GP_n Z(G_i)$$

is a stable equivalence, for each $n \in \mathbb{Z}$. Note that the induction has somewhere to start, because we are assuming that Z is bounded below.

Now, for the full statement of the theorem, the assumptions on Z imply that all of the fibres of the fibration sequences

$$GK(\pi_n Z, n) \to GP_n Z \to GP_{n-1} Z$$

have

$$\pi_j GK(\pi_n Z, n)(G_i) = 0 \qquad \text{if } j < n - M.$$

To see this, note that the restriction of the presheaf of spectra $GK(\pi_n Z, n)$ to the category of objects over

$$H_i - \mathbf{Sets}_{df} \cong G - \mathbf{Sets}_{df} \downarrow G_i$$

(see Remark 6.26) is globally fibrant, with homotopy groups of the associated global sections spectrum $GK(\pi_n Z, n)(G_i)$ given by

$$\pi_j GK(\pi_n Z, n)(G_i) \cong \begin{cases} H^{n-j}(H_i, \tilde{\pi}_n Z) & \text{if } j \leq n, \text{ and} \\ 0 & \text{otherwise.} \end{cases}$$

Now use Shapiro's lemma to see that

$$H^{n-j}(H_i, \tilde{\pi}_n Z) = 0 \qquad \text{if } j < n - M.$$

Write

$$\hat{Z} = \varprojlim_n GP_n Z,$$

as a presheaf of spectra on $G - \mathbf{Sets}_{df}$. Then $\hat{Z}$ is globally fibrant, and there are commutative diagrams composed of canonical maps

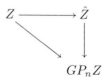

By the claim for the connectivity of the spectra $GK(\pi_r Z, r)(G_i)$, the canonical map $\hat{Z} \to GP_n Z$ induces isomorphisms in homotopy groups

$$\pi_j \hat{Z}(G_i) \cong \pi_j GP_n Z(G_i)$$

if $j < n - M$. Thus, that same map induces isomorphisms

$$\pi_j L\hat{Z} \cong \pi_j LGP_n Z$$

in homotopy groups of stalks in the same range. On the other hand, the map $Z \to GP_n Z$ induces isomorphisms

$$\pi_j LZ \cong \pi_j LGP_n Z$$

for $j \leq n$. It follows that the map $Z \to \hat{Z}$ is a stalkwise, and hence pointwise, stable equivalence of globally fibrant spectra. In particular, the induced map $Z(*) \to \hat{Z}(*)$ on global sections is a stable equivalence.

An important consequence of the previous paragraph is that the global sections spectrum $Z(*)$ is bounded below in the sense that

$$\pi_j Z(*) = 0 \qquad \text{if } j < N - M.$$

A similar argument shows that all fibres $GF_n Z$ of the maps $Z \to GP_n Z$ are bounded below in all G_i-sections. In particular, the spectrum $GF_n Z(G_i)$ is $(n-M)$-connected. But then a spectral sequence argument (via Corollary 4.22) implies that the spectrum $\varinjlim_{g \in G_i} GF_n Z(G_i)$ is also $(n - M)$-connected, so that the map of spectra

$$\varinjlim_{g \in G_i} Z(G_i) \to \varinjlim_{g \in G_i} GP_n Z(G_i)$$

induces an isomomorphism in stable homotopy groups π_j for $j \leq n - M$. Since Z is globally fibrant, there is a commutative diagram

$$
\begin{array}{ccc}
Z(*) & \xrightarrow{\quad i^* \quad} & \varprojlim_{g \in G_i} Z(G_i) \\
\downarrow & & \downarrow \\
GP_n Z(*) & \xrightarrow[\quad i^* \quad]{} & \varprojlim_{g \in G_i} GP_n Z(G_i)
\end{array}
$$

in the stable category, in which both horizontal maps i^* are stable equivalences. Finally, the induced map

$$\pi_j Z(*) \to \pi_j GP_n Z(*)$$

is an isomorphism if $j \leq n - M$. It follows that the hypernorm induces an isomorphism

$$\pi_i \varinjlim_{g \in G_i} Z(G_i) \xrightarrow{\cong} \pi_i \varprojlim_{g \in G} Z(G_i). \qquad \blacksquare$$

If the profinite group G has bounded cohomological dimension with respect to ℓ-torsion sheaves, then so does each of the subgroups $\tilde{H}$, since

$$cd_\ell(\tilde{H}) \leq cd_\ell(G) \tag{7.7}$$

by Shapiro's lemma. If A is an ℓ-torsion sheaf on $G - \mathbf{Sets}_{df}$ and $cd_\ell(G) \leq M$, then the inequality (7.7) also implies that $cd(G, A) \leq M$. The following is therefore a consequence of Theorem 7.2:

COROLLARY 7.8. *Suppose that G is a profinite group such that $cd_\ell(G) < \infty$. Suppose that Z is a globally fibrant presheaf of spectra on the site $G - \mathbf{Sets}_{df}$ whose presheaves of stable homotopy groups $\pi_* Z$ are ℓ-torsion, and which is bounded below in the sense that there is an integer N such that $\pi_j Z = 0$ for all $j < N$. Then the hypernorm*

$$N_h : \underset{g \in G_i}{\text{holim}}\, Z(G_i) \to \underset{g \in G_i}{\text{holim}}\, Z(G_i)$$

is a stable equivalence of spectra.

I shall refer to Corollary 7.8 as the Tate theorem in all that follows.

Suppose that a field k has bounded cohomological dimension with respect to ℓ-torsion sheaves, and that ℓ is a prime which is distinct from the characteristic of k. Suppose that L/k is a finite Galois extension of k with Galois group G. If F is a globally fibrant presheaf of spectra on some étale site for k whose presheaves of stable homotopy groups are ℓ-torsion and are bounded below, then the Tate theorem says that the hypernorm

$$N_h : \underset{G}{\text{holim}}\, F(L) \to \underset{G}{\text{holim}}\, F(L) \simeq F(k)$$

is a stable equivalence of spectra. This equivalence gives rise to a spectral sequence (Corollary 4.22), with

$$E_2^{p,q} = H_p(G, \pi_q F(L)) \Rightarrow \pi_{p+q} F(k), \tag{7.9}$$

that I shall refer to as the *Tate spectral sequence* for F and the extension L/k.

In particular, if $GK(\mathbb{Z}/\ell, 0)$ is a globally fibrant model for the Eilenberg-Mac Lane object $K(\mathbb{Z}/\ell, 0)$, then the Tate spectral sequence for $GK(\mathbb{Z}/\ell, 0)$ and the extension L/k has the form

$$E_2^{p,q} = H_p(G, \pi_q GK(\mathbb{Z}/\ell, 0)(L)) \Rightarrow \pi_{p+q} GK(\mathbb{Z}/\ell, 0)(k)$$

In view of the isomorphisms

$$\pi_q GK(\mathbb{Z}/\ell, 0)(k) \cong H^{-q}(k, \mathbb{Z}/\ell),$$

and the corresponding isomorphisms for the field L, the Tate spectral sequence for $GK(\mathbb{Z}/\ell, 0)$ has the form

$$E_2^{p,-q} = H_p(G, H^q(L, \mathbb{Z}/\ell)) \Rightarrow H^{q-p}(k, \mathbb{Z}/\ell). \tag{7.10}$$

7.2. Calculations in low degrees

Suppose that ℓ is a prime which is distinct from the characteristic of a field k, and that $\ell > 3$. Suppose that k contains a primitive ℓ^{th} root of unity ζ_ℓ.

Suppose that F is a presheaf of spectra on the big étale site $(Sch|_k)_{et}$, and let GF be a globally fibrant model for F. Recall that the descent spectral sequence (6.7) for the homotopy groups $\pi_* GF(k)$ of the global sections spectrum $GF(k)$ of GF has the form

$$E_2^{p,q} = H^p(k, \tilde{\pi}_q F) \Rightarrow \pi_{q-p} GF(k),$$

where $\tilde{\pi}_q F$ denotes the sheaf associated to the presheaf $\pi_q F$ of stable homotopy groups of F. Recall further that the differentials for the descent spectral sequence have the form

$$d_r : E_r^{p,q} \to E_r^{p+r,q+r-1}.$$

This spectral sequence converges to $\pi_* GF(k)$ if the sheaves of homotopy groups of F are ℓ-torsion and k has bounded Galois cohomological dimension with respect to ℓ-torsion sheaves.

Let K/ℓ denote the mod ℓ K-theory presheaf of spectra on the big étale site for k, and recall that there is a cofibre sequence of presheaves of spectra

$$K \xrightarrow{\times \ell} K \to K/\ell.$$

The purpose of this section is to analyse the map

$$j_* : \pi_* K/\ell(k) \to \pi_* GK/\ell(k)$$

induced by a choice $j : K/\ell \to GK/\ell$ of globally fibrant model for K/ℓ in low degrees. I shall begin by proving

PROPOSITION 7.11. *Suppose that ℓ is a prime which is distinct from the characteristic of a field k, and that $\ell > 3$. Suppose that k contains a primitive ℓ^{th} root of unity ζ_ℓ. Then the map*

$$j_* : \pi_i K/\ell(k) \to \pi_i GK/\ell(k)$$

is a monomorphism if $0 \leq i \leq 2$.

PROOF: Work over the finite étale site $et|_k$, so that the presheaves $\pi_0 K$ and $\pi_1 K$ are already sheaves up to isomorphism: $\pi_0 K$ is the constant sheaf associated to the integers $\mathbb{Z}$, and $\pi_1 K$ is a copy of the multiplicative group $\mathbb{G}_m$.

Consider the Postnikov truncation $P_1 K$ of the (integral) K-theory presheaf of spectra K, and form a diagram of cofibre sequences

$$
\begin{array}{ccccc}
P_1 K & \xrightarrow{\times \ell} & P_1 K & \longrightarrow & P_1 K/\ell \\
\downarrow{\scriptstyle j} & & \downarrow{\scriptstyle j} & & \downarrow{\scriptstyle j} \\
GP_1 K & \xrightarrow{\times \ell} & GP_1 K & \longrightarrow & GP_1 K/\ell.
\end{array}
$$

The non-trivial sheaves of homotopy groups of $P_1 K$ are

$$\tilde{\pi}_1 P_1 K \cong \mathbb{G}_m$$

and

$$\tilde{\pi}_0 P_1 K \cong \mathbb{Z},$$

by comparison with the corresponding sheaves of K-groups. The "descent spectral sequence" for $\pi_* G P_1 K(k)$ is really just the fibre sequence

$$GK(\mathbb{G}_m, 1)(k) \to G P_1 K(k) \to GK(\mathbb{Z}, 0)(k),$$

which fits into a comparison diagram

$$
\begin{array}{ccccc}
K(\pi_1 K(k), 1) & \longrightarrow & P_1 K(k) & \longrightarrow & K(\pi_0 K(k), 0) \\
\downarrow & & \downarrow & & \downarrow \\
GK(\mathbb{G}_m, 1)(k) & \longrightarrow & G P_1 K(k) & \longrightarrow & GK(\mathbb{Z}, 0)(k)
\end{array}
$$

in which the vertical maps on the group level are induced essentially be taking associated sheaves. Now,

$$\pi_0 GK(\mathbb{G}_m, 1)(k) = H^1(k, \mathbb{G}_m) = 0$$

by Hilbert theorem 90, so that $\pi_0 G P_1(k)$ can be identified with the kernel of the boundary map

$$\mathbb{Z} = \pi_0 GK(\mathbb{Z}, 0) \xrightarrow{\partial} \pi_{-1} GK(\mathbb{G}_m, 1)(k) = H^2(k, \mathbb{G}_m) = Br(k).$$

In particular, $\pi_0 G P_1(k)$ is torsion free. The same exact sequence gives an isomorphism

$$\pi_1 G P_1 K(k) \cong k^*,$$

induced on the π_1-level by the inclusion of the fibre $GK(\mathbb{G}_m, 1)(k) \to G P_1 K(k)$. The map

$$\pi_1 K(\pi_1 K(k), 1) \to \pi_1 GK(\mathbb{G}_m, 1)(k)$$

is an isomorphism by formal nonsense, so that the map

$$\pi_1 P_1 K(k) \xrightarrow{j_*} \pi_1 G P_1 K(k)$$

is an isomorphism as well. It follows that the comparison

$$0 \longrightarrow \pi_2 P_1 K/\ell(k) \longrightarrow \pi_1 P_1 K(k) \xrightarrow{\times \ell} \pi_1 P_1 K(k) \longrightarrow \pi_1 P_1 K/\ell(k) \longrightarrow 0$$

$$0 \longrightarrow \pi_2 GP_1 K/\ell(k) \longrightarrow \pi_1 GP_1 K(k) \underset{\times \ell}{\longrightarrow} \pi_1 GP_1 K(k) \longrightarrow \pi_1 GP_1 K/\ell(k) \longrightarrow 0$$

of exact sequences induces isomorphisms

$$j_* : \pi_i P_1 K/\ell(k) \xrightarrow{\cong} \pi_i GP_1 K/\ell(k)$$

for $i = 1, 2$. The induced map $\pi_1 K/\ell(k) \to \pi_1 P_1 K/\ell$ is an isomorphism, and so the commutativity of the diagram

$$\begin{array}{ccc} \pi_1 K/\ell(k) & \xrightarrow{\cong} & \pi_1 P_1 K/\ell \\ {\scriptstyle j_*}\downarrow & & \cong\downarrow{\scriptstyle j_*} \\ \pi_1 GK/\ell(k) & \longrightarrow & \pi_1 GP_1 K/\ell \end{array}$$

implies that $j_* : \pi_1 K/\ell(k) \to \pi_1 GK/\ell(k)$ is a monomorphism.

Note that $P_1 K/\ell$ is stalkwise stably equivalent to $P_2(K/\ell)$. It follows that the composite

$$\pi_1 K/\ell(k) \xrightarrow{j_*} \pi_1 GK/\ell(k) \to \pi_1 GP_2(K/\ell)(k)$$

is an isomorphism.

The presheaf of spectra $F_0 K/\ell$ is stalkwise 1-connected, and the map $F_0 K/\ell \to K/\ell$ induces an isomorphism $\tilde{\pi}_i F_0 K/\ell \cong \tilde{\pi}_i K/\ell$ for $i \geq 2$. Applying the functor P_2 to this map therefore gives a morphism in the stalkwise stable category

$$K(\pi_2 K/\ell, 2) \simeq P_2(F_0 K/\ell) \to P_2(K/\ell)$$

which induces an isomorphism in $\tilde{\pi}_2$. It follows that the induced map

$$\pi_1 GP_2(F_0 K/\ell)(k) \to \pi_1 GP_2(K/\ell)(k)$$

is an isomorphism. There is a homotopy commutative diagram of the form

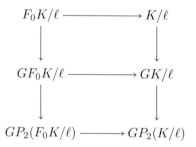

so the induced composite

$$\pi_1 F_0 K/\ell(k) \to \pi_1 GF_0 K/\ell(k) \to \pi_1 GP_2(F_0 K/\ell)(k)$$

is an isomorphism.

    Form the comparison diagram

$$
\begin{array}{ccccc}
F_1 K/\ell & \longrightarrow & K/\ell & \longrightarrow & P_1 K/\ell \\
{\scriptstyle j}\downarrow & & {\scriptstyle j}\downarrow & & \downarrow{\scriptstyle j} \\
GF_1 K/\ell & \longrightarrow & GK/\ell & \longrightarrow & GP_1 K/\ell
\end{array}
$$

of stalkwise fibre sequences in the category of presheaves of spectra over the étale site $et|_k$, and consider the induced comparison of exact sequences

$$
\begin{array}{ccccccccc}
0 & \longrightarrow & \pi_2 F_1 K/\ell(k) & \longrightarrow & \pi_2 K/\ell(k) & \longrightarrow & \pi_2 P_1 K/\ell(k) & \longrightarrow & 0 \\
& & {\scriptstyle j_*}\downarrow & & {\scriptstyle j_*}\downarrow & & {\scriptstyle \cong}\downarrow{\scriptstyle j_*} & & \\
0 & \longrightarrow & \pi_2 GF_1 K/\ell(k) & \longrightarrow & \pi_2 GK/\ell(k) & \longrightarrow & \pi_2 GP_1 K/\ell(k) & \longrightarrow & 0.
\end{array}
$$

The indicated map is an isomorphism by previous work. We will show that the map $j_* : \pi_2 K/\ell(k) \to \pi_2 GK/\ell(k)$ is a monomorphism by showing that the map

$$j_* : \pi_2 F_1 K/\ell(k) \to \pi_2 GF_1 K/\ell(k)$$

is a monomorphism. This is done by producing a map

$$\pi_2 GF_1 K/\ell(k) \to H^2(k, \mathbb{Z}/\ell)$$

whose composite with the map j_* is the norm residue homomorphism

$$nr : K_2(k) \otimes \mathbb{Z}/\ell \to H^2(k, \mathbb{Z}/\ell).$$

The norm residue homomorphism is an isomorphism — this is the main result of [40].

The cup product map $\pi_1 K/\ell(k) \otimes \pi_1 K/\ell(k) \to \pi_2 K/\ell(k)$ is induced by a restricted cup product map $\cup : F_0 K/\ell \wedge F_0 K/\ell \to F_1 K/\ell$, and one can construct a homotopy commutative diagram

$$
\begin{array}{ccc}
F_0 K/\ell \wedge F_0 K/\ell & \xrightarrow{\ \cup\ } & F_1 K/\ell \\
{\scriptstyle j \wedge j}\big\downarrow & & \big\downarrow{\scriptstyle j} \\
GF_0 K/\ell \wedge GF_0 K/\ell & \xrightarrow{\hspace{2cm}} & GF_1 K/\ell
\end{array}
$$

in the stable category, by taking appropriate globally fibrant models (see the remarks following (5.50)), and use the presheaf theoretic analogue of Lemma 3.14). The presheaves of spectra $F_2(F_0 K/\ell) \wedge F_0 K/\ell$ and $P_2(F_0 K/\ell) \wedge F_2(F_0 K/\ell)$ are both stalkwise 5-connected, so the map

$$F_0 K/\ell \wedge F_0 K/\ell \to P_2(F_0 K/\ell) \wedge P_2(F_0 K/\ell)$$

induces a stalkwise weak equivalence

$$P_5(F_0 K/\ell \wedge F_0 K/\ell) \to P_5(P_2(F_0 K/\ell) \wedge P_2(F_0 K/\ell))$$

It follows that there is a stalkwise homotopy commutative diagram

$$
\begin{array}{ccc}
F_0 K/\ell \wedge F_0 K/\ell & \xrightarrow{\hspace{2.5cm}} & F_1 K/\ell \\
\big\downarrow & & \big\downarrow \\
P_2(F_0 K/\ell) \wedge P_2(F_0 K/\ell) & \xrightarrow{\hspace{2cm}} & P_4(F_1 K/\ell).
\end{array}
$$

In the induced diagram

$$
\begin{array}{ccc}
G(F_0 K/\ell) \wedge G(F_0 K/\ell) & \xrightarrow{\hspace{2.5cm}} & G(F_1 K/\ell) \\
\big\downarrow & & \big\downarrow \\
GP_2(F_0 K/\ell) \wedge GP_2(F_0 K/\ell) & \xrightarrow{\hspace{2cm}} & GP_4(F_1 K/\ell)
\end{array}
$$

the presheaf of spectra $F_1 K/\ell$ is stalkwise 3-connected, and so the bottom horizontal map may be identified up to pointwise equivalence with the map

$$GK(\mathbb{Z}/\ell, 2) \wedge GK(\mathbb{Z}/\ell, 2) \to GK(\mathbb{Z}/\ell, 4)$$

which is induced by the pairing $\mathbb{Z}/\ell \otimes \mathbb{Z}/\ell \cong \mathbb{Z}/\ell$. The induced map

$$\pi_1 GK(\mathbb{Z}/\ell, 2)(k) \otimes \pi_1 GK(\mathbb{Z}/\ell, 2)(k) \to \pi_2 GK(\mathbb{Z}/\ell, 4)(k)$$

can therefore be identified with the cohomology cup product map

$$H^1(k, \mathbb{Z}/\ell) \otimes H^1(k, \mathbb{Z}/\ell) \to H^2(k, \mathbb{Z}/\ell).$$

The composite

$$\pi_2 F_1 K/\ell(k) \xrightarrow{j_*} \pi_2 GF_1 K/\ell(k) \to \pi_2 GP_4(F_1 K/\ell)(k) \cong H^2(k, \mathbb{Z}/\ell)$$

is therefore the norm residue homomorphism.

There is a commutative diagram

$$
\begin{array}{ccc}
\pi_0 K/\ell(k) & \longrightarrow & \pi_0 GK/\ell(k) \\
\cong \downarrow & & \downarrow \\
\pi_0 P_0 K/\ell(k) & \longrightarrow & \pi_0 GP_0 K/\ell(k)
\end{array}
$$

and a pointwise weak equivalence

$$P_0 K/\ell \simeq K(\Gamma^* \mathbb{Z}/\ell, 0).$$

In general, the map

$$\pi_0 K(A, 0)(k) \to \pi_0 GK(A, 0)(k)$$

induced by any globally fibrant model for a presheaf of Eilenberg-Mac Lane spectra arising from a presheaf of abelian groups A can be identified with the homomorphism

$$\eta : A(k) \to \tilde{A}(k)$$

induced by the associated sheaf map. It follows that the map

$$\pi_0 P_0 K/\ell(k) \to \pi_0 GP_0 K/\ell(k)$$

is an isomorphism, and so the map

$$\pi_0 K/\ell(k) \to \pi_0 GK/\ell(k)$$

is a monomorphism.   ■

In cases of low Galois cohomological dimension, we can say more:

PROPOSITION 7.12. *Suppose that ℓ is a prime which is distinct from the characteristic of a field k, and that $\ell > 3$. Suppose that k contains a primitive ℓ^{th} root of unity ζ_ℓ. Suppose further that k has finite Galois cohomological dimension with respect to ℓ-torsion sheaves, and suppose that $cd_\ell(k) = d$. Then the map*

$$j_* : \pi_i K/\ell(k) \to \pi_i GK/\ell(k)$$

is an isomorphism if $d - 1 \leq i \leq 2$. If $cd_\ell(k) = 0$, then j_* is an isomorphism for all i.

PROOF: Suppose that $cd_\ell(k) = 0$. In this case the proposition asserts that the map

$$j_* : \pi_i K/\ell(k) \to \pi_i GK/\ell(k)$$

is an isomorphism for all $i \geq 0$. One sees this by arguing over an étale site for k which is sufficiently big that it contains the algebraic closure $\overline{k}$. Then there is a commutative diagram of maps of spectra

$$
\begin{array}{ccc}
K/\ell(k) & \xrightarrow{\ j\ } & GK/\ell(k) \\
\downarrow & & \downarrow \\
K/\ell(\overline{k}) & \xrightarrow{\ j\ } & GK/\ell(\overline{k}),
\end{array}
\qquad (7.13)
$$

where the vertical maps are canonical maps into filtered colimits, since K/ℓ and GK/ℓ are both continuous functors. All finite algebraic extensions of the field k have index prime to ℓ, so transfer arguments for both K/ℓ and GK/ℓ imply that the induced maps

$$\pi_j K/\ell(k) \to \pi_j K/\ell(\overline{k}),$$

and

$$\pi_j GK/\ell(k) \to \pi_j GK/\ell(\overline{k})$$

are monomorphisms in all degrees. The maps

$$j_* : \pi_j K/\ell(\overline{k}) \to \pi_j GK/\ell(\overline{k})$$

are isomorphisms in all degrees (work over the étale site for the algebraically closed field $\overline{k}$ to see this), and we know from Suslin's calculations [52], [53] that there is a ring isomomorphism

$$\pi_* K/\ell(\overline{k}) \cong \mathbb{Z}/\ell[\beta].$$

Finally, the Bott element β lives in $\pi_2 K/\ell(k)$ since k has a primitive ℓ^{th} root of unity, and all maps in (7.13) are maps of ring spectra. It follows that all maps induced by the maps in (7.13) on the homotopy group level are isomorphisms of rings.

Suppose that $cd_\ell(k) \leq 3$, and consider the pointwise fibre sequence

$$F_4(F_1 K/\ell) \to F_1 K/\ell \xrightarrow{p} P_4(F_1 K/\ell),$$

arising from the Postnikov section construction, where the presheaf of spectra $F_1 K/\ell$ is defined in the proof of Proposition 7.11. The fibre $F_4(F_1 K/\ell)$ is stalkwise 5-connected, by the Gabber rigidity theorem [15], and so the groups $\pi_i GF_4(F_1 K/\ell)(k)$ vanish for $i \leq 2$. This implies that the induced map $p_* : \pi_2 GF_1 K/\ell(k) \to \pi_2 GP_4(F_1 K/\ell)(k)$ is an isomorphism, and so the proof of Proposition 7.11 implies that the maps $j_* : \pi_2 F_1 K/\ell(k) \to \pi_2 G(F_1 K/\ell)(k)$ and $j_* : \pi_2 K/\ell(k) \to \pi_2 GK/\ell(k)$ are isomorphisms.

Suppose that $cd_\ell(k) \leq 2$. In the pointwise fibre sequence

$$F_1 K/\ell \to K/\ell \xrightarrow{p} P_1 K/\ell,$$

the presheaf $F_1 K/\ell$ is stalkwise 3-connected, so that $\pi_i G(F_1 K/\ell)(k) = 0$ for $i \leq 1$. But then the map $p_* : \pi_1 GK/\ell(k) \to \pi_1 GP_1 K/\ell(k)$ is an isomorphism, so the proof of Proposition 7.11 implies that the map $j_* : \pi_1 K/\ell(k) \to \pi_1 GK/\ell(k)$ is an isomorphism.

If $cd_\ell(k) \leq 1$, there is an isomorphism $\pi_0 GK/\ell(k) \cong \mathbb{Z}/\ell$ which is induced by the Postnikov section $K/\ell \to P_0 K/\ell$. The monomorphism $j_* : \pi_0 K/\ell(k) \to \pi_0 GK/\ell(k)$ is therefore an isomorphism. ∎

REMARK 7.14. The degree 1 case in the proof of Proposition 7.12 is due to Thomason (see [30]). ∎

7.3. Inductors

Suppose that L/k is a finite Galois extension, with Galois group G. We have seen (Example 5.55) that the K-theory transfer defines a G-equivariant map $i_* : K(L) \to K(k)$, for the obvious G-action on $K(L)$ and the trivial action on $K(k)$. It follows that the K-theory transfer induces a map

$$i_h : \underset{g \in G}{\underrightarrow{\mathrm{holim}}}\, K/\ell(L) \to K/\ell(k).$$

This map i_h is called the *hypertransfer*.

The base change map $i^* : K(k) \to K(L)$ is also G-equivariant, and Theorem 5.72 implies that the resulting join transformation

$$K(L) \xrightarrow{i_*} K(k) \xrightarrow{i^*} K(L)$$

is $(G \times G)$-equivariantly homotopic to the abstract norm

$$N : K(L) \to K(L)$$

for the G-spectrum $K(L)$ (see Section 3.2). It follows that there is a commutative diagram

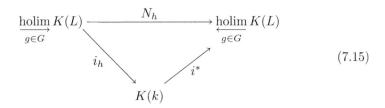

$$(7.15)$$

where N_h is the (abstractly defined) hypernorm, and the map i^* in the diagram is induced by base change. The same construction works for all of the presheaves of spectra which are constructed functorially from the K-theory presheaf by methods that preserve stable equivalences. In particular, there are commutative diagrams like (7.15), with the K-theory presheaf replaced by the mod ℓ K-theory presheaf K/ℓ, or by any suitable Postnikov section .

The following result asserts that the Bott element $\beta \in \pi_2 K/\ell(k)$ is in the image of the map

$$(i_h)_* : \pi_2(\operatorname*{holim}_{g \in G} K/\ell(L)) \to \pi_2 K/\ell(k)$$

in favourable circumstances. Any preimage of the element β is called an *inductor for* β. The fact that the Bott element has inductors in cases of low Galois cohomological dimension is the computational reason that Bott periodic K-theory satisfies étale, or Galois, cohomological descent (Theorem 7.27 below).

THEOREM 7.16. *Suppose that k is a field, that $\ell > 3$ is a prime which is distinct from the characteristic of k, and that k contains a primitive ℓ^{th} root of unity. Suppose that there is a sequence of extensions*

$$k \subset N \subset k_{sep}$$

where N/k is Galois with Galois group H such that $cd_\ell(H) \le 1$, and where $cd_\ell(N) \le 1$. Suppose that L/k is a finite Galois subextension of N/k with $G = Gal(L/k)$. Then there is an element

$$Ind(\beta) \in \pi_2 \operatorname*{holim}_{G} K/\ell(L)$$

such that $i_h(Ind(\beta)) = \beta$ in $\pi_2 K/\ell(k)$.

PROOF: Form the pointwise fibre sequence

$$F_1 K/\ell \to K/\ell \to P_1 K/\ell$$

as in the proof of Proposition 7.11, and observe that it induces a pointwise fibre sequence

$$F_1 K/\ell \to F_0(K/\ell) \to F_0(P_1 K/\ell).$$

This last sequence and the hypertransfer together induce a comparison of exact sequences of the form

$$\pi_2 \varinjlim_{G} F_1 K/\ell(L) \longrightarrow \pi_2 \varinjlim_{G} F_0(K/\ell)(L) \longrightarrow \pi_2 \varinjlim_{G} F_0(P_1 K/\ell)(L) \longrightarrow 0$$

$$\left\downarrow{i_h} \qquad\qquad \left\downarrow{i_h} \qquad\qquad \left\downarrow{i_h}$$

$$\pi_2 F_1 K/\ell(k) \longrightarrow \pi_2 F_0(K/\ell)(k) \longrightarrow \pi_2 F_0(P_1 K/\ell)(k) \longrightarrow 0.$$

The exactness on the right in both sequences follows from the fact that the presheaf of spectra $F_1 K/\ell$ is pointwise 1-connected, and a calculation involving the spectral sequence of Corollary 4.22.

The method of proof of this result is to show that $\beta \in \pi_2 F_0(P_1 K/\ell)(k)$ is in the image of the map i_h on the right, and to show that the map

$$i_h : \pi_2 \varinjlim_{G} F_1 K/\ell(L) \to \pi_2 F_1 K/\ell(k) \tag{7.17}$$

is surjective, for then the conclusion is just a diagram chase.

The latter statement is the easiest to deal with, since the Merkurjev-Suslin theorem [40] implies that the map (7.17) can be identified up to isomorphism with the map

$$H^2(L, \mathbb{Z}/\ell)_G \to H^2(k, \mathbb{Z}/\ell)$$

which is induced by the transfer map $i_* : H^2(L, \mathbb{Z}/\ell) \to H^2(k, \mathbb{Z}/\ell)$, and this transfer map is surjective since $cd_\ell(k) \le 2$ [49].

The techniques of proof of Proposition 7.11 imply that a globally fibrant model $j : P_1 K/\ell \to GP_1 K/\ell$ for $P_1 K/\ell$ on the étale site $et|_k$ induces a pointwise stable equivalence $j : F_0(P_1 K/\ell) \to F_0(GP_1 K/\ell)$ on 0-connected covers. Also, the hypertransfer and hypernorm maps for spectrum $F_0(P_1 K/\ell)$ fit into a commutative diagram

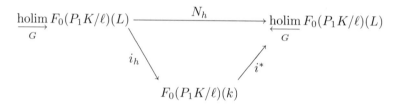

which is analogous to the diagram (7.15). Finally, the presheaf of stable homo-topy groups $\pi_2 P_1 K/\ell$ on the étale site $et|_k$ can be identified up to isomorphism with the constant sheaf $\mathbb{Z}/\ell$; this is the non-vanishing presheaf of homotopy groups of $P_1 K/\ell$ of highest degree, and so the map i^* induces an isomorphism

$$i^* : \pi_2 F_0(P_1 K/\ell)(k) \xrightarrow{\cong} \pi_2 \varprojlim_{G} F_0(P_1 K/\ell)(L).$$

It follows that β lifts to $\pi_2 \varinjlim_{G} F_0(P_1 K/\ell)(L)$ if and only if $i^*(\beta)$ is in the image of the map

$$N_h : \pi_2 \varinjlim_{G} F_0(P_1 K/\ell)(L) \to \pi_2 \varprojlim_{G} F_0(P_1 K/\ell)(L)$$

which is induced by the hypernorm.

The hypernorm for $F_0(P_1 K/\ell)(L)$ is part of a homotopy commutative diagram

$$
\begin{array}{ccc}
\varinjlim_{G} F_0(P_1 K/\ell)(L) & \xrightarrow{\ N_h\ } & \varprojlim_{G} F_0(P_1 K/\ell)(L) \\
{\scriptstyle j}\downarrow{\scriptstyle \simeq} & & {\scriptstyle \simeq}\downarrow{\scriptstyle j} \\
\varinjlim_{G} F_0(GP_1 K/\ell)(L) & \xrightarrow{\ N_h\ } & \varprojlim_{G} F_0(GP_1 K/\ell)(L)
\end{array}
$$

so it suffices to deal with the lifting problem for the image of β in

$$\pi_2 \varprojlim_{G} F_0(GP_1 K/\ell)(L).$$

The Bott element β determines a map of presheaves of spectra

$$\beta : \Gamma^* S[2]/\ell \to K/\ell$$

on the étale site $et|_k$, which takes the generator $\alpha \in \pi_2 S[2]/\ell \cong \mathbb{Z}/\ell$ to the element $\beta \in \pi_2 K/\ell(k)$. Recall that H is the Galois group of the subextension N/k, and form the diagram

$$
\begin{array}{ccc}
p_* \Gamma^* S[2]/\ell & \xrightarrow{\ \beta\ } & p_* K/\ell \\
{\scriptstyle j}\downarrow & & \downarrow{\scriptstyle j} \\
Gp_* \Gamma^* S[2]/\ell & \longrightarrow & Gp_* K/\ell \\
{\scriptstyle \simeq}\uparrow & & \uparrow \\
F_0 Gp_* \Gamma^* S[2]/\ell & \longrightarrow & F_0 Gp_* K/\ell
\end{array}
$$

in the H-world, where p_* denotes the restriction functor from presheaves on $et|_k$ to the site $H - \mathbf{Sets}_{df}$. The maps labelled j are choices of globally fibrant models in the H-world, and the indicated map is a pointwise stable equivalence by the assumption on the ℓ-cohomological dimension of H, since $\Gamma^* S[2]/\ell$ is pointwise 1-connected.

The hypernorm

$$\varinjlim_{G} \operatorname{holim} Gp_* \Gamma^* S[2]/\ell(L) \xrightarrow{N_h} \varprojlim_{G} \operatorname{holim} Gp_* \Gamma^* S[2]/\ell(L)$$

is a stable equivalence, by the Tate theorem (Corollary 7.8), since $Gp_* \Gamma^* S[2]/\ell$ is globally fibrant in the H-world. Furthermore, chasing homotopy group elements through the homotopy commutative diagrams

$$
\begin{array}{ccccc}
\varinjlim_{G} \operatorname{holim} Gp_* \Gamma^* S[2]/\ell(L) & \xleftarrow{\simeq} & \varinjlim_{G} \operatorname{holim} F_0 Gp_* \Gamma^* S[2](L) & \xrightarrow{\beta} & \varinjlim_{G} \operatorname{holim} F_0 Gp_* K/\ell(L) \\
\Big\downarrow N_h & & \Big\downarrow N_h & & \Big\downarrow N_h \\
\varprojlim_{G} \operatorname{holim} Gp_* \Gamma^* S[2]/\ell(L) & \xleftarrow{\simeq} & \varprojlim_{G} \operatorname{holim} F_0 Gp_* \Gamma^* S[2](L) & \xrightarrow{\beta} & \varprojlim_{G} \operatorname{holim} F_0 Gp_* K/\ell(L)
\end{array}
$$

and

$$
\begin{array}{ccc}
\varinjlim_{G} \operatorname{holim} F_0 Gp_* K/\ell(L) & \longrightarrow & \varinjlim_{G} \operatorname{holim} F_0 Gp_* (P_1 K/\ell)(L) \\
\Big\downarrow N_h & & \Big\downarrow N_h \\
\varprojlim_{G} \operatorname{holim} F_0 Gp_* K/\ell(L) & \longrightarrow & \varprojlim_{G} \operatorname{holim} F_0 Gp_* (P_1 K/\ell)(L)
\end{array}
$$

shows that the image of β in $\pi_2 \varprojlim_{G} \operatorname{holim} F_0 Gp_* (P_1 K/\ell)(L)$ is in the image of the map

$$N_h : \pi_2 \varinjlim_{G} \operatorname{holim} F_0 Gp_* (P_1 K/\ell)(L) \to \pi_2 \varprojlim_{G} \operatorname{holim} F_0 Gp_* (P_1 K/\ell)(L).$$

But the presheaf of spectra $p_*(GP_1 K/\ell)$ is globally fibrant in the H-world (Lemma 6.35), so there is a diagram

$$
\begin{array}{ccc}
p_*(P_1 K/\ell) & \xrightarrow{p_* j} & p_*(GP_1 K/\ell) \\
{\scriptstyle j} \Big\downarrow & \nearrow {\scriptstyle f} & \\
Gp_*(P_1 K/\ell) & &
\end{array}
$$

and so the map f induces a homotopy commutative diagram

$$
\begin{array}{ccc}
\underset{G}{\mathrm{holim}} \, F_0 G p_*(P_1 K/\ell)(L) & \xrightarrow{\ f\ } & \underset{G}{\mathrm{holim}} \, F_0(GP_1 K/\ell)(L) \\
N_h \Big\downarrow & & \Big\downarrow N_h \\
\underset{G}{\mathrm{holim}} \, F_0 G p_*(P_1 K/\ell)(L) & \xrightarrow{\ f\ } & \underset{G}{\mathrm{holim}} \, F_0(GP_1 K/\ell)(L).
\end{array}
$$

It follows that $\beta \in \pi_2 \underset{G}{\mathrm{holim}} \, F_0 G P_1 K/\ell(L)$ is in the image of the induced map

$$
N_h : \pi_2 \underset{G}{\mathrm{holim}} \, F_0(GP_1 K/\ell)(L) \to \pi_2 \underset{G}{\mathrm{holim}} \, F_0(GP_1 K/\ell)(L). \qquad \blacksquare
$$

COROLLARY 7.18. *Suppose that k is a field such that $cd_\ell(k) \le 1$, where $\ell > 3$ is a prime which is distinct from the characteristic of k, and suppose that k contains a primitive ℓ^{th} root of unity. Suppose that L/k is an arbitrary finite Galois extension of k with Galois group $G = Gal(N/k)$. Then there is an element*

$$
Ind(\beta) \in \pi_2 \underset{G}{\mathrm{holim}} \, K/\ell(L)
$$

such that $i_h(Ind(\beta)) = \beta$ in $\pi_2 K/\ell(k)$.

PROOF: This is the case $N = k_{sep}$ in Theorem 7.16. $\qquad \blacksquare$

7.4. Descent for Bott periodic K-theory of fields

For the time being, H will be the Galois group of a (possibly infinite) Galois extension N/k, whereas Ω will denote the absolute Galois group of k. Suppose as before that $\ell > 3$ is a prime which does not divide the characteristic of k, and that k contains a primitive ℓ^{th} root of unity.

Let $j : K/\ell \to GK/\ell$ be a globally fibrant model on the étale site $et|_k$ for the mod ℓ K-theory presheaf of spectra K/ℓ, and let $p_* j : p_* K/\ell \to p_* GK/\ell$ be the restriction of this map to the site $H - \mathbf{Sets}_{df}$ of finite discrete H-sets, where $p : \Omega \to H$ is the canonical epimorphism.

I shall now write K/ℓ for the presheaf of spectra $p_* K/\ell$: after all, there couldn't be any other meaning for the mod ℓ K-theory spectrum on the site $H - \mathbf{Sets}_{df}$.

Suppose that F is an additive presheaf of spectra on $H - \mathbf{Sets}_{df}$ whose sheaves of stable homotopy groups are ℓ-torsion. Suppose further that F is a module over the K-theory spectrum K/ℓ in the sense that there is a morphism

$$
F \wedge K/\ell \to F
$$

in the pointwise stable category on $H - \mathbf{Sets}_{df}$.

Suppose that L/k is a finite Galois extension, with $L \subset N$, and write $G = Gal(L/k)$. I say that the module spectrum F *admits transfers* if, for all such finite extensions L

(1) there is a G-equivariant map $i_* : F(L) \to F(k)$ which factors through the join transformation $N : F(L) \to F(L)$ in the sense that there is a diagram

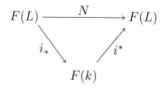

which commutes up to $G \times G$-equivariant homotopy, and

(2) The module structure on F satisfies a G-equivariant projection formula in the sense that the diagrams

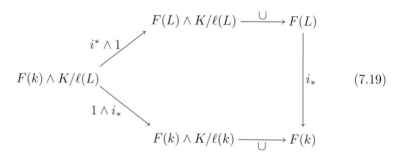

$$(7.19)$$

and

$$(7.20)$$

commute in the stable homotopy category of G-spectra.

Examples of presheaves module spectra over the K-theory presheaf K/ℓ which admit transfers include the K-theory presheaf K/ℓ itself, any presheaf of spectra $K/\ell \wedge E$, where E is constant (and we've abused some notation in a standard way). This is really the reason for all the hard work in Chapter 5: the G-equivariant transfer is developed in Example 5.55, the diagram in condition (1) is Theorem 5.72, the module structure is the point of Section 5.3, and the projection formulae are consequences of Corollary 5.57.

In particular, the *Bott periodic K-theory spectrum* $K/\ell(1/\beta)$ is best formed by smashing K/ℓ with the KU-theory localization S_K of the sphere spectrum (see Section 7.5), so that

$$K/\ell(1/\beta) = K/\ell \wedge S_K.$$

This is the slick — and homotopy coherent — way to formally invert multiplication by "the" Bott element β. A Bott element is any element $\beta \in K_2(k, \mathbb{Z}/\ell)$ which maps to the primitive ℓ^{th} root ζ_ℓ under the canonical map

$$K_2(k, \mathbb{Z}/\ell) \to \mathrm{Tor}(\mathbb{Z}/\ell, k^*).$$

The ambiguity of choice of β does not affect the pointwise stable homotopy type of $K/\ell(1/\beta)$, since we're just going to believe that this object is a (pointwise) K-theory localization.

Recall that $F_n F$ denotes the homotopy fibre of the Postnikov sections map $F \to P_n F$. We have seen (in Lemma 4.35 and Corollary 4.3) that, since the presheaf of spectra K/ℓ is pointwise connective, any K/ℓ-module structure on F induces K/ℓ-module structures on $P_n F$ and $F_n F$. Observe that the naturality of the identifications involved implies that if the module F admits transfers, then so do $P_n F$ and $F_n F$, for each $n \in \mathbb{Z}$. Write $P_m^n F$ for the K/ℓ-module $P_n F_{m-1} F$; then $P_m^n F$ admits transfers if F does.

I say that the Galois group H (or the extension N/k) *has inductors for the Bott element* if for all finite Galois subextensions L/k of N/k such that, if $G = Gal(L/k)$ and $i_h : \varinjlim_G K/\ell(L) \to K/\ell(k)$ is the corresponding hypertransfer, then there is an element $Ind(\beta) \in \pi_2 \varinjlim_G K/\ell(L)$ such that $(i_h)_*(Ind(\beta)) = \beta$ in $\pi_2 K/\ell(k)$.

I shall also say (following at least Thomason) that a field extension M'/M is *induced* from an extension L'/L if there is a diagram of field inclusions

$$
\begin{array}{ccc}
L' & \longrightarrow & M' \\
\uparrow & & \uparrow \\
L & \longrightarrow & M
\end{array}
$$

such that $M' = L' \cdot M$ and $L = L' \cap M$. Observe that, if M'/M is a Galois extension which is induced from a Galois extension L'/L which has inductors (and such that L satisfies the conditions imposed on k above), then M'/M also has inductors. This is a direct consequence of the naturality of the hypertransfer construction (see Example 5.57), which implies the existence of a commutative diagram of maps of spectra

$$
\begin{array}{ccc}
\varinjlim_{G} K/\ell(L'') & \xrightarrow{\ i_h\ } & K/\ell(L) \\
\downarrow & & \downarrow \\
\varinjlim_{G} K/\ell(L'' \cdot M) & \xrightarrow[\ i_h\ ]{} & K/\ell(M)
\end{array}
$$

for any finite subextension L''/L of L'/L with Galois group G.

THEOREM 7.21. *Suppose H has cohomological dimension 1 with respect to ℓ-torsion sheaves, and that H has inductors for the Bott element. Suppose that F is an additive presheaf of spectra on $H - \mathbf{Sets}_{df}$ as above, which is a module over the K-theory presheaf K/ℓ, and admits transfers. Suppose that $j : F \to GF$ is a globally fibrant model of F in the category of presheaves of spectra on the site $H - \mathbf{Sets}_{df}$. Then the map j induces a stable equivalence*

$$
j_* : F(1/\beta)(k) \to GF(1/\beta)(k).
$$

Theorem 7.21 is a consequence, in part, of the following technical result:

LEMMA 7.22. *Under the conditions of Theorem 7.21, suppose that L/k is a finite Galois subextension of N/k, with $G = Gal(L/k)$. Then there is a commutative diagram in the stable category*

$$
\begin{array}{ccccc}
F(k) & \xrightarrow{\ i^*\ } & \varprojlim_{G} F(L) & \longrightarrow & \Omega^2 F(k) \\
j\downarrow & & j\downarrow & & \downarrow j \\
GF(k) & \xrightarrow[\ i^*\ ]{\simeq} & \varprojlim_{G} GF(L) & \longrightarrow & \Omega^2 GF(k),
\end{array}
$$

in which the top and bottom composites are multiplication by the Bott element $\beta \in \pi_2 K/\ell(k)$.

Modulo the proof of Lemma 7.22, we have the following:

Proof of Theorem 7.21: The Galois group H has cohomological dimension 1 with respect to ℓ-torsion sheaves, so that the K/ℓ-module maps

$$P_m^n F = P_n F_{m-1} F \leftarrow F_{m-1} F \rightarrow F$$

induce isomorphisms

$$\pi_i G P_m^n F(k) \cong \pi_i G F_{m-1} F(k) \cong \pi_i G F(k)$$

for $m \leq i \leq n-1$, for any choices of globally fibrant models for all of the objects in sight (Corollary 6.14). The presheaf $P_m^n F$ is a module over K/ℓ admitting transfers, so Lemma 7.22 asserts that there is a commutative diagram

$$
\begin{array}{ccccc}
P_m^n F(k) & \xrightarrow{\;i^*\;} & \underset{G}{\mathrm{holim}}\, P_m^n F(L) & \longrightarrow & \Omega^2 P_m^n F(k) \\
{\scriptstyle j}\big\downarrow & & {\scriptstyle j}\big\downarrow & & \big\downarrow{\scriptstyle j} \\
G P_m^n F(k) & \xrightarrow[\;i^*\;]{\sim} & \underset{G}{\mathrm{holim}}\, G P_m^n F(L) & \longrightarrow & \Omega^2 G P_m^n F(k),
\end{array}
$$

for each member of a cofinal list of finite Galois subextensions L/k, where $G = Gal(L/k)$. Furthermore, one knows that the map of spectra

$$\varinjlim_{L \subset N}\; \underset{G=Gal(L/k)}{\mathrm{holim}}\; P_m^n F(L) \xrightarrow{\;j\;} \varinjlim_{L \subset N}\; \underset{G=Gal(L/k)}{\mathrm{holim}}\; G P_m^n F(L)$$

is a stable equivalence, since the additive presheaf of spectra $P_m^n F$ has only finitely many non-trivial presheaves of homotopy groups (Lemma 6.49).

Fix $i \in \mathbb{Z}$, and choose integers m and n such that $m \leq i \leq n-3$. Take

$$x \in \pi_i P_m^n F(k) \cong \pi_i F(k).$$

If $j_*(x) = 0$ in $\pi_i G P_m^n F(k) \cong \pi_i G F(k)$, then $i^*(x) = 0$ in $\pi_i \varprojlim_G P_m^n F(L)$ for some Galois extension $L \subset N$, so that $x \cup \beta = 0$ in $\pi_{i+2} P_m^n F(k) = \pi_{i+2} F(k)$.

It follows that the induced maps

$$j_* : \pi_* F(1/\beta)(k) \rightarrow \pi_* G F(1/\beta)(k)$$

are injective.

Now take $y \in \pi_i G P_m^n F(k)$. Then $i^*(y) = j_*(z)$ in $\pi_i \varprojlim_G G P_m^n F(L)$, where $z \in \pi_i \varprojlim_G P_m^n F(L)$, for some $L \subset N$. Thus, $y \cup \beta$ is in the image of the map j_*.

It follows that the maps

$$j_* : \pi_* F(1/\beta)(k) \to \pi_* GF(1/\beta)(k)$$

are surjective.   ∎

PROOF OF LEMMA 7.22: Suppose that $j : F \to GF$ is a globally fibrant model for F, and observe that the K/ℓ module structure $\cup : F \wedge K/\ell \to F$ induces a K/ℓ-module structure $\cup : GF \wedge K/\ell \to GF$ on GF, in such a way that the map j is a K/ℓ-module map. One sees this by replacing K/ℓ by a cofibrant object up to pointwise equivalence if necessary, so that the dotted arrow in the diagram

$$
\begin{array}{ccc}
F \wedge K/\ell & \xrightarrow{\;\;\cup\;\;} & F \\
{\scriptstyle j \wedge 1}\downarrow & & \downarrow{\scriptstyle j} \\
GF \wedge K/\ell & \dashrightarrow{\;\;\cup\;\;} & GF
\end{array}
$$

exists in the category of presheaves of bispectra, because GF is globally fibrant and $j \wedge 1$ is a cofibration (Lemma 3.14). For the same reason, it is also harmless to assume that the presheaf of spectra F is pointwise globally fibrant.

The abstract norm homomorphism induces a G-equivariant diagram

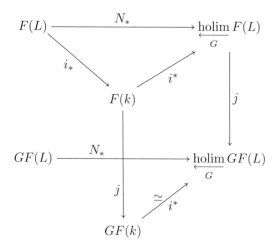

where the maps labelled i^* are induced by the inclusion $i : k \subset L$. The map $i^* : GF(k) \to \underleftarrow{\text{holim}}_G \, GF(L)$ is a stable equivalence since GF is globally fibrant (Proposition 6.39).

Let $\tilde{j} : F(k) \to \varprojlim_G GF(L)$ be the composite

$$F(k) \xrightarrow{j} GF(k) \xrightarrow{i^*} \varprojlim_G GF(L).$$

Then there is a G-equivariant homotopy commutative diagram

$$
\begin{array}{ccccc}
F(L) \wedge K/\ell(L) & \xrightarrow{\cup} & F(L) & \xrightarrow{i_*} & F(k) \\
{\scriptstyle j \wedge 1}\downarrow & & {\scriptstyle j}\downarrow & & \downarrow{\scriptstyle \tilde{j}} \\
GF(L) \wedge K/\ell(L) & \xrightarrow[\cup]{} & GF(L) & \xrightarrow[N_*]{} & \varprojlim_G GF(L).
\end{array}
$$

Form the adjoint diagram

$$
\begin{array}{ccc}
F(L) & \xrightarrow{(i_*\cup)_*} & \mathbf{hom}_*(K/\ell(L), F(k)) \\
{\scriptstyle j}\downarrow & & \downarrow{\scriptstyle \tilde{j}_*} \\
GF(L) & \xrightarrow[(N_*\cup)_*]{} & \mathbf{hom}_*(K/\ell(L), \varprojlim_G GF(L)),
\end{array}
$$

and apply the functor $\varprojlim_G$ to get the homotopy commutative diagram of spectra

$$
\begin{array}{ccc}
\varprojlim_G F(L) & \xrightarrow{(i_*\cup)_*} & \varprojlim_G \mathbf{hom}_*(K/\ell(L),F(k)) \\
{\scriptstyle j}\downarrow & & \downarrow{\scriptstyle \tilde{j}_*} \\
\varprojlim_G GF(L) & \xrightarrow[(N_*\cup)_*]{} & \varprojlim_G \mathbf{hom}_*(K/\ell(L),\varprojlim_G GF(L)),
\end{array}
\qquad (7.23)
$$

There are commutative diagrams

$$
\begin{array}{ccc}
\varprojlim_G \mathbf{hom}_*(K/\ell(L),F(k)) & \xrightarrow{\cong} & \mathbf{hom}_*(\varinjlim_G K/\ell(L),F(k)) \\
{\scriptstyle \tilde{j}_*}\downarrow & & \downarrow{\scriptstyle \tilde{j}_*} \\
\varprojlim_G \mathbf{hom}_*(K/\ell(L),\varprojlim_G GF(L)) & \xrightarrow{\cong} & \mathbf{hom}_*(\varinjlim_G K/\ell(L),\varprojlim_G GF(L))
\end{array}
$$

$$(7.24)$$

and

$$\begin{array}{ccc}
\mathbf{hom}_*(\varinjlim_G K/\ell(L),F(k)) & \xrightarrow{\;\;Ind(\beta)^*\;\;} & \mathbf{hom}_*(S[2],F(k)) \\
\tilde{j}_* \downarrow & & \downarrow \tilde{j}_* \\
\mathbf{hom}_*(\varinjlim_G K/\ell(L),\varprojlim_G GF(L)) & \xrightarrow[\;Ind(\beta)^*\;]{} & \mathbf{hom}_*(S[2],\varprojlim_G GF(L)),
\end{array} \qquad (7.25)$$

where the indicated isomorphisms are canonical, and the map $Ind(\beta)^*$ is induced by precomposition with the inductor

$$Ind(\beta) : S[2] \to \varinjlim_G K/\ell(L)$$

of the Bott element, wherever it occurs.

Finally, there is a diagram

$$\begin{array}{ccc}
F(k) & \xrightarrow{\;\;i^*\;\;} & \varprojlim_G F(L) \\
j \downarrow & & \downarrow j_* \\
GF(k) & \xrightarrow[\;\;i^*\;\;]{} & \varprojlim_G GF(L)
\end{array} \qquad (7.26)$$

I claim that composing diagrams (7.26), (7.23), (7.24) and (7.25) gives the diagram required in the statement of the lemma. We have only to check that the resulting top and bottom composite maps are induced by multiplication by the Bott element β.

For the top composite, the projection formula (7.19) and naturality of the canonical isomorphism together imply that there is a commutative diagram

$$\begin{array}{ccccc}
F(k) & \xrightarrow{\;\;i^*\;\;} & \varprojlim_G F(L) & \xrightarrow{\;\;(i_*\cup)_*\;\;} & \varprojlim_G \mathbf{hom}_*(K/\ell(L),F(k)) \\
\cup_* \downarrow & & & & \downarrow \cong \\
\mathbf{hom}_*(K/\ell(k),F(k)) & & \xrightarrow[\;\;i_h^*\;\;]{} & & \mathbf{hom}_*(\varinjlim_G K/\ell(L),F(k)),
\end{array}$$

where the map $i_h : \varinjlim_G K/\ell(L) \to K/\ell(k)$ is the hypertransfer. It follows that the top composite coincides with the composite

$$F(k) \xrightarrow{\cup_*} \mathbf{hom}_*(K/\ell(k), F(k))$$

$$\downarrow i_h^*$$

$$\mathbf{hom}_*(\varinjlim_G K/\ell(L), F(k)) \xrightarrow{Ind(\beta)^*} \mathbf{hom}_*(S[2], F(k)),$$

which is multiplication by β, since $i_h(Ind(\beta)) = \beta$.

The projection formula for the hypernorm (see (3.22)) is a homotopy commutative diagram of G-equivariant maps

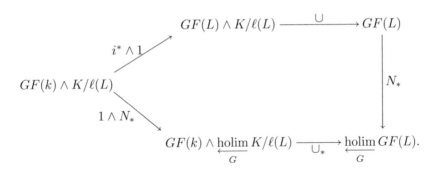

But there is also a G-equivariant homotopy commutative diagram

$$GF(k) \wedge K/\ell(k) \xrightarrow{\cup} GF(k)$$

$$GF(k) \wedge K/\ell(L) \xrightarrow[1 \wedge N_*]{} GF(k) \wedge \varprojlim_G K(L) \xrightarrow{\cup_*} \varprojlim_G GF(L),$$

with maps $1 \wedge i^*$, $1 \wedge i^*$, i^*

so the bottom composite coincides up to homotopy with the composite

$$GF(k) \xrightarrow{\cup_*} \mathbf{hom}_*(K/\ell(k), GF(k)) \xrightarrow{i_h^*} \mathbf{hom}_*(\varinjlim_{G} K/\ell(L), GF(k))$$

$$(\cup(1 \wedge \beta))_* \searrow \qquad \qquad \downarrow Ind(\beta)^*$$

$$\mathbf{hom}_*(S[2], GF(k))$$

$$\simeq \downarrow i^*$$

$$\mathbf{hom}_*(S[2], \varprojlim_{G} GF(L)),$$

which is multiplication by β, up to isomorphism.   ∎

We can now prove Thomason's étale cohomological descent theorem for the Bott periodic K-theory of fields:

THEOREM 7.27. *Suppose that k is a field containing a primitive ℓ^{th} root of unity ζ_ℓ as above, and suppose that the inclusion of k in its separable closure k_{sep} has a finite filtration*

$$k = L_0 \subset L_1 \subset \cdots \subset L_r = k_{sep},$$

such that each extension L_{i+1}/L_i is Galois, and $G_i = Gal(L_{i+1}/L_i)$ has cohomological dimension at most one with respect to ℓ-torsion sheaves. Suppose further that each Galois group G_i has inductors for the Bott element if $cd_\ell(G_i) = 1$. Then any globally fibrant model

$$j : K/\ell(1/\beta) \to G(K/\ell(1/\beta))$$

for the presheaf of spectra $K/\ell(1/\beta)$ on the étale site $et|_k$ for k induces a stable equivalence of spectra

$$j : K/\ell(1/\beta)(k) \to G(K/\ell(1/\beta))(k)$$

in global sections.

PROOF: By induction on r, we can assume that

$$j : K/\ell(1/\beta)(L_1) \to G(K/\ell(1/\beta))(L_1)$$

is a stable equivalence. Here, $G(K/\ell(1/\beta))$ is a globally fibrant model for $K/\ell(1/\beta)$, chosen on some étale site for k which contains the fields L_i. The induction starts with the observation that j is a stalkwise weak equivalence, and so induces a stable equivalence

$$j : K/\ell(1/\beta)(k_{sep}) \to G(K/\ell(1/\beta))(k_{sep}).$$

Let Ω denote the absolute Galois group $Gal(k_{sep}/k)$, and let $p : \Omega \to G_1$ be the canonical epimorphism. Recall that p_* denotes the direct image functor associated to this epimorphism.

The inductive assumption ensures that the map

$$p_* j : p_* K/\ell(1/\beta) \to p_* G(K/\ell(1/\beta))$$

is a stalkwise equivalence, since "stalk" in the G_1-world means "evaluation at L_1", and $G(K/\ell(1/\beta))$ is continuous (Theorem 6.60). Furthermore, the presheaf of spectra $p_* G(K/\ell(1/\beta))$ is globally fibrant (Lemma 6.35), so that the map $p_* j$ is a globally fibrant model of $p_* K/\ell(1/\beta)$. It therefore remains to show that any globally fibrant model

$$j : K/\ell(1/\beta) \to G(K/\ell(1/\beta))$$

of $K/\ell(1/\beta)$ in the category of presheaves of spectra on the site $G_1 - \mathbf{Sets}_{df}$ induces a stable equivalence

$$j : K/\ell(1/\beta)(k) \to G(K/\ell(1/\beta))(k)$$

in global sections.

In the case that $cd_\ell(G_1) = 0$, one knows that all finite Galois subextensions L/k of L_1 have index prime to ℓ, and so the induced maps

$$i^* : K/\ell(1/\beta)(k) \to K/\ell(1/\beta)(L)$$

and

$$i^* : G(K/\ell(1/\beta))(k) \to G(K/\ell(1/\beta))(L)$$

induce split monomorphisms in all associated maps of homotopy groups. The K-theory transfer is used to prove the K-theory statement, while the abstract norm is used to prove the statement for the globally fibrant object $G(K/\ell)(1/\beta))$. But then the map

$$\varinjlim_{L \subset L_1} K/\ell(1/\beta)(L) \xrightarrow{j_*} \varinjlim_{L \subset L_1} G(K/\ell(1/\beta))(L)$$

is a stable equivalence by assumption, so one sees by chasing elements in homotopy groups that the global sections map is a stable equivalence as well.

If $cd_\ell(G_1) = 1$, the Bott periodic K-theory presheaf $K/\ell(1/\beta)$ is a module over the K-theory presheaf K/ℓ which admits transfers, and so the induced map

$$j_* : (K/\ell(1/\beta))(1/\beta)(k) \to G(K/\ell(1/\beta))(1/\beta)(k)$$

is a stable equivalence, by Theorem 7.21. But multiplication by β is a weak equivalence on both $K/\ell(1/\beta)(k)$ and $G(K/\ell(1/\beta))(k)$, and so the global sections map

$$j : K/\ell(1/\beta)(k) \to G(K/\ell(1/\beta))(k)$$

is also a stable equivalence.   ∎

Say that a filtration of the extension k_{sep}/k of the sort appearing in Theorem 7.27 is *admissible*. Examples of fields k such that the extension k_{sep}/k has an admissible filtration include:

(1) all fields k such that $cd_\ell(k) \leq 1$, and
(2) all fields k such that $cd_\ell(k(\mu_{\ell^\infty})) \leq 1$, where $k(\mu_{\ell^\infty})$ is obtained from k by adjoining all ℓ-primary roots of unity.

If $cd_\ell(k) = 1$, then the absolute Galois group has inductors for the Bott element, by Corollary 7.18, so the filtration

$$k \subset k_{sep}$$

is admissible. In the other case, the filtration

$$k \subset k(\mu_{\ell^\infty}) \subset k_{sep}$$

is admissible, by Corollary 7.18 and Theorem 7.16.

The fields described in (2) are contained in a more general class of fields k such that the inclusion $k \subset k_{sep}$ has an admissible filtration, namely those fields k which fit the conditions of Theorem 7.16, for the same reasons.

Note that both classes of fields are closed under finite algebraic extension. All finite fields $\mathbb{F}_p(\zeta_\ell)$, $p \neq \ell$, belong to the first class. The second class contains the fields $\mathbb{Q}(\zeta_\ell)$, all "p-adic" fields $\mathbb{Q}_{\hat{p}}(\zeta_\ell)$, and the field $\mathbb{F}_p((t))(\zeta_\ell)$.

THEOREM 7.28. *Suppose that a field L has finite transcendance degree over a field k, where k belongs to one of the two classes above. Then the comparison map*

$$K/\ell(1/\beta)(L) \to G(K/\ell(1/\beta))(L)$$

is a stable homotopy equivalence.

PROOF: It suffices to assume that L is a separable extension of the field $k(t_1, \ldots, t_n)$: if L/L' is a purely inseparable extension where L' is separable over $k(t_1, \ldots, t_n)$, then the induced map

$$K/\ell(L') \to K/\ell(L)$$

is a stable homotopy equivalence, by a result of Quillen [47, Prop. 4.8]. Furthermore, finite Galois extensions of L are cofinal in Galois extensions of the form $L \cdot K/L$, where K/L' is a finite Galois extension of L'. The field L has finite Galois cohomological dimension with respect to ℓ-torsion sheaves, by assumption, so that the existence of commutative diagrams

$$
\begin{array}{ccc}
P_m^n K/\ell(1/\beta)(L') & \xrightarrow{\ \simeq\ } & P_m^n K/\ell(1/\beta)(L) \\
\Big\downarrow{\scriptstyle j} & & \Big\downarrow{\scriptstyle j} \\
\underset{G}{\operatorname{holim}}\, P_m^n K/\ell(1/\beta)(K) & \xrightarrow[\ \simeq\ ]{} & \underset{G}{\operatorname{holim}}\, P_m^n K/\ell(1/\beta)(L \cdot K)
\end{array}
$$

for $G = Gal(K/L')$ implies that the globally fibrant model $j : K/\ell(1/\beta) \to G(K/\ell(1/\beta))$ induces a weak equivalence

$$ j : K/\ell(1/\beta)(L) \to G(K/\ell(1/\beta))(L) $$

in L-sections if and only if it does so in L'-sections.

The presheaves $K/\ell(1/\beta)$ and $G(K/\ell(1/\beta))$ are continuous, so we can now presume that L is a finite separable extension of $k(t_1, \dots, t_n)$.

We now argue that the extension L_{sep}/L has an admissible filtration, by induction on transcendance degree.

Suppose that L is a finite separable extension of a field $M(t)$, where M has lower transcendance degree over k. Then $L_{sep} = M(t)_{sep}$, and the inclusion $L \subset M(t)_{sep}$ has a filtration

$$ L \subset M_{sep}(t) \cdot L \subset M(t)_{sep}. $$

The extension $M(t)_{sep}/(M_{sep}(t) \cdot L)$ has cohomological dimension with respect to ℓ-torsion sheaves bounded above by 1, by Tsen's theorem, and the extension $(M_{sep} \cdot L)/L$ is induced by the extension $M_{sep}/(M_{sep} \cap L)$. The field $M_{sep} \cap L$ is a finite separable extension of M, and therefore has lower transcendance degree over k. An admissible filtration for $(M_{sep}(t) \cdot L)/L$ is then induced from an admissible filtration for $M_{sep}/(M_{sep} \cap L)$, which exists by the inductive hypothesis. ∎

7.5. Arbitrary powers and regular schemes

I shall persist in avoiding the primes $\ell = 2$ and $\ell = 3$ in all that follows, on the grounds that each of these cases is a bit of a zoo that is well addressed by other authors [55], [44]. In fact, I shall only sketch the development at arbitrary powers for the cases that will be dealt with — this is really the only place where traditional stable homotopy theory comes into this theory.

Bousfield shows [7] that the KU-localization Y_K of an arbitrary spectrum Y is achieved by smashing with the KU-localization S_K of the sphere spectrum S, in the sense that

$$Y_K \simeq Y \wedge S_K.$$

He also shows [7] that the KU-localization $(Y_\ell)_K$ of the Moore spectrum Y_ℓ is stably equivalent to the spectrum $Y_\ell(1/A_1)$, which is obtained by formally inverting the Adams map $A_1 : Y_\ell[2(\ell-1)] \to Y_\ell$. This last result can be bootstrapped to a stable equivalence

$$(Y_{\ell^\nu})_K \simeq Y_{\ell^\nu}(1/A_\nu),$$

where $A_\nu : Y_{\ell^\nu}[2(\ell-1)\ell^{\nu-1}] \to Y_{\ell^\nu}$ is the Adams map corresponding to the power ν (see [44]).

The Adams map A_ν can be interpreted as multiplication by the Adams element $a_\nu \in \pi_{2(\ell-1)\ell^\nu} Y_{\ell^\nu}$, and a result of Snaith [51] implies that the element $a_1 \in \pi_{2(\ell-1)} Y_\ell$ maps to $\beta^{\ell-1} \in \pi_{2(\ell-1)} K/\ell(k)$ under the map $e : Y_\ell \to K/\ell$ corresponding to the unit in K_0. The Adams element a_ν is chosen (by a Bockstein spectral sequence argument) to map to the element $a_{\nu-1}^\ell$ under the map

$$\pi_{2(\ell-1)\ell^\nu} Y_{\ell^\nu} \to \pi_{2(\ell-1)\ell^\nu} Y_{\ell^{\nu-1}},$$

and so the image of $a_\nu \in \pi_{2(\ell-1)\ell^\nu} K/\ell^\nu(k)$ under the unit map

$$Y_{\ell^\nu} \xrightarrow{e} K/\ell^\nu(k)$$

is an obvious choice of a Bott element β_ν for $K/\ell^\nu(k)$.

The Bott periodic K/ℓ^ν-theory for the field k was originally defined to be $K/\ell^\nu(k)(1/\beta_\nu)$. But the results just quoted imply that there are stable equivalences

$$K/\ell^\nu(k)(1/\beta_\nu) \simeq K(k) \wedge Y_{\ell^\nu}(1/a_\nu) \simeq K(k) \wedge Y_{\ell^\nu} \wedge S_K.$$

This means that we can ignore the Bott elements themselves in many circumstances.

A first observation to be made, along the road to more general results, is that the primitive root in Theorem 7.28 can be removed.

COROLLARY 7.29. *Suppose that a field L has finite transcendance degree over a field k, where either $cd_\ell(k) \le 1$ or $cd_\ell(k(\mu_{\ell^\infty})) \le 1$ and ℓ is a prime larger than 3 which is distinct from the characteristic of k. Then the comparison map*

$$K/\ell \wedge S_K(L) \to G(K/\ell \wedge S_K)(L)$$

is a stable homotopy equivalence.

PROOF: Let ζ_ℓ be a primitive ℓ^{th} root of unity. Then $L(\zeta_\ell)$ has finite transcendance degree of $k(\zeta_\ell)$, and $k(\zeta_\ell)$ satisfies the conditions of Theorem 7.28. It therefore follows from Theorem 7.28 that the comparison map

$$K/\ell^\nu \wedge S_K(L(\zeta_\ell)) \to G(K/\ell^\nu \wedge S_K)(L(\zeta_\ell))$$

is a stable equivalence. The top and bottom composites in the diagram

$$
\begin{array}{ccccc}
K/\ell \wedge S_K(L) & \xrightarrow{\;i^*\;} & K/\ell \wedge S_K(L(\zeta_\ell)) & \xrightarrow{\;i_*\;} & K/\ell \wedge S_K(L) \\
\Big\downarrow{\scriptstyle j} & & \Big\downarrow{\scriptstyle j} & & \Big\downarrow{\scriptstyle j} \\
G(K/\ell \wedge S_K)(L) & \xrightarrow{\;i^*\;} & G(K/\ell \wedge S_K)(L(\zeta_\ell)) & \xrightarrow{\;i_*\;} & G(K/\ell \wedge S_K)(L)
\end{array}
$$

are multiplication by a number dividing the unit $\ell - 1$, so the map

$$K/\ell \wedge S_K(L) \to G(K/\ell \wedge S_K)(L)$$

is an isomorphism as well. ∎

The following is now a triviality:

COROLLARY 7.30. *Suppose that a field L has finite transcendance degree over a field k, where either $cd_\ell(k) \leq 1$ or $cd_\ell(k(\mu_{\ell^\infty})) \leq 1$, and ℓ is a prime larger than 3 which is distinct from the characteristic of k. Then the comparison map*

$$K/\ell^\nu \wedge S_K(L) \to G(K/\ell^\nu \wedge S_K)(L)$$

is a stable homotopy equivalence for all powers $\nu \geq 1$.

PROOF: The proof is by induction on ν, using the fibre sequences of presheaves of spectra

$$K/\ell \wedge S_K \to K/\ell^\nu \wedge S_K \to K/\ell^{\nu-1} \wedge S_K.$$

The induction starts with the case $\nu = 1$, which is given by Corollary 7.29. ∎

We shall now extend Corollary 7.30 to an assertion for regular separated Noetherian scheme whose residue fields satisfy the conditions of Corollary 7.30.

THEOREM 7.31. *Suppose that ℓ is a prime such that $\ell > 3$. Suppose that X be a scheme which is separated, Noetherian and regular, of finite Krull dimension, and has $1/\ell \in \Gamma(X, \mathcal{O}_X)$. Suppose further that each of the residue fields $k(x)$, $x \in X$ is of finite transcendance degree over some subfield k_x such that either $cd_\ell(k_x) \leq 1$ or $cd_\ell(k_x(\mu_{\ell^\infty})) \leq 1$. Then the comparison map*

$$K/\ell^\nu \wedge S_K(X) \xrightarrow{\;j\;} G(K/\ell^\nu \wedge S_K)(X)$$

is a stable equivalence of spectra for all powers $\nu \geq 1$.

Recall from Section 6.5 that, by imposing an appropriate cardinality bound, one can assume that the comparison map $j : K/\ell^\nu \wedge S_K \to G(K/\ell^\nu \wedge S_K)$ underlying the statement of Proposition 7.31 is a globally fibrant model for $K/\ell^\nu \wedge S_K$, which is defined on an étale site for L which is sufficiently large that it contains X and all spectra $Sp(O_x)$ of local rings for X and their respective residue fields $Sp(k(x))$.

REMARK 7.32. Theorem 7.31 applies to separated regular schemes X which are of finite type over some field L satisfying the conditions of Corollary 7.30. The field L could, in particular, be algebraically closed. Theorem 7.31 also applies to separated regular schemes which are of finite type over some ring of integers in a number field.   ∎

I shall give two proofs of Theorem 7.31. The first of these is essentially Thomason's original argument [55]. It involves minimal technology, except insofar as one has to introduce a "new" étale site to effect the proof.

The standard definition (as in [42, p.47]) for the small étale site $et|_X$ of a locally Noetherian scheme X asserts that its objects are all scheme homomorphisms $U \to X$ which are étale and of finite type. The category $et|_X$ contains a full subcategory $sep - et|_X$ whose objects are the morphisms $V \to X$ which are separated, étale and of finite type. The class of scheme homomorphisms which are separated, étale and of finite type contains all isomorphisms, and is closed under composition and base change, and so the category $sep - et|_X$, with the topology arising from the étale covering families within the category, is a perfectly good Grothendieck site, which will be called the *separated étale site* for X. Any open immersion is separated [20, p.99], so that any map $U \to X$ which is étale and of finite type is locally separated in the sense that there is a Zariski open covering V_α of U such that all composite maps $V_\alpha \subset U \to X$ are separated, and hence in $sep - et|_X$. It follows that restriction of sheaves along the inclusion $\omega : sep - et|_X \subset et|_X$ is exact on sheaves, and has an exact left adjoint. In particular, if F is a presheaf of spectra on $et|_X$, and $j : F \to GF$ is a globally fibrant model, then the restriction $\omega_* j$ of j to $sep - et|_X$ is a globally fibrant model for the restriction $\omega_* F$ of F to that site. This means in particular that the cohomology theories defined by F on either of these sites are canonically isomorphic. The advantage of performing such a construction is that if X is separated, Noetherian and regular and $V \to X$ is a member of $sep - et|_X$, then the scheme V is separated, Noetherian and regular.

FIRST PROOF OF THEOREM 7.31:

The proof is by induction on the Krull dimension of X. If every point x of X has height 0, then X is a finite disjoint union of schemes of the form $Sp(k(x))$. In this case, the comparison map

$$K/\ell^\nu \wedge S_K(X) \xrightarrow{\ j\ } G(K/\ell^\nu \wedge S_K)(X)$$

is a stable equivalence by Corollary 7.30, since both displayed presheaves of spectra are additive.

Suppose that X has Krull dimension r, and the result has been proved for all schemes satisfying the conditions of the theorem and having lower dimension.

The restricted presheaf of spectra $K/\ell^\nu \wedge S_K$ on the Zariski site X_{Zar} satisfies "Zariski descent". In effect, since X is separated, Noetherian and regular, Quillen's localization theorem [47, p.119] implies that, if U and V are open subschemes of X, then the diagram of K-theory spectra

$$
\begin{array}{ccc}
K(U \cup V) & \longrightarrow & K(V) \\
\downarrow & & \downarrow \\
K(U) & \longrightarrow & K(U \cap V)
\end{array}
$$

is homotopy cartesian. It follows that the diagram

$$
\begin{array}{ccc}
K/\ell^\nu \wedge S_K(U \cup V) & \longrightarrow & K/\ell^\nu \wedge S_K(V) \\
\downarrow & & \downarrow \\
K/\ell^\nu \wedge S_K(U) & \longrightarrow & K/\ell^\nu \wedge S_K(U \cap V)
\end{array}
$$

is homotopy cartesian, and so any globally fibrant model

$$
j : K/\ell^\nu \wedge S_K \to G(K/\ell^\nu \wedge S_K)
$$

of presheaves of spectra on the Zariski site X_{Zar} induces a stable equivalence

$$
j : K/\ell^\nu \wedge S_K(X) \to G(K/\ell^\nu \wedge S_K)(X)
$$

in global (and hence all) sections — this is the Brown-Gersten descent theorem [11, p.286].

The restriction of comparison map

$$
j : K/\ell^\nu \wedge S_K(X) \to G(K/\ell^\nu \wedge S_K)(X)
$$

on $et|_X$ to the Zariski site gives a map

$$
\pi_* j : K/\ell^\nu \wedge S_K(X) \to \pi_* G(K/\ell^\nu \wedge S_K)(X)
$$

of presheaves of spectra on $Zar|_X$, where π_* denotes the direct image functor. The presheaf of spectra $\pi_* G(K/\ell^\nu \wedge S_K)$ is globally fibrant over $Zar|_X$, and therefore satisfies Zariski descent, and so we shall be done if we can show that $\pi_* j$ is a stalkwise weak equivalence, or equivalently that the maps

$$j : K/\ell^\nu \wedge S_K(O_x) \to \pi_* G(K/\ell^\nu \wedge S_K)(O_x) \tag{7.33}$$

are stable equivalences for every point x of X.

Presume inductively that the map (7.33) is a stable equivalence if the height of the point x is less than r, so pick a point x of height r. Write $U = Sp(O_x) - \{x\}$, and let $j : U \subset Sp(O_x)$ be the canonical inclusion. Let $i : Sp(k(x)) \to Sp(O_x)$ be the inclusion of the closed point. Quillen's localization theorem (see also the remarks following this proof) implies that there is a pointwise fibre sequence of presheaves of spectra on the separated étale site $sep - et|_{O_x}$

$$i_*(K/\ell^\nu \wedge S_K) \to K/\ell^\nu \wedge S_K \to j_*(K/\ell^\nu \wedge S_K). \tag{7.34}$$

Form the comparison diagram

$$\begin{array}{ccccc}
i_*(K/\ell^\nu \wedge S_K) & \longrightarrow & K/\ell^\nu \wedge S_K & \longrightarrow & j_*(K/\ell^\nu \wedge S_K) \\
\downarrow{\scriptstyle j} & & \downarrow{\scriptstyle j} & & \downarrow{\scriptstyle j} \\
Gi_*(K/\ell^\nu \wedge S_K) & \longrightarrow & G(K/\ell^\nu \wedge S_K) & \longrightarrow & Gj_*(K/\ell^\nu \wedge S_K)
\end{array} \tag{7.35}$$

in the category of presheaves of spectra on $sep - et|_{O_x}$, but recall that there are comparison maps $j : K/\ell^\nu \wedge S_K \to G(K/\ell^\nu \wedge S_K)$ defined everywhere, in particular on the sites $sep - et|_U$ and $sep - et|_{k(x)}$.

The map $j : K/\ell^\nu \wedge S_K \to G(K/\ell^\nu \wedge S_K)$ is a pointwise stable equivalence on the site $et|_{k(x)} = sep - et|_{k(x)}$, by Corollary 7.30, and so the direct image map

$$i_* j : i_*(K/\ell^\nu \wedge S_K) \to i_* G(K/\ell^\nu \wedge S_K)$$

is a pointwise stable equivalence as well. Also, the direct image $i_* G(K/\ell^\nu \wedge S_K)$ on $sep - et|_{O_x}$ is globally fibrant, and so the map $i_* j$ is a globally fibrant model for the presheaf $i_*(K/\ell^\nu \wedge S_K)$. It follows that any globally fibrant model

$$j : i_*(K/\ell^\nu \wedge S_K) \to Gi_*(K/\ell^\nu \wedge S_K)$$

for the direct image presheaf of spectra $i_*(K/\ell^\nu \wedge S_K)$ is a pointwise stable equivalence.

Similarly, the inductive hypotheses imply that any globally fibrant model

$$j : K/\ell^\nu \wedge S_K \to G(K/\ell^\nu \wedge S_K)$$

on the site $sep - et|_U$ for $K/\ell^\nu \wedge S_K$ is a pointwise stable equivalence, so the map

$$j : j_*(K/\ell^\nu \wedge S_K) \to Gj_*(K/\ell^\nu \wedge S_K)$$

is a pointwise stable equivalence of presheaves of spectra on the site $sep-et|_{O_x}$. One can therefore use the comparison diagram (7.35) to show that the map (7.33) is a stable equivalence for the current choice of point x. This is true for all such points of height r.   ∎

It's more than a little glib to assert the existence of the pointwise fibre sequence (7.34) with Quillen's localization theorem as the sole justification, as is done in the above proof. Suppose that $i \mapsto X(i)$ is an I-diagram in the category of schemes with flat transition maps. Then the categories $\mathcal{M}(X(i))$ of coherent sheaves of each of the schemes $X(i)$ define a contravariant pseudo-functor $i \mapsto \mathcal{M}(X(i))$ taking values in exact categories. As is the case for K-theory, supercoherence theory and Waldhausen's constructions together give rise to an I^{op}-diagram of spectra $i \mapsto K'(X(i))) \simeq K(\mathcal{M}(X(i)))$. This is the the K'-theory diagram — any special case of it corresponding to the index category I being some geometrically defined site whose morphisms are flat is called the K'-theory presheaf on that site. Note as well that the inclusions $\mathcal{P}(X(i)) \subset \mathcal{M}(X(i))$ define a pseudo-natural transformation on I^{op}, and hence give rise to a natural transformation $K(X(i)) \to K'(X(i))$ of I^{op}-diagrams of spectra.

Suppose that Z is a closed reduced subscheme of a separated regular Noetherian scheme X, let $j : Z \subset X$ denote the inclusion, and let the scheme homomorphism $\phi : V \to X$ be separated, étale and of finite type. All étale maps are flat, so the transfer maps

$$t : \mathcal{M}(Z \times_X V) \to \mathcal{M}(V)$$

are pseudo-natural on $sep-et|_X$ (by a sequence of ideas similar to those involved in Example 5.54), and hence determine a "Gysin map"

$$t : j_*K'(V) \to K'(V)$$

of presheaves of spectra on $sep - et|_X$. The restriction maps

$$K'(V) \to K'(\phi^{-1}(X - Z))$$

also determine a map

$$p : K'(V) \to i_*K'(V)$$

on $sep - et|_X$, where i denotes the inclusion $X - Z \subset X$ of the open subset $X - Z$. Quillen's localization theorem implies that the sequence

$$j_*K' \xrightarrow{t} K' \xrightarrow{p} i_*K' \tag{7.36}$$

is a pointwise fibre sequence of presheaves of spectra on $sep - et|_X$.

Now, X is a separated regular Noetherian scheme, as is each scheme V appearing as the "total space" of an object $V \to X$ in $sep-et|_X$, so the natural map $K \to K'$ of presheaves of spectra is a pointwise equivalence on $sep-et|_X$ by the resolution theorem [47, p.100]. Also, the sequence (7.36) remains exact after smashing with any constant spectrum E. One concludes that there is a pointwise fibre sequence

$$j_*(K' \wedge E) \xrightarrow{t} K \wedge E \xrightarrow{p} i_*(K \wedge E).$$

In the cases of immediate interest, we get pointwise fibre sequences

$$j_*(K'/\ell^\nu) \xrightarrow{t} K/\ell^\nu \xrightarrow{p} i_*(K/\ell^\nu) \tag{7.37}$$

and

$$j_*(K'/\ell^\nu \wedge S_K) \xrightarrow{t} K/\ell^\nu \wedge S_K \xrightarrow{p} i_*(K/\ell^\nu \wedge S_K) \tag{7.38}$$

on the separated étale site $sep-et|_X$. Observe that if the closed subscheme Z has the good manners to be regular (as it is in the case underlying the sequence (7.34)), then the sole remaining occurence of K'-theory in (7.37) and (7.38) can be replaced with K-theory.

7.6. The Nisnevich topology

The Nisnevich site for a locally Noetherian scheme X has the same underlying category as does the separated étale site $sep-et|_X$: the objects of the category $Nis|_X$ are the separated étale maps $\phi : U \to X$ which are of finite type, and the morphisms of this category are the X-scheme morphisms between such maps. A collection $\{\phi_i : U_i \to U\}$ of morphisms in $Nis|_X$ is said to be a *covering family* if, for every point $y \in U$, the map $Sp(k(y)) \to U$ lifts to some U_i. The collection of covering families satisfies the axioms for a pretopology — the resulting topology is called the *Nisnevich topology* for X, and the *Nisnevich site* consists of the category $Nis|_X$, equipped with this topology.

The Nisnevich topology is called the *cd-topology* (or completely decomposed topology) in Nisnevich's paper [45]. He writes X_{cd} to denote the Nisnevich site for a scheme X.

EXAMPLE 7.39. Suppose that k is a field, and write $Nis|_k$ for the Nisnevich site for the scheme $Sp(k)$. The objects of $Nis|_k$ can be identified with finite disjoint unions
$$U = Sp(L_1) \sqcup \cdots \sqcup Sp(L_n)$$
of Zariski spectra of finite separable extensions of k, and a family $\{\phi_i : U_i \to Sp(L)\}$ in $Nis|_k$ is covering if and only if it contains a morphism of the form

$$Sp(L) \sqcup Sp(L_2) \sqcup \cdots \sqcup Sp(L_n) \to Sp(L).$$

There is therefore only one covering sieve in $Nis|_k$ for each finite separable extension L/k, namely the trivial sieve which is generated by the identity map on $Sp(L)$. It follows that a presheaf F on $Nis|_k$ is a sheaf if and only if F is additive in the sense that each canonical map

$$pr : F(Sp(L_1) \sqcup \cdots \sqcup Sp(L_n)) \to \prod_{i=1}^{n} F(Sp(L_i)) \qquad (7.40)$$

is an isomorphism. The triviality of the covering sieves for $Sp(L)$ also implies that the associated sheaf map $\eta : F \to \tilde{F}$ induces an isomorphism $F(L) \cong \tilde{F}(L)$ for each finite separable extension L/k. (Following standard practice, I shall most often write $F(R)$ for $F(Sp(R))$). It is a trivial observation that a map $f : F_1 \to F_2$ of sheaves on $Nis|_k$ is an isomorphism if and only if, for all such L, the induced map $F_1(L) \to F_2(L)$ is an isomorphism. Thus, the map pr of (7.40) can be identified up to isomorphism with the associated sheaf map η in sections corresponding to $Sp(L_1) \sqcup \cdots \sqcup Sp(L_n)$. ∎

Suppose that x is a point of X, and let $i_x : Sp(k(x)) \to X$ be the scheme homomorphism arising from the residue field $k(x)$ at x. Composition with the usual induced functor $et|_X \to et|_{k(x)}$ defines a direct image functor

$$(i_x)_* : PreShv(Nis|_{k(x)}) \to PreShv(Nis|_X)$$

between the respective categories of presheaves, which preserves sheaves. The direct image functor has a left adjoint

$$i_x^* : PreShv(Nis|_X) \to PreShv(Nis|_{k(x)})$$

which is defined by left Kan extension. In particular, if y is a point of U, where $U \to X$ is an object of $Nis|_X$, and F is a presheaf on $Nis|_X$, then one can show that $i_x^*(k(y))$ is given up to isomorphism by a filtered colimit

$$i_x^*(k(y)) = \varinjlim F(U) \qquad (7.41)$$

indexed over all liftings of $i_y : Sp(k(y)) \to U$ of the form

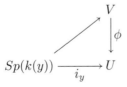

If the presheaf F on $Nis|_X$ is the restriction of a contravariant functor defined on a sufficiently large collection of schemes, and if this functor F is continuous in the standard sense, then there is an isomorphism

$$i_x^*(k(y)) \cong F(\mathcal{O}_y^h), \qquad (7.42)$$

where $\mathcal{O}_y^h$ is the henselization of the local ring $O_{y,U}$ at the point y.

Lemma 7.43. *Suppose that F is an additive presheaf on $Nis|_X$, and that $i_x : Sp(k(x)) \to X$ is the scheme homomorphism arising from a point $x \in X$. Then $i_x^* F$ is an additive presheaf on $Nis|_{k(x)}$.*

Proof: We have to show that the canonical map

$$i_x^* F(S_1 \sqcup S_2) \xrightarrow{pr} i_x^*(S_1) \times i_x^*(S_2) \tag{7.44}$$

is an isomorphism for any finite étale $k(x)$-scheme having the form $S_1 \sqcup S_2$. Any two elements of $i_x^* F(S_1 \sqcup S_2)$ can be represented by elements $s_1, s_2 \in F(U)$, where there is a commutative diagram

$$
\begin{array}{ccc}
S_1 \sqcup S_2 & \xrightarrow{(f_1, f_2)} & U \\
\downarrow & & \downarrow \phi \\
Sp(k(x)) & \xrightarrow{\ \ i_x\ \ } & X,
\end{array}
$$

and ϕ is étale. If s_1 and s_2 represent the same element in $i_x^*(S_1) \times i_x^*(S_2)$, there are liftings

$$
\begin{array}{ccc}
& & V_i \\
& {}^{g_i}\nearrow & \downarrow \phi_i \\
S_i & \xrightarrow{\ f_i\ } & U
\end{array}
$$

with ϕ_i separated, étale and of finite type for $i = 1, 2$, such that s_1 and s_2 map to a common element in $F(V_i)$. But then s_1 and s_2 both map to the same element in $F(V_1 \sqcup V_2) \cong F(V_1) \times F(V_2)$ along the étale map $(\phi_1, \phi_2) : V_1 \sqcup V_2 \to U$, since F is additive. There is also a lift of the map (f_1, f_2) of the form

$$
\begin{array}{ccc}
& & V_1 \sqcup V_2 \\
& {}^{(g_1, g_2)}\nearrow & \downarrow (\phi_1, \phi_2) \\
S_1 \sqcup S_2 & \xrightarrow{\ (f_1, f_2)\ } & U,
\end{array}
$$

so the canonical map (7.44) is injective. One shows that this map is surjective by using the same circle of ideas. ∎

COROLLARY 7.45. *Under the assumptions of the Lemma 7.43, if F is a sheaf on $Nis|_X$, then $i_x^* F$ is a sheaf on $Nis|_{k(x)}$.*

The isomorphisms (7.41), Corollary 7.45 and the development in Example 7.39 together give one the ability to think of stalks for the Nisnevich topology from two different points of view. In the first place, if F is a presheaf on $Nis|_X$ then the isomorphisms (7.41) and a standard argument show that the associated sheaf map $\eta : F \to \tilde{F}$ induces isomorphisms

$$\eta_* : i_{\phi(y)}^* F(k(y)) \cong i_{\phi(y)}^* \tilde{F}(k(y))$$

for all objects $\phi : U \to X$ of $Nis|_X$ and all $y \in U$. Similarly, a map $f : F_1 \to F_2$ of sheaves on $Nis|_X$ is an isomorphism if and only if the induced maps

$$f_* : i_{\phi(y)}^* F_1(k(y)) \to i_{\phi(y)}^* F_2(k(y))$$

are isomorphisms for all objects $\phi : U \to X$ in $Nis|_X$ and all $y \in U$. Any finite separable extension $L/k(x)$ is of the form $L = k(y)$ for some point $y \in U$, where $U \to X$ is a separated étale map of finite type. It follows that the associated sheaf map $\eta : F \to \tilde{F}$ induces isomorphisms $i_x^* F(L) \cong i_x^* \tilde{F}(L)$ for all finite separable extensions $L/k(x)$ and all $x \in X$. Also, Corollary 7.45 and the isomorphism (7.42) together imply that a map $f : F_1 \to F_2$ of sheaves on $Nis|_X$ is an isomorphism if and only if the induced map

$$i_x^* f : i_x^* F_1 \to i_x^* F_2$$

is an isomorphism of sheaves on $Nis|_{k(x)}$ for each point x of X. This means that the various presheaves $i_x^* F$, $x \in X$, for a presheaf F, act like stalks for F in the Nisnevich topology on X, even though the toposes corresponding to the sites $Nis|_{k(x)}$ are not actually points.

In many cases, maps $f : F_1 \to F_2$ of presheaves arise from natural transformations of functors which are continuous and "globally defined". In this case the induced map $f_* : \tilde{F}_1 \to \tilde{F}_2$ of associated sheaves is an isomorphism if and only if the map

$$f_* : F_1(\mathcal{O}_y^h) \to F_2(\mathcal{O}_y^h)$$

is an isomorphism for each separated étale map $U \to X$ of finite type, and each point $y \in U$. Such maps of presheaves tend, for us, to arise as comparison maps of presheaves of stable homotopy groups arising from K-theory presheaves of spectra. The K-theory presheaf of spectra K on $Nis|_X$ is the restriction of a globally defined spectrum-valued functor, and it is continuous up to stable equivalence, so there are stable equivalences

$$i_x^* K(k(y)) \simeq K(\mathcal{O}_y^h)$$

for all $y \in U$, $U \to X$ an object of $Nis|_X$. There are similar equivalences

$$i_x^* K/\ell^\nu(k(y)) \simeq K/\ell^\nu(\mathcal{O}_y^h),$$

and

$$i_x^*(K/\ell^\nu \wedge S_K)(k(y)) \simeq (K/\ell^\nu \wedge S_K)(\mathcal{O}_y^h),$$

because smashing with a fixed (constant) spectrum does not disturb the continuity property.

Let F be a presheaf of spectra on the Nisnevich site $Nis|_X$ for X. The object F is said to have the *cd-excision property* (or have cd-excision) if the following conditions hold:

(1) for each map $\phi : U \to V$ in $Nis|_X$ and a closed subscheme $Z \subset V$ such that ϕ induces an isomorphism $Z \times_V U \cong Z$, the commutative diagram

$$
\begin{array}{ccc}
F(V) & \longrightarrow & F(V - Z) \\
\downarrow & & \downarrow \\
F(U) & \longrightarrow & F(\phi^{-1}(V - Z))
\end{array}
$$

of maps of spectra is homotopy cartesian, and

(2) $F(\emptyset)$ is contractible.

EXAMPLES 7.46.

(1) If the Noetherian scheme X is also separated and regular, then the K-theory presheaf of spectra K on $Nis|_X$ has this property. See the development following the proof of Theorem 7.31 — the extra hypotheses are required to invoke Quillen's localization theorem.

(2) If F has the cd-excision property, then so does each presheaf of spectra $F \wedge E = F \wedge \Gamma^* E$ that is obtained by smashing F with a fixed spectrum (ie. constant presheaf of spectra) E. If X is regular, the presheaves K/ℓ^ν and $K/\ell^\nu \wedge S_K$ have the cd-excision property, so that all Bott periodic K-theory presheaves of spectra on $Nis|_X$ have the cd-excision property.

(3) If F' is pointwise stably equivalent to a presheaf of spectra F which has cd-excision, then F' also has cd-excision. ∎

LEMMA 7.47. *Suppose that X is a Noetherian scheme, and that F is a presheaf of spectra on $Nis|_X$ which has the cd-excision property. Then there is a pointwise weak equivalence $j : F \to G_{Zar}F$, where $G_{Zar}F$ is a presheaf of spectra such that every open subset $V \subset U$ induces a stable fibration $G_{Zar}F(U) \to G_{Zar}F(V)$, where $\phi : U \to X$ is an object of $Nis|_X$.*

PROOF: Since F has cd-excision, F has Zariski excision with respect to the Zariski open subset $V \subset U$, for all objects $\phi : U \to X$. In effect, given open subsets V_1 and V_2 of U, it's easy to see that $(V_1 \cup V_2) - V_1 = V_2 - (V_1 \cap V_2)$, and so the cd-excision property for F implies that the induced diagram of restriction maps

$$
\begin{array}{ccc}
F(V_1 \cup V_2) & \longrightarrow & F(V_1) \\
\downarrow & & \downarrow \\
F(V_2) & \longrightarrow & F(V_1 \cap V_2)
\end{array}
$$

is homotopy cartesian. The Brown-Gersten descent theorem then implies that any globally fibrant model $F|_U \to GF|_U$ for the restriction of F to the Zariski site $Zar|_U$ is a pointwise weak equivalence.

But now choose a globally fibrant model $j : F \to G_{Zar}F$ for F with respect to the Zariski topology on the category $Nis|_X = et|_X$. Then restriction along the functor

$$
\phi_* : Zar|_U \to Nis|_X
$$

corresponding to each object $\phi : U \to X$ of $Nis|_X$ is exact and preserves globally fibrant objects for the Zariski topology [22, p.219]. It follows that the map $j : F \to G_{Zar}F$ is a pointwise weak equivalence, and that $G_{Zar}F$ has Zariski descent. In particular, restriction along every Zariski open subset $V \subset U$ for $\phi : U \to X$ in $Nis|_X$ induces a fibration

$$
G_{Zar}F(U) \to G_{Zar}F(V) \qquad \blacksquare
$$

We shall mostly presume that X is a Noetherian scheme henceforth. In general, we will be looking at properties of presheaves of spectra on $Nis|_X$ that are invariant of the pointwise stable homotopy type. Lemma 7.47 implies that it is harmless to assume that all restriction maps induced by inclusions of Zariski open subsets induce fibrations for a presheaf of spectra F on $Nis|_X$ having cd-excision.

Suppose that F is a fixed choice of presheaf spectra on $Nis|_X$ which has the cd-excision property. Note that the fact that F has Zariski excision implies that F is *additive up to stable equivalence* (or just "additive" if confusion is unlikely to result), meaning that the corresponding presheaves $\pi_* F$ of stable homotopy groups are additive in the sense of Lemma 7.43.

Suppose that Z is a closed subset of U, where $\phi : U \to X$ is a separated étale map of finite type (ie. $\phi \in Nis|_X$). The spectrum $\Gamma_Z F$ is defined to be the fibre of the map $F(U) \to F(U - Z)$.

Suppose that Y is locally closed in U, so that $Y = \overline{Y} \cap V$, for some Zariski open subset V of U. Then V is is separated, étale and of finite type over X, so that $\Gamma_Y F$ is defined to be the fibre of $F(V) \to F(V - Y)$. The homotopy type of $\Gamma_Y F$ is independent of the choice of V: if $V \subset V'$ are open subsets of U such that $Y = V \cap \overline{Y} = V' \cap \overline{Y}$, then the diagram of restriction maps

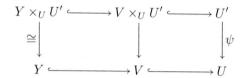

is homotopy cartesian since F satisfies cd-excision, and the category of all open subsets $V \subset U$ such that $Y = V \cap \overline{Y}$ is filtered.

If $\psi : U' \to U$ is a map of $Nis|_X$, and Y is a locally closed subscheme of U such that the map ψ induces an isomorphism $Y \times_U U' \cong Y$, then restriction along ψ induces a stable equivalence $\Gamma_Y F \simeq \Gamma_{\psi^{-1}(Y)} F$. To see this, stare at the diagram of scheme homomorphisms

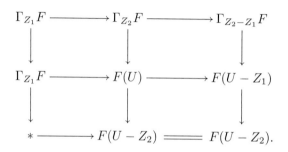

where V is chosen to be an open subscheme of U such that Y is closed in V. Then $Y \times_U U'$ is closed in $V \times_U U'$, which is open in U'. Now use cd-excision.

Suppose that $Z_1 \subset Z_2$ are closed subsets of U, where $\phi : U \to X$ is an object of $Nis|_X$. Then $Z_2 - Z_1 = \overline{Z_2 - Z_1} \cap (U - Z_1)$ so that $Z_2 - Z_1$ is locally closed in U. Furthermore, there are canonically defined maps

$$\Gamma_{Z_1} F \to \Gamma_{Z_2} F \to \Gamma_{Z_2 - Z_1} F \tag{7.48}$$

which form a homotopy fibre sequence, on account of the commutative diagram

$$
\begin{array}{ccccc}
\Gamma_{Z_1} F & \longrightarrow & \Gamma_{Z_2} F & \longrightarrow & \Gamma_{Z_2 - Z_1} F \\
\downarrow & & \downarrow & & \downarrow \\
\Gamma_{Z_1} F & \longrightarrow & F(U) & \longrightarrow & F(U - Z_1) \\
\downarrow & & \downarrow & & \downarrow \\
* & \longrightarrow & F(U - Z_2) & = = & F(U - Z_2).
\end{array}
$$

As a consequence, the diagrams

$$
\begin{array}{ccc}
\Gamma_{Z_1 \cap Z_2} F & \longrightarrow & \Gamma_{Z_1} F \\
\downarrow & & \downarrow \\
\Gamma_{Z_2} F & \longrightarrow & \Gamma_{Z_1 \cup Z_2} F
\end{array}
\tag{7.49}
$$

arising from pairs of closed subsets Z_1, Z_2 of U are homotopy cocartesian.

The collection of all closed subsets $Z \subset U$ such that $codim_U(Z) \geq p$ with inclusions between them forms a filtered category. The spectrum $S^p F(U)$ is defined to be the corresponding filtered colimit

$$
S^p F(U) = \varinjlim_{codim_U(Z) \geq p} \Gamma_Z F
$$

LEMMA 7.50. *Suppose that X is a locally Noetherian scheme, let $\phi : U \to X$ be a finite separated étale morphism, and let Z be a closed subscheme of U with $Z = Z_1 \cup Z_2$, where Z_1 is irreducible and $Z_1 \cap Z_2$ is a proper subscheme of Z_1. Suppose that the presheaf of spectra F on $Nis|_X$ satisfies cd-excision. Then the cofibre of the map*

$$
\varinjlim_{codim_Z(W) \geq 1} \Gamma_W F \to \Gamma_Z F
$$

is a wedge of the cofibres of the maps

$$
\varinjlim_{codim_{Z_i} W \geq 1} \Gamma_W F \to \Gamma_{Z_i} F,
$$

for $i = 1, 2$.

PROOF: Consider the collection of diagrams

$$
\begin{array}{ccc}
\Gamma_{Z_1 \cap Z_2 \cap W} F & \longrightarrow & \Gamma_{Z_1 \cap W} F \\
\downarrow & & \downarrow \\
\Gamma_{Z_2 \cap W} F & \longrightarrow & \Gamma_W F
\end{array}
\tag{7.51}
$$

indexed over the collection of closed subschemes W such that $codim_Z(W) \geq 1$. Then $codim_{Z_i}(Z_i \cap W) \geq 1$, and all closed subschemes $W' \subset Z_i$ with

$codim_{Z_i}(W') \geq 1$ are of the form $W' = Z_i \cap W$, for $i = 1, 2$. Also, the subscheme $Z_1 \cap Z_2$ is one of the subschemes W, so that the map

$$\varinjlim_{codim_Z(W) \geq 1} \Gamma_{Z_1 \cap Z_2 \cap W} F \to \Gamma_{Z_1 \cap Z_2} F$$

is a stable equivalence. The map from the filtered colimit of the diagrams (7.51) to the diagram (7.49) therefore induces a homotopy cocartesian diagram

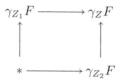

of homotopy cofibres, so that

$$\gamma_Z F \simeq \gamma_{Z_1} F \vee \gamma_{Z_2} F,$$

as required.   ∎

According to the notation appearing in the proof of Lemma 7.50, write $\gamma_x F = \gamma_{\overline{\{x\}}} F$ for the cofibre of the map

$$\varinjlim_{codim_{\overline{\{x\}}}(W) \geq 1} \Gamma_W F \to \Gamma_{\overline{\{x\}}} F,$$

for each point $x \in U$.

COROLLARY 7.52. *Suppose that X is a Noetherian scheme, and let $\phi : U \to X$ be a finite separated étale morphism. Then there is a cofibre sequence*

$$S^{p+1} F(U) \xrightarrow{i} S^p F(U) \to \bigvee_{codim_U(x) = p} \gamma_x F.$$

PROOF: The scheme U is Noetherian, so that each closed subset $Z \subset U$ is a finite union $\overline{\{x_1\}} \cup \cdots \cup \overline{\{x_n\}}$ of its irreducible components. It follows from Lemma 7.50 that there are cofibre sequences of the form

$$\varinjlim_{codim_Z(W) \geq 1} \Gamma_W F \to \Gamma_Z F \to \bigvee_{i=1}^{n} \gamma_{x_i} F$$

Taking a filtered colimit of these, indexed over all closed subschemes $Z \subset U$ such that $codim_U Z \geq p$ gives the desired cofibre sequence.   ∎

The assignment $U \mapsto S^p F(U)$ is a presheaf of spectra on $Nis|_X$, and the maps $i : S^{p+1} F(U) \to S^p F(U)$ induce a map $i : S^{p+1} F \to S^p F$ of presheaves of spectra.

Choose a point $x \in X$, and an object $\phi : U \to X$ of $Nis|_X$. There is a cofibre sequence

$$\varinjlim_{codim\frac{}{\phi^{-1}(x)} Z \geq 1} \Gamma_Z F \to \Gamma_{\overline{\phi^{-1}(x)}} F \to \Gamma_x F(U), \tag{7.53}$$

which defines the spectrum $\Gamma_x F(U)$. The sequence (7.53) is functorial in $\phi : U \to X$, and hence defines a cofibre sequence of presheaves of spectra on $Nis|_X$, with cofibre object denoted by $\Gamma_x F$. Lemma 7.50 implies the spectrum $\Gamma_x F(U)$ of U-sections of $\Gamma_x F(U)$ is a finite wedge

$$\Gamma_x F(U) \simeq \bigvee_{\phi(y)=x} \gamma_y F,$$

and hence that the cofibre of the map $i : S^{p+1} F \to S^p F$ is a wedge

$$\bigvee_{x \in X, codim(x)=p} \Gamma_x F$$

of presheaves of spectra. Observe that $\Gamma_x F$ is additive up to stable equivalence.

LEMMA 7.54. *Suppose that X is a locally Noetherian scheme, and that F is a presheaf of spectra on $Nis|_X$ having cd-excision. Suppose that $\psi : U_1 \to U_2$ is a morphism of $Nis|_X$, such that $\psi(x_1) = x_2$ and that $\psi^{-1}(x_2)$ is the singleton set $\{x_1\}$. Suppose that ψ induces an isomorphism of residue fields $k(x_2) \cong k(x_1)$. Then restriction along ψ induces a stable equivalence of spectra $\gamma_{x_2} F \simeq \gamma_{x_1} F$.*

PROOF: We shall first deal with the case corresponding to

$$x \in V \subset U \xrightarrow{\phi} X,$$

where V is open in U. Write $\gamma_x^U F$ for the spectrum $\gamma_x F$ — this corresponds to presuming that $x \in U$. Then

$$\gamma_x^U F = \varinjlim_{x \in W \subset U} \Gamma_{W \cap \overline{x}} F,$$

where W varies over the open subsets of U which contain x, and $\overline{x}$ means closure of $\{x\}$ in U. The closure of the set $\{x\}$ in V has the form $V \cap \overline{x}$, so that the spectrum $\gamma_x^V F$ which corresponds to $x \in V$ has the form

$$\gamma_x^V F = \varinjlim_{x \in W' \subset V} \Gamma_{W' \cap V \cap \overline{x}} F,$$

where W' varies over the open subsets of V containing x. Restriction along the inclusion $V \subset U$ induces a map of spectra $\gamma_x^U F \to \gamma_x^V F$, which can also be viewed as induced by the collection of maps

$$\Gamma_{W \cap \overline{x}} F \to \Gamma_{V \cap W \cap \overline{x}} F.$$

The collection of open subsets of V which contain x is cofinal in the collection of open subsets of U which contain x, so the restriction map $\gamma_x^U F \to \gamma_x^V F$ is a stable equivalence of spectra.

More generally, the scheme homomophism ψ is separated, étale and of finite type, and we are assuming that ψ induces an isomorphism $k(x_2) \cong k(x_1)$. It follows (from Corollary I.3.12 of [42] plus elementary nonsense: the conditions on ψ and the Nakayama lemma together imply that ψ induces an isomorphism of local rings $\mathcal{O}_{U_2,x_2} \cong \mathcal{O}_{U_1,x_1}$) that there is a Zariski open neighbourhood V of x_1 in U_1 such that the composite

$$V \subset U_1 \xrightarrow{\psi} U_2$$

is an open immersion. ∎

Lemma 7.55. *Suppose that X is a Noetherian scheme, and that F is a presheaf of spectra on $Nis|_X$ which has cd-excision. Let x be an element of X. Then the canonical map*

$$\Gamma_x F \to (i_x)_* i_x^* \Gamma_x F$$

is a pointwise stable equivalence.

Proof: Suppose that $\phi : U \to X$ is an object of $Nis|_X$ such that $\phi^{-1}(x) = \{y\}$. Then $\Gamma_x F(U) = \gamma_y F$, and

$$(i_x)_* i_x^* \Gamma_x F(U) = i_x^* \Gamma_x F(k(y))$$
$$= \varinjlim \Gamma_x F(V),$$

where the colimit is indexed over all liftings

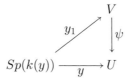

of $y : Sp(k(y)) \to U$. We can assume, up to cofinality, that $\psi^{-1}(y) = \{y_1\}$. In effect, if $\psi^{-1}(y) = \{y_1, y_2, \ldots, y_n\}$, y_1 lives in the Zariski open subset $V - (\overline{y_2} \cup \cdots \cup \overline{y_n})$. But then the map $\Gamma_x F(U) \to \Gamma_x F(V)$ is a stable equivalence, by Lemma 7.54. This is true for all such $\psi : V \to U$, so that the canonical map $\Gamma_x F(U) \to (i_x)_* i_x^* F(U)$ is a stable equivalence.

More generally,

$$\Gamma_x F(U) = \bigvee_{i=1}^{n} \gamma_{y_i} F \simeq \prod_{i=1}^{n} \gamma_{y_i} F,$$

where $\phi^{-1}(y) = \{y_1, \ldots, y_n\}$, and restriction along the inclusion

$$(U - \bigcup_{j \neq i} \overline{y_j}) \subset U \tag{7.56}$$

induces projection onto the ith factor $\gamma_{y_i} F$ in the product. But $i_x^* \Gamma_x F$ is also additive, and so there is a stable equivalence

$$(i_x)_* i_x^* \Gamma_x F(U) = i_x^* \Gamma_x F(Sp(k(y_1)) \sqcup \cdots \sqcup Sp(k(y_n)))$$
$$\simeq \prod_{i=1}^{n} i_x^* \Gamma_x F(k(y_i)),$$

where projection onto the ith factor in the product is similarly induced by restriction along the inclusion map (7.56). ∎

Lemma 7.57. *Suppose that X is Noetherian, F is a presheaf of spectra on $Nis|_X$ having the cd-excision property, and take $x \in X$. Then any globally fibrant model $j : \Gamma_x F \to G\Gamma_x F$ for $\Gamma_x F$ is a pointwise stable equivalence.*

Proof: By Lemma 7.55, $\Gamma_x F$ is pointwise equivalent to a presheaf of spectra $(i_x)_* F'$, where F' is an additive presheaf of spectra on the site $Nis|_{k(x)}$. It suffices to show that a globally fibrant model $j : (i_x)_* F' \to G(i_x)_* F'$ is a pointwise stable equivalence, for any such presheaf of spectra F'. Let $j : F' \to GF'$ be a globally fibrant model for F' on $Nis|_{k(x)}$. Then F' is additive, so j is a pointwise stable equivalence. It follows that the induced map $(i_x)_* j : (i_x)_* F' \to (i_x)_* GF'$ is a pointwise stable equivalence. Furthermore, $(i_x)_* GF'$ is globally fibrant, so the map $(i_x)_* j$ must be a globally fibrant model for $(i_x)_* F'$. ∎

It's time to quote a theorem [45, p.279], [32]:

Theorem 7.58 (Kato-Saito). *Suppose X is a Noetherian scheme of Krull dimension d, and let F be a sheaf of abelian groups on $Nis|_X$. Then $H^i_{Nis}(X, F) = 0$ if $i > d$. In other words, the Krull dimension d is a uniform bound on cohomological dimension for all abelian sheaves (and hence for all additive abelian presheaves) on $Nis|_X$.*

The proof of this result is not particularly difficult, but I'm not going to reproduce it here. The reader should be reminded that results of this type force descent spectral sequences to converge.

LEMMA 7.59. *Suppose X is a Noetherian scheme of Krull dimension d. Suppose that $i \mapsto F(i)$ is a filtered system of presheaves of spectra on $Nis|_X$, defined for objects i in some filtered category I. Suppose that, for each $i \in I$, any choice of globally fibrant model $j : F(i) \to GF(i)$ is a pointwise stable equivalence. Then any choice of globally fibrant model*

$$j : \varinjlim_{i \in I} F(i) \to G(\varinjlim_{i \in I} F(i))$$

for the filtered colimit presheaf of spectra $\varinjlim_i F(i)$ is a pointwise stable equivalence.

PROOF: Choose a globally fibrant model $j : F \to GF$ in the category of I-diagrams of presheaves of spectra on $Nis|_X$, according to Proposition 2.37. Then each induced map $j : F(i) \to GF(i)$ is a globally fibrant model in the category of presheaves of spectra on $Nis|_X$, by Lemma 2.38, and is therefore a pointwise stable equivalence, by assumption. The map j induces a pointwise stable equivalence $j_* : \varinjlim_i F(i) \to \varinjlim_i GF(i)$. It therefore suffices to assume that F is globally fibrant in the category of I-diagrams of presheaves of spectra on $Nis|_X$, and show that any globally fibrant model

$$\varinjlim F(i) \to G(\varinjlim F(i))$$

of the filtered colimit is a pointwise stable equivalence.

Form the fibre sequence

$$F_n F \to F \to P_n F$$

of I-diagrams of presheaves of spectra, and observe that the functors P_n and F_n commute with filtered colimits in the stable category. Form the comparison diagram

$$
\begin{array}{ccccc}
F_n F & \longrightarrow & F & \longrightarrow & P_n F \\
\downarrow{\scriptstyle j} & & \downarrow{\scriptstyle j}{\simeq} & & \downarrow{\scriptstyle j} \\
GF_n F & \longrightarrow & GF & \longrightarrow & GP_n F
\end{array}
\qquad (7.60)
$$

where the vertical maps are globally fibrant models in the category of I-diagrams of spectra, and the indicated map is a pointwise stable equivalence because F is already globally fibrant. Now form the comparison

$$
\begin{array}{ccccc}
\varinjlim GF_n F & \xrightarrow{\;i\;} & \varinjlim GF & \longrightarrow & \varinjlim GP_n F \\
\downarrow{\scriptstyle j_F} & & \downarrow{\scriptstyle j} & & \downarrow{\scriptstyle j_P} \\
G(\varinjlim GF_n F) & \xrightarrow[Gi]{} & G(\varinjlim GF) & \longrightarrow & G(\varinjlim GP_n F)
\end{array}
\qquad (7.61)
$$

of pointwise fibre sequences of presheaves of spectra on $Nis|_X$. The presheaves $\pi_i \varinjlim GP_n F$ and the presheaves $\pi_i G(\varinjlim GP_n F)$ vanish if $i > n$. Thus, if we can show that the map j_F is a pointwise stable equivalence, then the map

$$j_* : \pi_i \varinjlim GF \to \pi_i G(\varinjlim GF) \qquad (7.62)$$

is an isomorphism of presheaves for $i > n$. This is true for every n, so it suffices to prove the claim for globally fibrant I-diagrams of presheaves of spectra F which are bounded below in the sense that the I-diagrams of presheaves of abelian groups $\pi_i F$ vanish if $i < N$ for some fixed number N.

Take such an I diagram F and look at the comparison diagrams (7.60) and (7.61) once again. The maps of I-diagrams of abelian presheaves $\pi_i GF \to \pi_i GP_n F$ are isomorphisms if $i \leq n - d$ since $\pi_i GF_n F = 0$ for $i \leq n - d$ by Theorem 7.58 (see also the argument for Lemma 6.9). But then F is bounded below and $\pi_i GP_n F = 0$ for $i > n$, so that $\pi_i GP_n F = 0$ except for finitely many i. Also, $\pi_i \varinjlim GF_n F = 0$ for $i \leq n - d$ so that $\pi_i G(\varinjlim GF_n F) = 0$ for $i \leq n - 2d$. It follows that, if the map j_P is a pointwise stable equivalence, then the induced map (7.62) is an isomorphism for $i \leq n - 2d$. Once again, this is true for every n, so it is enough to consider only globally fibrant I-diagrams of spectra having only finitely many non-trivial I-diagrams of sheaves of stable homotopy groups $\tilde{\pi}_i F$.

Suppose that F is such an object, and suppose that $\tilde{\pi}_n F$ is the top non-vanishing I-diagram of sheaves of homotopy groups for F. Form the comparison diagram

$$
\begin{array}{ccccc}
F_{n-1} F & \longrightarrow & F & \longrightarrow & P_{n-1} F \\
\downarrow j & & \downarrow j \simeq & & \downarrow j \\
GF_{n-1} F & \longrightarrow & GF & \longrightarrow & GP_{n-1} F
\end{array}
$$

in the category of I-diagrams of presheaves of spectra. Then $GF_{n-1} F$ is pointwise stably equivalent to $G(\tilde{\pi}_n F, n)$, so that there is an induced diagram

$$
\begin{array}{ccccc}
\varinjlim GK(\tilde{\pi}_n F, n) & \longrightarrow & \varinjlim GF & \longrightarrow & \varinjlim GP_{n-1} F \\
\downarrow j_K & & \downarrow j & & \downarrow j_{n-1} \\
G(\varinjlim GK(\tilde{\pi}_n F, n)) & \longrightarrow & G(\varinjlim GF) & \longrightarrow & G(\varinjlim GP_{n-1} F)
\end{array}
$$

in the category of presheaves of spectra on $Nis|_X$. The globally fibrant I-diagram $GP_{n-1} F$ has fewer non-trivial presheaves of homotopy groups than does F, so we can assume inductively that the map j_{n-1} is a pointwise stable equivalence. The map j_K is a pointwise stable equivalence, since there are isomorphisms

$$H^*_{Nis}(U, \varinjlim_{i \in I} A_i) \cong \varinjlim_{i \in I} H^*_{Nis}(U, A_i)$$

for all objects $\phi : U \to X$ of $Nis|_X$, and all I diagrams $i \mapsto A_i$ of abelian sheaves on $Nis|_X$, by a hypercover argument. It follows that the globally fibrant model $j : \varinjlim GF \to G(\varinjlim GF)$ is a pointwise stable equivalence. ∎

THEOREM 7.63. *Suppose that X is a Noetherian scheme having Krull dimension d, and suppose that F is a presheaf of spectra on $Nis|_X$ which has the cd-excision property. Then any globally fibrant model $j : F \to GF$ is a pointwise stable equivalence.*

PROOF: Form the filtration $S^{p+1}F \subset S^pF$, and observe that $S^0F = F$, $S^{d+1}F = *$ and there are pointwise cofibre (but also fibre) sequences

$$S^{p+1}F \hookrightarrow S^pF \to \bigvee_{codim(x)=p} \Gamma_x F.$$

Form the comparison diagram of fibre sequences

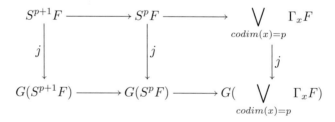

by taking appropriate globally fibrant models, and presume inductively that the map $j : S^{p+1}F \to G(S^{p+1}F)$ is a pointwise stable equivalence. Then every globally fibrant model $j : \Gamma_x F \to G\Gamma_x F$ is a pointwise stable equivalence, by Lemma 7.57, and so the map

$$j : \bigvee_{codim(x)=p} \Gamma_x F \to G(\bigvee_{codim(x)=p} \Gamma_x F)$$

is a pointwise stable equivalence by Lemma 7.59. ∎

Theorem 7.63 is the Nisnevich descent theorem, but it can only be recognized as the result that Nisnevich actually proves in [45] with some extra work, since the original result is formulated in terms of a type of Godement resolution G^*F for a presheaf of spectra F, which resolution will now be rapidly introduced.

Continue to suppose that X is a Noetherian scheme having finite Krull dimension d. The functor

$$i_* : \prod_{x \in X} PreShv(Nis|_{k(x)}) \to PreShv(Nis|_X)$$

is defined by

$$i_*(F_x) = \prod_{x \in X} (i_x)_* F_x,$$

and the functor

$$i^* : PreShv(Nis|_X) \to \prod_{x \in X} PreShv(Nis|_{k(x)})$$

is defined by

$$(i^*F)_x = i_x^* F.$$

It's easily seen that the composite functor $i_* i^*$ preserves pointwise fibrations of simplicial presheaves. With a little more work, one can show that the composite $i_* i^*$ also preserves and reflects finite limits of sheaves and exactness of sequences of abelian sheaves. For the proof of the latter statement, it's handy to know that if $\phi : U \to X$ is an étale map of finite type then, for all $x \in X$, pulling back ϕ along the map $i_x : Sp(k(x)) \to X$ gives a diagram

$$\begin{array}{ccc} \bigsqcup_{\phi(y)=x} Sp(k(y)) & \longrightarrow & U \\ \Big\downarrow & & \Big\downarrow \phi \\ Sp(k(x)) & \longrightarrow & X. \end{array}$$

The functor i^* is plainly left adjoint to i_*. Suppose that F is a presheaf. The cosimplicial object

$$i_* i^* F \rightrightarrows i_* i^* i_* i^* F \substack{\longrightarrow \\ \longrightarrow \\ \longrightarrow} \cdots$$

arising from the adjunction is called the *Godement resolution* of F and is denoted by G^*F.

Note that, if F is an additive presheaf, then the associated sheaf map $\eta : F \to \tilde{F}$ induces an isomorphism $\eta_* : G^*F \cong G^*\tilde{F}$.

If F is a sheaf of sets on $Nis|_X$, then the following is an equalizer in the sheaf category

$$F \xrightarrow{\eta} G^0 F \rightrightarrows G^1 F.$$

If A is a sheaf of abelian groups, then the sequence

$$0 \to A \xrightarrow{\eta} G^0 A \xrightarrow{\partial} G^1 A \xrightarrow{\partial} \cdots$$

is exact, where $\partial = \sum_{i=0}^{n+1} (-1)^i d^i : G^n A \to G^{n+1} A$ is the boundary operator. The proofs of both of these statements are standard categorical moves (see, for example, [4, p.104] for the equalizer statement).

If A is an abelian sheaf on $Nis|_X$, $\phi : U \to X$ is an object of that category, and $\phi(y) = x$, then

$$i_x^* A(k(y)) = i_y^* A|_U(k(y)).$$

Observe further that

$$(i_x)_* i_x^* A(U) = i_x^* A(\emptyset) = 0$$

if $\phi^{-1}(x) = \emptyset$. It follows that there are isomorphisms

$$i_* i^* A(U) \cong \prod_{y \in U} (i_y)_* i_y^* A|_U(U). \tag{7.64}$$

The functor i_* is exact, as is its left adjoint i^*, so for each abelian group object

$$B = (B_x) \in \prod_{x \in X} Shv(Nis|_{k(x)}),$$

there is an adjunction isomorphism

$$H_{Nis}^n(X, i_* B) \cong \prod_{x \in X} H_{Nis}^n(k(x), B_x).$$

But global sections is an exact functor on $Shv(Nis|_{k(x)})$, and so

$$H_{Nis}^n(k(x), B_x) = 0 \qquad \text{for } n > 0,$$

and $H_{Nis}^n(X, i_* B) = 0$ for $n > 0$. Thus, if A is an abelian sheaf on $Nis|_X$ then the cochain complex

$$0 \to A \xrightarrow{\eta} G^0 A \xrightarrow{\partial} G^1 A \xrightarrow{\partial} \cdots$$

is a resolution of A by flabby sheaves. In particular, there are isomorphisms

$$H_{Nis}^n(X, A) \cong H^n(G^* A(X))$$

for $n \geq 0$. Note as well that the identification (7.64) implies that there is an isomorphism

$$G^* A(U) \cong (G^* A|_U)(U)$$

for each separated étale map $\phi : U \to X$ of finite type. We therefore have natural isomorphisms

$$H^n_{Nis}(U, A|_U) \cong H^n(G^* A(U))$$

for each such ϕ.

The Godement reolution construction applies to simplicial presheaves, simplicial sheaves and presheaves of spectra on $Nis|_X$. If F is an object in one of these categories, then $G^* F$ is a cosimplicial object in that category, and then the Bousfield-Kan Tot construction produces an object Tot $G^* F$ in either simplicial presheaves or presheaves of spectra. This is *not* the construction that we use, however, because the functor $F \mapsto$ Tot $G^* F$ does not necessarily preserve any of the fibrations of interest to us. In order to recover at least some fibration structure, we use the Bousfield-Kan "cosimplicial replacement" $\Pi^* G^* F$ (aka. the homotopy inverse limit $\underleftarrow{\mathrm{holim}}\, G^* F$) for the object $G^* F$. This method has the advantage that the functor $F \mapsto$ Tot $\Pi^* G^* F$ takes global fibrations to pointwise fibrations in all cases of interest, while preserving the cohomological information of $G^* F$. The construction still does not preserve global fibrations, in contrast with the Godement resolution construction for the étale site (see [23]) — this is the source of what technical difficulty there is in the following:

PROPOSITION 7.65. *Suppose that X is a Noetherian scheme of finite Krull dimension d, and let F be a globally fibrant simplicial sheaf on $Nis|_X$ which is locally connected in the sense that the sheaf $\tilde{\pi}_0 F$ is trivial. Then the canonical map $F \to$ Tot $\Pi^* G^* F$ is a pointwise weak equivalence.*

PROOF: The map $F \to$ Tot $\Pi^* G^* F$ is a stalkwise equivalence, and Tot $\Pi^* Y$ is globally fibrant if Y is a cosimplicial simplicial sheaf which consists of globally fibrant objects. These two claims are proved by analogy with the corresponding statements for the Godement resolution for the étale topology [23, p.76].

In fact, these statements suffice. Let $j : G^* F \to G(G^* F)$ be a globally fibrant model for $G^* F$ in the category of cosimplicial objects in simplicial sheaves on $Nis|_X$ (from Proposition 2.37). Then the level map $j : G^n F \to G(G^n F)$ is a globally fibrant model for the simplicial sheaf $G^n F$ for each $n \geq 0$, by Lemma 2.38. But $G^n F$ has the form

$$G^n F = \prod_{x \in X} (i_x)_* F_x$$

for some collection of simplicial sheaves F_x on $Nis|_{k(x)}$, $x \in X$. Any globally fibrant model $j_x : F_x \to GF_x$ on $Nis|_{k(x)}$ is a pointwise weak equivalence (the assumption that F is a simplicial sheaf is used at this point), and so there is a pointwise weak equivalence

$$(j_x) : \prod_{x \in X} (i_x)_* F_x \to \prod_{x \in X} (i_x)_* GF_x,$$

where the product on the right is globally fibrant. It follows that each of the level maps $j : G^n F \to G(G^n F)$ is a pointwise weak equivalence, and so the induced map

$$j_* : \mathrm{Tot}\ \Pi^* G^* F \to \mathrm{Tot}\ \Pi^* G(G^* F)$$

is a pointwise weak equivalence. But then the composite

$$F \to \mathrm{Tot}\ \Pi^* G^* F \to \mathrm{Tot}\ \Pi^* G(G^* F)$$

is a stalkwise equivalence of globally fibrant simplicial presheaves, and is therefore a pointwise weak equivalence. ∎

COROLLARY 7.66. *Suppose that F is a globally fibrant simplicial presheaf on $Nis|_X$, where X is a Noetherian scheme of finite Krull dimension. Suppose as well that F is locally connected in the sense that $\tilde{\pi}_0 F = *$. Then the canonical map $F \to \mathrm{Tot}\ \Pi^* G^* F$ is a pointwise weak equivalence.*

PROOF: Choose a stalkwise weak equivalence $f : F \to F'$, where F' is a globally fibrant simplicial sheaf. Then f is a pointwise weak equivalence, and so the induced map

$$f_* : \mathrm{Tot}\ \Pi^* G^* F \to \mathrm{Tot}\ \Pi^* G^* F'$$

is a pointwise weak equivalence. Now use Proposition 7.65. ∎

COROLLARY 7.67. *Suppose that F is a globally fibrant presheaf of spectra on $Nis|_X$, where X is a Noetherian scheme of finite Krull dimension. Then the canonical map $F \to \mathrm{Tot}\ \Pi^* G^* F$ is a pointwise stable equivalence.*

PROOF: Corollary 7.66 implies that $F \to \mathrm{Tot}\ \Pi^* G^* F$ is a pointwise stable equivalence if F is bounded below in the sense that the presheaves $\pi_i F$ vanish for i below some fixed number.

More generally, form comparison diagrams of fibre sequences

$$
\begin{array}{ccccc}
F_n F & \longrightarrow & F & \longrightarrow & P_n F \\
\downarrow{\scriptstyle j} & & \downarrow{\scriptstyle j}{\simeq} & & \downarrow{\scriptstyle j} \\
G F_n F & \longrightarrow & G F & \longrightarrow & G P_n F
\end{array}
$$

and

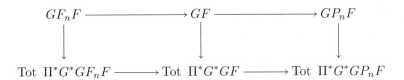

where the vertical maps labelled j in the first diagram are globally fibrant models. The presheaf of spectra GF_nF is globally fibrant and is bounded below by the assumption on Krull dimension (Theorem 7.58), so that the map

$$GF_nF \to \text{Tot } \Pi^*G^*GF_nF$$

is a pointwise stable equivalence. The presheaves of homotopy groups $\pi_i GP_n F$ vanish for $i > n$, so the presheaves $\pi_i(\text{Tot } \Pi^*G^*GP_nF)$ vanish for $i > n$ by Lemma 6.50. It follows that the induced map of presheaves

$$\pi_i GF \to \pi_i(\text{Tot } \Pi^*G^*GF)$$

is an isomorphism for $i > n$. This is true for every n. ∎

COROLLARY 7.68 (NISNEVICH). *Suppose X is a Noetherian scheme of finite Krull dimension, and that F is a presheaf of spectra on the Nisnevich site $Nis|_X$ which has the cd-excision property and is pointwise fibrant. Then the canonical map*

$$F \to \text{Tot } \Pi^*G^*F$$

is a pointwise stable equivalence.

PROOF: Note that F is presumed to be pointwise fibrant so that the construction Tot Π^*G^*F makes (pointwise) homotopical sense.

The statement of the corollary is an invariant of pointwise stable homotopy type, so it suffices to assume that F is globally fibrant for the Zariski topology on $Nis|_X$. Let $j : F \to GF$ be a globally fibrant model for the Nisnevich topology, and consider the diagram

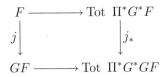

The map j is a pointwise stable equivalence by the Nisnevich descent theorem (Theorem 7.63), and so the map j_* is a pointwise stable equivalence as well. The map $GF \to \text{Tot } \Pi^*G^*GF$ is a pointwise stable equivalence, by Corollary 7.67. ∎

COROLLARY 7.69. *Suppose that X is a separated regular Noetherian scheme, let E be a spectrum, and let $K \wedge E$ be the presheaf of spectra which is obtained by smashing the K-theory presheaf K with the spectrum E. Let $j : K \wedge E \to G(K \wedge E)$ be a globally fibrant model for $K \wedge E$ for the Nisnevich topology on X. Then the map j is a pointwise stable equivalence.*

PROOF: This is really a direct corollary of Theorem 7.63. As was pointed out in Example 7.46, all such presheaves $K \wedge E$ have the cd-excision property. ∎

REMARK 7.70. It is possible to drop the regularity hypotheses of Corollary 7.69, if one is willing to replace K-theory by Bass K-theory, and also use the localization theorem of Thomason and Trobaugh [56]. ∎

I promised, in the last section, that there would be a second proof of Theorem 7.30. Of course, a Nisnevich descent argument will be used for this, but we need to first establish a rigidity result for étale Bott periodic K-theory. Rigidity for mod ℓ^ν étale K-theory is proved at the same time.

LEMMA 7.71. *Suppose that $\mathcal{O}$ is a regular Noetherian henselian local ring, with residue field k. Suppose that F is a globally fibrant presheaf of spectra on an étale site $(\kappa - Sch|_S)_{et}$ which contains $Sp(\mathcal{O})$ and $Sp(k)$, and that F is rigid in the sense that the stable homotopy group sheaves $\tilde{\pi}_* F$ are constant on that site. Then the residue homomorphism $p : \mathcal{O} \to k$ induces a stable equivalence $F(\mathcal{O}) \simeq F(k)$ of spectra.*

PROOF: The respective restrictions $F|_\mathcal{O}$ and $F|_k$ of the presheaf of spectra F to each of the sites $et|_\mathcal{O}$ and $et|_k$ are globally fibrant, and the residue map $F(\mathcal{O}) \to F(k)$ can be identified with the morphism in global sections which is induced by the composite

$$F|_\mathcal{O} \xrightarrow{\eta} p_* p^* F|_\mathcal{O} \xrightarrow{p_* c} p_* F|_k.$$

Here, η is the adjunction map associated to the scheme homomorphism $p : Sp(k) \to Sp(\mathcal{O})$, and $c : p^* F|_\mathcal{O} \to F|_k$ is a canonical map of presheaves of spectra which arises from the fact that F is globally defined on $\kappa - Sch|_S$.

Suppose that H is a presheaf on $et|_\mathcal{O}$. The functor $B \mapsto B \otimes_\mathcal{O} k$ induces an equivalence of the category of finite étale $\mathcal{O}$-algebras with the category of finite étale k-algebras [42, p.34]. Thus, if L/k is a finite separable extension of k, there is, up to ismorphism, a unique finite étale henselian local $\mathcal{O}$-algebra B such that $B \otimes_\mathcal{O} k \cong L$. Furthermore, any such $\mathcal{O}$-algebra B arises in this way. This $\mathcal{O}$-algebra B is the henselization arising from the composite map

$$Sp(L) \to Sp(k) \to Sp(\mathcal{O}),$$

and so the canonical map $\eta : H \to p_* p^* H$ induces an isomorphism $H(B) \cong p_* p^* H(B)$. This is true for all such $\mathcal{O}$-algebras B, so that the presheaf map

$\eta : H \to p_*p^*H$ induces an isomorphism of associated sheaves. Similarly, the canonical presheaf map $\epsilon : p^*p_*G \to G$ induces an isomorphism of associated sheaves on $et|_k$, and the direct image functor p_* preserves stalkwise isomorphisms of presheaves.

It follows that the scheme homomorphism $p : Sp(k) \to Sp(\mathcal{O})$ induces an equivalence of stable homotopy categories

$$Ho(\mathbf{Spt}Pre(et|_{\mathcal{O}})) \simeq Ho(\mathbf{Spt}Pre(et|_k)).$$

This statement includes the assertion that the direct image functor p_* preserves stalkwise stable equivalences.

The proof is finished by showing that the canonical map

$$c : p^*F|_{\mathcal{O}} \to F|_k$$

is a stalkwise stable equivalence. For this, we show that the map c induces an isomorphism in all sheaves of homotopy groups. But the induced map in sheaves of stable homotopy groups can be identified up to isomorphism with the corresponding map

$$c : (\tilde{\pi}_*F)|_{\mathcal{O}} \to (\tilde{\pi}_*F)|_k$$

associated to the collection of sheaves $\tilde{\pi}_*F$ on the big site $(\kappa - Sch|_S)_{et}$. In the setting above, where L/k a finite separable extension with associated henselization B, the $\mathcal{O}$-algebra B is regular, hence connected, and the sheaves $\tilde{\pi}_*F$ are constant, so that the induced map

$$\tilde{\pi}_*F(B) \to \tilde{\pi}_*F(L)$$

is an isomorphism. This is true for each finite separable extension L/k, so that the map of sheaves $c : (\tilde{\pi}_*F)|_{\mathcal{O}} \to (\tilde{\pi}_*F)|_k$ is an isomorphism. ∎

THEOREM 7.72. *Suppose that $\mathcal{O}$ is a regular Noetherian henselian local ring with residue field k, and suppose that $1/\ell \in \mathcal{O}$. Suppose that $G(K/\ell^\nu)$ and $G(K/\ell^\nu \wedge S_K)$ are globally fibrant models for the presheaves of spectra K/ℓ^ν and $K/\ell^\nu \wedge S_K$ on a sufficiently large étale site. Then the residue morphism $p : \mathcal{O} \to k$ induces stable equivalences*

$$\begin{cases} G(K/\ell^\nu)(\mathcal{O}) \simeq G(K/\ell^\nu)(k), & \text{and} \\ G(K/\ell^\nu \wedge S_K)(\mathcal{O}) \simeq G(K/\ell^\nu \wedge S_K)(k). \end{cases}$$

PROOF: Suppose, first of all that $S = Spec(\mathbb{Z}[1/\ell](\zeta_\ell))$, where ζ_ℓ is a primitive ℓ^{th} root of unity, and that $\zeta_\ell \in \mathcal{O}$ so that $Sp(\mathcal{O})$ is an S-scheme. Choose a cardinal κ sufficiently large so that $Sp(\mathcal{O})$ is a member of the category of S-schemes whose cardinality is bounded above by κ. Take a globally fibrant model $j : K/\ell \wedge S_K \to G(K/\ell \wedge S_K)$ for the mod ℓ Bott periodic K-theory presheaf on the site $(\kappa - Sch|_S)_{et}$.

There is a map of presheaves

$$\Gamma^* \mathbb{Z}/\ell[\beta, \beta^{-1}] \to \pi_* G(K/\ell \wedge S_K)$$

of graded abelian groups on $\kappa - Sch|_S$ which is defined by the Bott element $\beta \in \pi_2 G(K/\ell \wedge S_K)(S)$, and this map induces an isomorphism of associated sheaves by Gabber rigidity [15]. In particular, the associated sheaves $\tilde{\pi}_* G(K/\ell \wedge S_K)$ on $(\kappa - Sch|_S)_{et}$ are constant. Now just apply Lemma 7.71 to show that the residue map

$$G(K/\ell \wedge S_K)(\mathcal{O}) \to G(K/\ell \wedge S_K)(k)$$

is a stable equivalence.

If ζ_ℓ is not in $\mathcal{O}$, then the ring $\mathcal{O}(\zeta_\ell)$ is a henselian local ring with residue field $k(\zeta_\ell)$. The equivalence of finite étale k-algebras with finite étale $\mathcal{O}$-algebras can be used to show that the extension $\mathcal{O}(\zeta_\ell)/\mathcal{O}$ is Galois, with Galois group G isomorphic to $Gal(k(\zeta_\ell/k)$. The presheaf of spectra $G(K/\ell \wedge S_K)$ is globally fibrant, so the ring homomorphism $i : \mathcal{O} \to \mathcal{O}(\zeta_\ell)$ induces a stable equivalence

$$G(K/\ell \wedge S_K)(\mathcal{O}) \xrightarrow{i^*} \underset{g \in G}{\mathrm{holim}}\, G(K/\ell \wedge S_K)(\mathcal{O}(\zeta_\ell)).$$

It follows (see Section 3.2) that the abstract norm for the G-action on the spectrum $G(K/\ell \wedge S_K)(\mathcal{O}(\zeta_\ell))$ induces a transfer map

$$N_* : G(K/\ell \wedge S_K)(\mathcal{O}(\zeta_\ell)) \to G(K/\ell \wedge S_K)(\mathcal{O})$$

in the stable category, and that there is a commutative diagram in the stable category

$$
\begin{array}{ccccc}
G(K/\ell \wedge S_K)(\mathcal{O}) & \xrightarrow{i^*} & G(K/\ell \wedge S_K)(\mathcal{O}(\zeta_\ell)) & \xrightarrow{N_*} & G(K/\ell \wedge S_K)(\mathcal{O}) \\
\downarrow{p^*} & & \downarrow{p^*} & & \downarrow{p^*} \\
G(K/\ell \wedge S_K)(k) & \xrightarrow[i^*]{} & G(K/\ell \wedge S_K)(k(\zeta_\ell)) & \xrightarrow[N_*]{} & G(K/\ell \wedge S_K)(k)
\end{array}
$$

in which the top and bottom horizontal composites are multiplication by some number dividing $\ell - 1$, and are therefore isomorphisms. The middle vertical map is a stable equivalence, and so the map

$$p^* : G(K/\ell \wedge S_K)(\mathcal{O}) \to G(K/\ell \wedge S_K)(k)$$

is a stable equivalence as well.

The assertion that the map

$$p^* : G(K/\ell^\nu \wedge S_K)(\mathcal{O}) \to G(K/\ell^\nu \wedge S_K)(k)$$

is a stable equivalence for all henselian local rings satisfying the conditions of the theorem may now be proved by using the observation that there are pointwise fibre sequences

$$G(K/\ell \wedge S_K) \to G(K/\ell^\nu \wedge S_K) \to G(K/\ell^{\nu-1} \wedge S_K)$$

on all étale sites.

The proof that the map

$$p^* : G(K/\ell^\nu)(\mathcal{O}) \to G(K/\ell^\nu)(k)$$

is a stable equivalence is entirely similar, and starts from the observation that Gabber rigidity implies that the sheaf of stable homotopy groups $\tilde{\pi}_* G(K/\ell)$ on the site $(\kappa - Sch|_S)_{et}$ is the constant sheaf associated to the graded abelian group $\mathbb{Z}/\ell[\beta]$. ∎

We have, finally, the

SECOND PROOF OF THEOREM 7.31: Recall that X is a regular, separated, Noetherian scheme, with $1/\ell \in \Gamma(X, \mathcal{O}_X)$. We are also supposing that each of the residue fields $k(x)$ for X is of finite transcendence degree over a field k_x such that either $cd_\ell(k_x) \leq 1$ or $cd_\ell(k_x(\mu_{\ell^\infty})) \leq 1$. Suppose that $j : K/\ell^\nu \wedge S_K \to G(K/\ell^\nu \wedge S_K)$ is a globally fibrant model for the presheaf of spectra $K/\ell^\nu \wedge S_K$ on some étale site which contains X. We want to show that the induced map of spectra

$$j : (K/\ell^\nu \wedge S_K)(X) \to G(K/\ell^\nu \wedge S_K)(X)$$

in X-sections is a stable equivalence.

It suffices to show that the restriction of the map $j|_{Nis|_X}$ to the Nisnevich site $Nis|_X$ induces a stable equivalence in global sections. The restricted presheaf of spectra $G(K/\ell^\nu \wedge S_K)|_{Nis|_X}$ is globally fibrant for the Nisnevich topology, and the Bott periodic K-theory presheaf

$$K/\ell^\nu \wedge S_K = (K/\ell^\nu \wedge S_K)|_{Nis|_X}$$

satisfies Nisnevich descent, by the Nisnevich descent theorem (Theorem 7.63, Corollary 7.69), so it suffices to show that the restricted map $j|_{Nis|_X}$ is a stalkwise weak equivalence for the Nisnevich topology. This amounts to showing that, if $\phi : U \to X$ is a separated étale map of finite type and y is a point of U, then the induced map

$$(K/\ell^\nu \wedge S_K)(\mathcal{O}_y^h) \xrightarrow{j_*} G(K/\ell^\nu \wedge S_K)(\mathcal{O}_y^h)$$

is a stable equivalence, where $\mathcal{O}_y^h$ is the henselization of the local ring $\mathcal{O}_{y,U}$ at y. There is a commutative diagram of maps of spectra

$$
\begin{array}{ccc}
(K/\ell^\nu \wedge S_K)(\mathcal{O}_y^h) & \xrightarrow{\ j\ } & G(K/\ell^\nu \wedge S_K)(\mathcal{O}_y^h) \\
\simeq \downarrow & & \downarrow \simeq \\
(K/\ell^\nu \wedge S_K)(k(y)) & \xrightarrow{\ j\ } & G(K/\ell^\nu \wedge S_K)(k(y))
\end{array}
$$

in which the vertical maps are stable equivalences by Gabber rigidity and Theorem 7.72. Finally, the map

$$ j : K/\ell^\nu \wedge S_K(k(y)) \to G(K/\ell^\nu \wedge S_K)(k(y)) $$

is a stable equivalence, by Corollary 7.30.   ∎

7.7. Post Script: The Lichtenbaum-Quillen conjecture
We shall begin by using the assumptions of Section 7.4 on the field k and the prime ℓ.

CONJECTURE 7.73 (LICHTENBAUM-QUILLEN). *Suppose ℓ is a prime which is distinct from the characteristic of a field k, and that $\ell > 3$. Suppose that k contains a primitive ℓ^{th} root of unity ζ_ℓ. Suppose that k_{sep}/k has a finite filtration*

$$ k = L_0 \subset L_1 \subset \cdots \subset L_r = k_{sep}, $$

by Galois subextensions such that each Galois group $G_i = Gal(L_{i+1}/L_i)$ has $cd_\ell(G_i) \leq 1$. Choose a globally fibrant model $j : K/\ell \to GK/\ell$ on an étale site which contains all of the fields L_i. Then if $cd_\ell(k) \leq d$, the induced map

$$ \pi_i K/\ell(k) \to \pi_i GK/\ell(k) $$

in stable homotopy groups is an isomorphism if $i \geq d-1$ and is a monomorphism if $i = d - 2$.

The preliminary goal of this section is to reduce this conjecture to a statement about Galois groups of cohomological dimension 1. The proof is quite short, perhaps too much so — the rather delicate nature of the induction in the proof of the descent result for Bott periodic K-theory would lead one to believe that the formulation of Conjecture 7.73 is still a bit naive.

Note first of all that a Leray spectral sequence argument shows that, under the assumptions of Conjecture 7.73, the cohomological dimension $cd_\ell(k)$ is bounded above by r. More precisely, if $cd_\ell(L_1) \leq d$ then

$$
\begin{cases}
cd_\ell(k) \leq d & \text{if } cd_\ell(G_1) = 0, \text{ and} \\
cd_\ell(k) \leq d+1 & \text{if } cd_\ell(G_1) = 1.
\end{cases}
$$

Suppose that $cd_\ell(G_1) = 0$, and that the conjecture is true for L_1. Suppose further that $cd_\ell(L_1) \le d$. Then, as in the proof of the descent theorem for Bott periodic K-theory, L_1 is a filtered colimit of finite Galois subextensions L/k of index prime to ℓ. It follows that the maps i^* induced by the inclusion $i : k \subset L$ in the diagram

$$
\begin{array}{ccc}
\pi_i K/\ell(k) & \xrightarrow{\ j_* \ } & \pi_i GK/\ell(k) \\
{\scriptstyle i^*} \downarrow & & \downarrow {\scriptstyle i^*} \\
\pi_i K/\ell(L) & \xrightarrow[\ j_* \ ]{} & \pi_i GK/\ell(L)
\end{array}
$$

are natural split inclusions. The map

$$
\varinjlim_L \pi_i K/\ell(L) \xrightarrow{\ j_* \ } \varinjlim_L \pi_i GK/\ell(L)
$$

is an isomorphism for $i \ge d - 1$ and is a monomorphism if $i = d - 2$ by the inductive assumption, so that

$$
\pi_i K/\ell(k) \xrightarrow{\ j_* \ } \pi_i GK/\ell(k)
$$

is an isomorphism (respectively monomorphism) in the same range.

Now suppose that $cd_\ell(G_1) = 1$, and presume once again that $cd_\ell(L_1) \le d$. Form a pointwise fibre sequence

$$
F \to K/\ell \xrightarrow{\ j \ } GK/\ell
$$

on a sufficiently large étale site for k. Then $\pi_i F(L_1) = 0$ if $i \ge d - 2$. Let

$$
p_* F \to p_* K/\ell \to p_* GK/\ell
$$

denote the direct image of this fibre sequence in the G_1-world, along the topos morphism induced by the canonical surjection $p : \Omega \to G_1$. Further, take globally fibrant models of everything in sight in the G_1-world to form a map of pointwise fibre sequences

$$
\begin{array}{ccc}
p_* F & \longrightarrow p_* K/\ell \xrightarrow{\ p_* j \ } & p_* GK/\ell \\
{\scriptstyle j_{G_1}} \downarrow & {\scriptstyle j_{G_1}} \downarrow & \downarrow {\scriptstyle j_{G_1}} \\
Gp_* F & \longrightarrow Gp_* K/\ell \xrightarrow[\ Gp_* j \ ]{} & Gp_* GK/\ell
\end{array}
$$

Then global sections of the map $p_* j$ is the original map

$$j : K/\ell(k) \to GK/\ell(k).$$

Also, the presheaf of spectra $p_* GK/\ell$ is globally fibrant in the G_1-world, so the global sections map

$$j_{G_1} : p_* GK/\ell(k) \to Gp_* GK/\ell(k)$$

is a stable equivalence of spectra. Finally, formal nonsense (see Proposition 7.4) implies that $\pi_i Gp_* F(k) = 0$ if $i \geq d - 2$, since the homotopy groups of the stalk $F(L_1)$ vanish in the same range. It follows that the induced map

$$\pi_i Gp_* K/\ell(k) \to \pi_i Gp_* GK/\ell(k)$$

is an isomorphism if $i \geq d - 1$ and is a monomorphism if $i = d - 2$. Thus, in order to prove the Lichtenbaum-Quillen conjecture in the cases that we're dealing with, it suffices to show the following:

CONJECTURE 7.74. *Under the assumptions of Conjecture 7.73, suppose that $cd_\ell(G_1) = 1$ and $cd_\ell(L_1) \leq d$. Then the map*

$$j_* : \pi_i p_* K/\ell(k) \to \pi_i Gp_* K/\ell(k),$$

which arises from a globally fibrant model for the restricted K-theory presheaf $p_* K/\ell = K/\ell$ in the G_1-world, is an isomorphism for $i \geq d$ and a monomorphism if $i \geq d - 1$.

Conjecture 7.73 and Conjecture 7.74 are equivalent.

The lower bound d in the statement of Conjecture 7.74 is the best possible. Consider the sequence of field inclusions

$$\mathbb{Q}(\zeta_\ell) \subset \mathbb{Q}(\mu_{\ell^\infty}) \subset \overline{\mathbb{Q}}.$$

Write $L = \mathbb{Q}(\mu_{\ell^\infty})$ and let $H = Gal(L/\mathbb{Q}(\zeta_\ell))$. Let $p : \Omega \to H$ be the canonical surjection of the absolute Galois group $\Omega = Gal(\overline{\mathbb{Q}}/\mathbb{Q}(\zeta_\ell))$ onto H. Choose a globally fibrant model $j : p_* K/\ell \to Gp_* K/\ell$ for the direct image presheaf of spectra $p_* K/\ell$ in the H-world, and observe that Conjecture 7.74 predicts that the map

$$j_* : \pi_i K/\ell(\mathbb{Q}(\zeta_\ell)) \to \pi_i Gp_* K/\ell(\mathbb{Q}(\zeta_\ell))$$

is an isomorphism if $i \geq 1$.

The descent spectral sequence for the presheaf of spectra $Gp_* K/\ell$ collapses, and gives a short exact sequence of the form

$$0 \to H^1(H, L^*/(L^*)^{\times \ell}) \to \pi_0 Gp_* K/\ell(\mathbb{Q}(\zeta_\ell)) \to H^0(H, \mathbb{Z}/\ell) \to 0.$$

On the other hand, the Leray spectral sequence for $H^*(\mathbb{Q}(\zeta_\ell), \mathbb{Z}/\ell)$ which arises from the topos morphism associated to $p : \Omega \to H$ gives an isomorphism

$$H^1(H, L^*/(L^*)^{\times\ell}) \cong H^2(\Omega, \mathbb{Z}/\ell),$$

and the latter is well-known to coincide up to isomorphism with the group $_\ell Br(\mathbb{Q}(\zeta_\ell))$ of ℓ-torsion elements in the Brauer group of $\mathbb{Q}(\zeta_\ell)$. Class field theory shows that this piece of the Brauer group is infinite, so it follows that $\pi_0 Gp_* K/\ell(\mathbb{Q}(\zeta_\ell))$ is not isomorphic to $\pi_0 K/\ell(\mathbb{Q}(\zeta_\ell)) \cong \mathbb{Z}/\ell$.

I shall close by indicating some of the corollaries of Conjecture 7.73. The first step is to show that the hypothesis that requires the existence of a primitive root of unity can be removed, and that the statement "works" for arbitrary powers of ℓ.

COROLLARY 7.75. *Suppose that ℓ is a prime which is distinct from the characteristic of a field k, and that $\ell > 3$. Suppose that k_{sep}/k has a finite filtration*

$$k = L_0 \subset L_1 \subset \cdots \subset L_r = k_{sep},$$

by Galois subextensions such that each Galois group $G_i = Gal(L_{i+1}/L_i)$ has $cd_\ell(G_i) \leq 1$. Choose a globally fibrant model $j : K/\ell \to GK/\ell$ on an étale site which contains all of the fields L_i. Then if $cd_\ell(k) \leq d$, the induced map

$$\pi_i K/\ell^\nu(k) \to \pi_i GK/\ell^\nu(k)$$

in stable homotopy groups is an isomorphism if $i \geq d-1$ and is a monomorphism if $i = d - 2$.

PROOF: Suppose that ζ_ℓ is a primitive ℓ^{th} root of unity in the separable closure k_{sep}. A Shapiro's lemma argument shows that the filtration

$$k(\zeta_\ell) = L_0(\zeta_\ell) \subset L_1(\zeta_\ell) \subset \ldots L_r(\zeta_\ell) = k_{sep}$$

is a filtration of the extension $k_{sep}/k(\zeta_\ell)$ which satisfies the conditions of Conjecture 7.73, and that $cd_\ell(k(\zeta_\ell)) \leq d$. The comparison map

$$j_* : \pi_i K/\ell(k(\zeta_\ell)) \to \pi_i GK/\ell(k(\zeta_\ell))$$

is an isomorphism if $i \geq d - 1$ and a monomorphism if $i = d - 2$ according to Conjecture 7.73, so a transfer argument implies that the comparison map

$$j_* : \pi_i K/\ell(k) \to \pi_i GK/\ell(k)$$

is an isomorphism (respectively monomorphism) in the same range.

For higher powers of ℓ, we use a diagram of pointwise fibre sequences

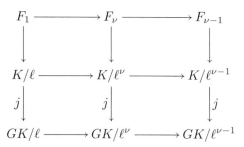

Conjecture 7.73 says that the homotopy groups $\pi_i F_1(k)$ of the spectrum $F_1(k)$ vanish if $i \geq d - 2$. Inductively, we assume that the homotopy groups $\pi_i F_{\nu-1}(k)$ vanish if $i \geq d - 2$. But then the long exact sequence associated to the fibre sequence

$$F_1(k) \to F_\nu(k) \to F_{\nu-1}(k)$$

in global sections implies that $\pi_i F_\nu(k) = 0$ for $i \geq d - 2$. ∎

We can now say something about regular separated Noetherian schemes.

COROLLARY 7.76. *Suppose that X is a regular separated Noetherian scheme, and suppose that $1/\ell \in \Gamma(X, \mathcal{O}_X)$, where ℓ is a prime such that $\ell > 3$. Suppose that the extension $k(x)_{sep}/k(x)$ each of the residue fields of X has a filtration of the form appearing in the statement of Corollary 7.75. Suppose finally that $cd_\ell(k(x)) \leq d$ uniformly for all $x \in X$, where d is some finite number. Let $j : K/\ell^\nu \to GK/\ell^\nu$ be a globally fibrant model for the mod ℓ^ν K-theory presheaf of spectra on a sufficiently large étale site which contains the scheme X. Then the induced map*

$$j_* : \pi_i K/\ell^\nu(X) \to \pi_i GK/\ell^\nu(X)$$

is an isomorphism if $i \geq d - 1$ and a monomorphism if $i = d - 2$.

PROOF: Let F be the pointwise fibre of the comparison map $j : K/\ell^\nu \to GK/\ell^\nu$, and consider the restricted pointwise fibre sequence

$$F|_{Nis|_X} \to K/\ell^\nu|_{Nis|_X} \xrightarrow{j} GK/\ell^\nu|_{Nis|_X}$$

on the Nisnevich site $Nis|_X$. Both $K/\ell^\nu|_{Nis|_X}$ and $GK/\ell^\nu|_{Nis|_X}$ satisfy Nisnevich descent (Corollary 7.69 and formal nonsense, respectively), so that the fibre $F|_{Nis|_X}$ does as well.

The presheaf F is also rigid. Suppose that $\phi : U \to X$ is a separated étale map of finite type, and that $y \in U$. Then the residue map $p : \mathcal{O}_y^h \to k(y)$ for the henselization $\mathcal{O}_y^h$ of the local ring $\mathcal{O}_y$ induces a diagram of fibre sequences

$$
\begin{array}{ccccc}
F(\mathcal{O}_y^h) & \longrightarrow & K/\ell^\nu(\mathcal{O}_y^h) & \longrightarrow & GK/\ell^\nu(\mathcal{O}_y^h) \\
{\scriptstyle p^*}\downarrow & & {\scriptstyle p^*}\downarrow{\scriptstyle \simeq} & & {\scriptstyle \simeq}\downarrow{\scriptstyle p^*} \\
F(k(y)) & \longrightarrow & K/\ell^\nu(k(y)) & \longrightarrow & GK/\ell^\nu(k(y))
\end{array}
$$

in which the indicated maps are stable equivalences by Gabber rigidity and Theorem 7.72. It follows that the map $p^* : F(\mathcal{O}_y^h) \to F(k(y))$ is a stable equivalence.

Each such field $k(y)$ is a finite separable algebraic extension of some $k(x)$, and therefore satisfies the conditions of Corollary 7.75. Also, $cd_\ell(k(y)) \leq d$, so that the map

$$
j_* : \pi_i K/\ell(k(y)) \to \pi_i GK/\ell(k(y))
$$

is an isomorphism if $i \geq d - 1$ and a monomorphism if $i = d - 2$ (according to Conjecture 7.73). It follows that $\pi_i F(\mathcal{O}_y^h) = 0$ for $i \geq d - 2$ for all $y \in U$, $\phi : U \to X$ chosen as above. In particular the stable homotopy group sheaves $\tilde{\pi}_i F|_{Nis|X}$ on the Nisnevich site for X vanish if $i \geq d - 2$. But $F|_{Nis|X}$ satisfies Nisnevich descent, so the groups $\pi_i F(X)$ vanish for $i \geq d - 2$. $\blacksquare$

REFERENCES

[1] J.F. Adams, *On the groups J(X) I–IV*, Topology **5** (1966), 21–71.

[2] J.F. Adams, *Stable homotopy and generalised cohomology*, University of Chicago Press, Chicago, 1974.

[3] J.F. Adams, *Infinite Loop Spaces*, Princeton University Press, Princeton, 1978.

[4] M. Barr and C. Wells, *Toposes, Triples and Theories*, Springer-Verlag, New York, 1985.

[5] J.L. Bell and A.B. Slomson, *Models and Ultraproducts*, 3rd revised printing, North-Holland, Amsterdam, 1974.

[6] A.K. Bousfield, *The localization of spaces with respect to homology*, Topology **14** (1975), 133–150.

[7] A.K. Bousfield, *The localization of spectra with respect to homology*, Topology **18** (1979), 257–281.

[8] A.K. Bousfield and E.M. Friedlander, *Homotopy theory of Γ-spaces, spectra, and bisimplicial sets*, Springer Lecture Notes in Math. **658** (1978), 80–150.

[9] A.K. Bousfield and D.M. Kan, *Homotopy limits completions and localizations*, Springer Lecture Notes in Math., Vol. 304 (2nd corrected printing), Springer-Verlag, Berlin-Heidelberg-New York, 1987.

[10] W. Browder, *Algebraic K-theory with coefficients $\mathbb{Z}/p$*, Springer Lecture Notes in Math. **657** (1978), 40–84.

[11] K.S. Brown and S.M. Gersten, *Algebraic K-theory as generalized sheaf cohomology*, Springer Lecture Notes in Math. **341** (1973), 266–292.

[12] W.G. Dwyer and E.M. Friedlander, *Algebraic and étale K-theory*, Trans. AMS **292** (1985), 247–280.

[13] W. Dwyer, E. Friedlander, V. Snaith and R. Thomason, *Algebraic K-theory eventually surjects onto topological K-theory*, Invent. Math. **66** (1982), 481–491.

[14] E.M. Friedlander, *Étale Homotopy of Simplicial Schemes*, Annals of Mathematics Studies, Vol. 104, Princeton University Press, Princeton, 1982.

[15] O. Gabber, *K-theory of Henselian local rings and Henselian pairs*, Contemp. Math. **126** (1992), 59–70.

[16] H. Gillet and D. Grayson, *The loop space of the Q-construction*, Ill. J. Math. **31(4)** (1987), 574–597.

[17] H. Gillet and R.W. Thomason, *The K-theory of strict hensel local rings and a theorem of Suslin*, J. Pure Applied Algebra **34** (1984), 241–254.

[18] P.G. Goerss, *Homotopy fixed points for Galois groups*, Contemp. Math. **181** (1995), 187–224.

[19] D. Grayson, *Higher algebraic K-theory II*, Springer Lecture Notes in Math. **551** (1974), 217–240.

[20] R. Hartshorne, *Algebraic Geometry*, Graduate Texts in Mathematics, Vol. 52, Springer-Verlag, New York Heidelberg Berlin, 1977.

[21] J.F. Jardine, *Algebraic homotopy theory*, Can. J. Math. **33(2)** (1981), 302–319.

[22] J.F. Jardine, *Simplicial objects in a Grothendieck topos*, Contemp. Math. **55** (1986), 193–239.

[23] J.F. Jardine, *Simplicial presheaves*, J. Pure Applied Algebra **47** (1987), 35–87.

[24] J.F. Jardine, *Stable homotopy theory of simplicial presheaves*, Can. J. Math. **39(3)** (1987), 733–747.

[25] J.F. Jardine, *The multiple Q-construction*, Can. J. Math. **39(5)** (1987), 1174–1209.

[26] J.F. Jardine, *The homotopical foundations of algebraic K-theory*, Contemp. Math. **83** (1989), 57–82.

[27] J.F. Jardine, *The Leray spectral sequence*, J. Pure Applied Algebra **61** (1989), 189–196.

[28] J.F. Jardine, *Supercoherence*, J. Pure Applied Algebra **75** (1991), 103–194.

[29] A. Joyal, *Letter to A. Grothendieck*, (1984).

[30] B. Kahn, *Some conjectures on the algebraic K-theory of fields I: K-theory with coefficients and étale K-theory*, NATO ASI Series C **279** (1989), 117–176.

[31] D.M. Kan, *Semisimplicial spectra*, Ill. J. Math. **7** (1963), 463–478.

[32] K. Kato and S. Saito, *Global class field theory of arithmetic schemes*, Contemp. Math. **55(I)** (1986), 255–332.

[33] M. Levine, *The indecomposable K_3 of fields*, Ann. scient. Ec. Norm. Sup. **22** (1989), 255–344.

[34] L.G. Lewis, J.P. May and M. Steinberger, *Equivariant Stable Homotopy Theory*, Springer Lecture Notes in Math., Vol. 1213, Springer-Verlag, Berlin-Heidelberg-New York, 1986.

[35] S. Mac Lane, *Natural associativity and commutativity*, Rice University Studies **49** (1963), 28–46.

[36] S. Mac Lane, *Categories for the Working Mathematician*, Graduate Texts in Math., Vol. 5, Springer, Berlin-Heidelberg-New York, 1971.

[37] J.P. May, *Simplicial Objects in Algebraic Topology*, Van Nostrand, Princeton, 1967.

[38] J.P. May (with contributions by F. Quinn, N. Ray, and J. Tornehave), *E_∞ ring spaces and E_∞ ring spectra*, Springer Lecture Notes in Math., Vol. 577, Springer-Verlag, Berlin-Heidelberg-New York, 1977.

[39] J.P. May, *Pairings of categories and spectra*, J. Pure Applied Algebra **19** (1980), 299–346.

[40] A.S. Merkurjev and A.A. Suslin, *K-cohomology of Severi-Brauer varieties and the norm residue homomorphism*, Math. USSR Izvestiya **21** (1983), 307–340.

[41] A.S. Merkurjev and A.A. Suslin, *On the norm residue homomorphism of degree 3*, Math. USSR Izvestiya **36** (1991), 349–367.

[42] J.S. Milne, *Étale Cohomology*, Princeton University Press, Princeton, 1980.

[43] S.A. Mitchell, *The Morava K-Theory of Algebraic K-Theory Spectra*, K-Theory **3** (1989), 607–626.

[44] S.A. Mitchell, *Harmonic localization of algebraic K-theory spectra*, Trans. AMS **332** (1992), 823–837.

[45] Y.A. Nisnevich, *The completely decomposed topology on schemes and associated descent spectral sequences in algebraic K-theory*, Algebraic K-theory: Connections with Geometry and Topology, NATO ASI Series C, Vol. 279, Kluwer, Dordrecht, 1989, pp. 241–342.

[46] D. Quillen, *Homotopical algebra*, Springer Lecture Notes in Math., Vol., 43, Springer-Verlag, Berlin-Heidelberg-New York, 1967.

[47] D. Quillen, *Higher algebraic K-theory I*, Springer Lecture Notes in Math. **341** (1973), 85–147.

[48] G. Segal, *Categories and cohomology theories*, Topology **13** (1974), 293–312.

[49] J-P. Serre, *Cohomologie Galoisienne*, Springer Lecture Notes in Math., Vol. 5 (4th Edition), Springer-Verlag, Berlin-Heidelberg-New York-Tokyo, 1973.

[50] J-P. Serre, *Local Fields*, Springer Graduate Texts in Math., Vol. 67, Springer-Verlag, New York-Heidelberg-Berlin, 1979.

[51] V.P. Snaith, *Unitary K-homology and the Lichtenbaum-Quillen conjecture on the algebraic K-theory of schemes*, Spinger Lecture Notes in Math. **1051** (1984), 128–155.

[52] A.A. Suslin, *On the K-theory of algebraically closed fields*, Invent. Math. **73** (1983), 241–245.

[53] A.A. Suslin, *On the K-theory of local fields*, J. Pure Applied Algebra **34** (1984), 301–318.

[54] R.M. Switzer, *Algebraic Topology — Homotopy and Homology*, Springer-Verlag, Berlin-Heidelberg-New York, 1975.

[55] R.W. Thomason, *Algebraic K-theory and étale cohomology*, Ann. Scient. Éc. Norm. Sup., 4e série **18** (1985), 437–552.

[56] R.W. Thomason and Thomas Trobaugh, *Higher Algebraic K-Theory of Schemes and of Derived Categories*, The Grothendieck Festschrift, Volume III, Progress in Mathematics, Vol. 88, Birkhäuser, Boston-Basel-Berlin, 1990, pp. 247–436.

[57] H. Toda, *Composition Methods in Homotopy Groups of Spheres*, Annals of Mathematics Studies, Vol. 49, Princeton University Press, Princeton, 1962.

[58] F. Waldhausen, *Algebraic K-theory of spaces*, Springer Lecture Notes in Math. **1126** (1985), 318–419.

INDEX

Progress in Mathematics

Edited by:

H. Bass
Columbia University
New York
10027
U.S.A.

J. Oesterlé
Dépt. de Mathématiques
Université de Paris VI
4, Place Jussieu
75230 Paris Cedex 05, France

A. Weinstein
Dept. of Mathematics
University of CaliforniaNY
Berkeley, CA 94720
U.S.A.

Progress in Mathematics is a series of books intended for professional mathematicians and scientists, encompassing all areas of pure mathematics. This distinguished series, which began in 1979, includes authored monographs, and edited collections of papers on important research developments as well as expositions of particular subject areas.

We encourage preparation of manuscripts in such form of TeX for delivery in camera-ready copy which leads to rapid publication, or in electronic form for interfacing with laser printers or typesetters.

Proposals should be sent directly to the editors or to: Birkhäuser Boston, 675 Massachusetts Avenue, Cambridge, MA 02139, U.S.A.